HALF-HOURS

WITH THE

BEST HUMOROUS AUTHORS.

SELECTED AND ARRANGED BY

CHARLES MORRIS.

VOL. II.

AMERICAN.

PHILADELPHIA:
J. B. LIPPINCOTT COMPANY.
1889.

Copyright, 1889, by J. B. Lippincott Company.

CONTENTS.

3

4 *CONTENTS.*

CONTENTS.

II.   1*

CONTENTS.

HALF-HOURS

WITH THE

BEST HUMOROUS AUTHORS.

BROWN-BREAD CAKES.

GAIL HAMILTON.

[The sprightly humor and keen satire of the author who signs herself Gail Hamilton (and prefers to be known only by this *nom-de-guerre*) is too well known to American readers to need description. We have given in the preceding volume a selection from her works, and add to it, from her "Country Living and Country Thinking," the following lively edict from the "kitchen cabinet."]

LET me give the *modus operandi*. Of fine maize flour, yellow as the locks of the lovely Lenore, take—well, take enough: I cannot tell exactly how much; it depends upon circumstances. Of fresh new milk, white as the brow of the charming Arabella, take—I don't know exactly how much of that either; it depends upon circumstances, particularly upon the quantity of the meal. If you have not new milk, take blue milk, provided it be sweet; or, if you have none that is sweet, sour milk will answer; or, if "your folks don't keep a cow," take water, clear and sparkling as the eyes of the peerless Amanda; but, whether it be milk or water, let it be scalding as the

7

tears of the outraged Isabel. Of molasses, sweet as the
tones of the tuneful Lisette, take—a great deal, if it is
summer; in the winter not quite so much (for the reasons
therefor, see Newton's Treatise on the Expansive Power
of Fluids, vol. i. p. 175). Of various other substances,
animal, vegetable, and mineral, which it becomes not me
to mention,—first, because I have forgotten what they are;
secondly, because I never knew; and thirdly, because, as the
immortal Toots remarks, " it is of no consequence,"—take
whatever seems good in your sight, and cast them together
into the kneading-trough, and knead with all your might
and main. Provide yourself, then, with a tin plate, not
bright and new, for so your cakes will be heavy, your
crust cracked, and your soul sorrowful, but one blackened
by fire and venerable with time and rough with service.
With your own roseate fingers scoop out a portion of the
pulpy mass. Fear not to touch it; it is soft, yielding, and
plastic as the heart of the affectionate Clara. Turn it
lovingly over in your hands; round it; mould it; caress
it; soften down its asperities; smooth off its angularities;
repress its bold protuberances; encourage its timid shrink-
ings; and when it is smooth as the velvet cheek of Ida,
and oval as the classic face of Helen, give one " last, long,
lingering look," and lay it tenderly in the swart arms of its
tutelar plate. Repeat the process until your cakes shall
equal the sands on the sea-shore or the stars in the sky for
multitude, or as long as your meal holds out, or till you are
tired. I am prescribing for one only. *Ab uno disce omnes.*

To the Stygian cave, that yawns dismally from the
kitchen stove, consign it without a murmur. Item: said
stove must have a prodigious crack up and down the front.
A philosophical reason for this I am unable to give. I
refer the curious in cause and effect to Galen's deservedly
celebrated Disquisition on the Relations of Fire and Metals,

passim ; also, Debrauche on Dough, p. 35, appendix. I only
know that the only stove whence I ever saw brown-bread
cakes issue had an immense crack up and down the front.
(Since writing the above, a new stove has been substituted
for the old one, and still brown-bread cakes are duly marshalled every morning. Consequently, you need not be
particular about the crack. Still, I would advise all amateurs to consult the authorities I have mentioned. It will
be a good exercise.)

When your cake has for a sufficient length of time under-
gone the ordeal of fire, bring it again to the blessed light
of day. If the edge be black and blistered, like a giant
tree blasted by the lightning's stroke, or if the crust be
rent and torn as by internal convulsions, cast it away. It
is worthless. Trample it under foot. Item : put on your
stoutest boots, and provide yourself with cork soles ; otherwise the trampling may prove to be anything but an agreeable pastime. But if the surface be a, beautiful auburn
brown, crisp, brittle, and unbroken,—

> " Joy, joy, forever ! your task is done !
> The gates are past, and breakfast is won."

Or, as the clown said of the apple-dumplings, " Them's the
jockeys for me."

If you are an outside barbarian, ignorant of the refine-
ments of civilized life, you will at once proceed to cut open
with your knife the steaming cake as you would an oyster,
and thereby render it heavy as the heart of the weeping
Niobe ; but if you are a gentleman and a scholar, you will
gently sunder its clinging sides without " armed interfer-
ence," and so preserve its spongy, porous texture. To the
uninitiated one part is as good as another ; but let me confidently whisper in your ear, if it should be your duty to

pass the plate, present to your neighbor that side which bears the under-crust, as that is liable to be burnt and unpalatable, and reserve to yourself the smoothly-rounded upper crust, which is deliciously toothsome. Lay your portion on your plate crust downward. With your own polished knife (the reason of this you will presently perceive), carve from the ball of golden butter a lump of magnificent dimensions. Be not niggardly in this respect. Exercise towards yourself a large-hearted generosity; for butter sinks into itself and in itself is lost with wonderful rapidity, when it rests on a pedestal of hot bread. Press your butter, still adhering to your knife, down into the warm, soft bread, in various places, forming little wells, whose walls are unctuous with the melted luxury, and then—OH, THEN! but I cannot sustain the picture which my fancy has drawn.

THE OLD CLOCK.

JAMES NACK.

[The following poem, which has gone the round of humorous literature for the last sixty years, has, like the old clock which it celebrates, go in it still, and is well worthy of preservation as a specimen of Yankee humor.]

Two Yankee wags, one summer day,
Stopped at a tavern on their way,
Supped, frolicked, late retired to rest,
And woke to breakfast on the best.

The breakfast over, Tom and Will
Sent for the landlord and the bill;

Will looked it over: "Very right:
But hold! what wonder meets my sight?—
Tom, the surprise is quite a shock!"—
"What wonder? where?"—"The clock! the clock!"

Tom and the landlord in amaze
Stared at the clock with stupid gaze,
And for a moment neither spoke;
At last the landlord silence broke:

"You mean the clock that's ticking there?
I see no wonder, I declare,
Though maybe, if the truth were told,
'Tis rather ugly,—somewhat old;
Yet time it keeps to half a minute:
But, if you please, what wonder's in it?"

"Tom, don't you recollect," said Will,
"The clock at Jersey near the mill,
The very image of this present,
With which I won the wager pleasant?"
Will ended with a knowing wink.
Tom scratched his head and tried to think.
"Sir, begging pardon for inquiring,"
The landlord said, with grin admiring,
"What wager was it?"

                              "You remember
It happened, Tom, in last December.
In sport I bet a Jersey Blue
That it was more than he could do,
To make his finger go and come
In keeping with the pendulum,

Repeating, till one hour should close,
Still ' *Here she goes—and there she goes.*'
He lost the bet in half a minute."

"Well, if I would, the deuce is in it!"
Exclaimed the landlord: "try me yet,
And fifty dollars be the bet." ·
"Agreed; but we will play some trick
To make you of the bargain sick!"
"I'm up to that!"

      "Don't make us wait.
Begin: the clock is striking eight."
He seats himself, and left and right
His finger wags with all his might,
And hoarse his voice and hoarser grows,
With "*Here she goes—and there she goes!*"

"Hold!" said the Yankee; "plank the ready!"
The landlord wagged his finger steady,
While his left hand, as well as able,
Conveyed a purse upon the table.
"Tom, with the money let's be off!"
This made the landlord only scoff;
He heard them running down the stair,
But was not tempted from his chair:
Thought he, "The fools! I'll bite them yet!
So poor a trick shan't win the bet."
And loud and loud the chorus rose
Of " *Here she goes—and there she goes!*"
While right and left his finger swung,
In keeping to his clock and tongue.

His mother happened in, to see
Her daughter.   "Where is Mrs. B——?

When will she come, as you suppose?
Son!"
  " Here she goes—and there she goes!"

"Here!—where?"—the lady in surprise
His finger followed with her eyes;
"Son, why that steady gaze and sad?
Those words,—that motion,—are you mad?
But here's your wife: perhaps she knows,
And——"
  " Here she goes—and there she goes!"

His wife surveyed him with alarm,
And rushed to him and seized his arm;
He shook her off, and to and fro
His fingers persevered to go,
While curled his very nose with ire
That *she* against him should conspire,
And with more furious tone arose
The *" Here she goes—and there she goes!"*

"Lawks!" screamed the wife, "I'm in a whirl!
Run down and bring the little girl:
She is his darling, and who knows
But——"
  " Here she goes—and there she goes!"

"Lawks! he is mad! what made him thus?
Good Lord! what will become of us?
Run for a doctor!—run,—run,—run!—
For Doctor Brown, and Doctor Dun,
And Doctor Black, and Doctor White,
And Doctor Gray, with all your might."

II.   2

The doctors came, and looked and wondered,
And shook their heads, and paused and pondered,
Till one proposed he should be bled;
"No; leeched, you mean," the other said.
"Clap on a blister," roared another;
"No, cup him,"—"No, trepan him, brother!"
A sixth would recommend a purge,
The next would an emetic urge;
The eighth, just come from a dissection,
His verdict gave for an injection;
The last produced a box of pills,
A certain cure for earthly ills:
"I had a patient yesternight,"
Quoth he, "and wretched was her plight,
And, as the only means to save her,
Three dozen patent pills I gave her,
And by to-morrow I suppose
That——"
                    "*Here she goes—and there she goes!*"

"You all are fools," the lady said,
"The way is, just to shave his head.
Run, bid the barber come anon——"
"Thanks, mother," thought her clever son:
"*You* help the knaves that would have bit me,
But all creation shan't outwit me!"
Thus to himself, while to and fro
His finger perseveres to go,
And from his lips no accent flows
But "*Here she goes—and there she goes!*"

The barber came: "Lord help him! what
A queerish customer I've got!

But we must do our best to save him:
So hold him, gemmen, while I shave him!"
But here the doctors interpose:
" A woman never——"
                              " *There she goes!*"

" A woman is no judge of physic,
Not even when her baby *is* sick.
He must be bled."—" No, no! a blister!"—
" A purge, you mean!"—" I say a clyster!"
" No, cup him!"—" Leech him!"—" Pills! pills! pills!"
And all the house the uproar fills.

What means that smile? what means that shiver?
The landlord's limbs with rapture quiver,
And triumph brightens up his face,—
His finger yet shall win the race!
The clock is on the stroke of nine,
And up he starts: " 'Tis mine! 'tis mine!"
" What do you mean ?"

                              " I mean the fifty!
I never spent an hour so thrifty;
But you, who tried to make me lose,
Go, burst with envy, if you choose!
But how is this? where are they ?"

                              " Who ?"
" The gentlemen,—I mean the two
Came yesterday: are they below ?"
" They galloped off an hour ago."
" Oh, purge me! blister! shave and bleed!
For, hang the knaves, I'm mad indeed!"

A PIANO IN ARKANSAS

THOMAS B. THORPE.

[Thomas Bangs Thorpe, born at Westfield, Massachusetts, in 1815, was an artist of some distinction and a humorous writer of considerable ability. His works consist of sketches of Western and Southern life, comprising "Tom Owen the Bee-Hunter" and other volumes of tales and sketches. He was a frequent contributor to *Harper's Magazine*. He died in 1878.]

WE shall never forget the excitement which seized upon the inhabitants of the little village of Hardscrabble as the report spread through the community that a real piano had actually arrived within its precincts.

Speculation was afloat as to its appearance and its use. The name was familiar to everybody; but what it precisely meant, no one could tell. That it had legs was certain; for a stray volume of some literary traveller was one of the most conspicuous works in the floating library of Hardscrabble, and said traveller stated that he had seen a piano somewhere in New England with pantalets on; also, an old foreign paper was brought forward, in which there was an advertisement headed "Soirée," which informed the "citizens, generally," that Mr. Bobolink would preside at the piano.

This was presumed by several wiseacres, who had been to a menagerie, to mean that Mr. Bobolink stirred the piano with a long pole, in the same way that the showman did the lions and rhi-no-ce-rus.

So, public opinion was in favor of its being an animal, though a harmless one; for there had been a land-speculator through the village a few weeks previously, who distributed circulars of a "Female Academy" for the accomplishment of young ladies. These circulars distinctly stated "the use of the piano to be one dollar per month."

One knowing old chap said, if they would tell him what so-i-ree meant, he would tell them what a piano was, and no mistake.

The owner of this strange instrument was no less than a very quiet and very respectable late merchant of a little town somewhere "north," who, having failed at home, had emigrated into the new and hospitable country of Arkansas, for the purpose of bettering his fortune and escaping the heartless sympathy of his more lucky neighbors, who seemed to consider him a very bad and degraded man because he had become honestly poor.

The new-comers were strangers, of course. The house in which they were setting up their furniture was too little arranged "to admit of calls;" and, as the family seemed very little disposed to court society, all prospects of immediately solving the mystery that hung about the piano seemed hopeless. In the mean time, public opinion was "rife."

The depository of this strange thing was looked upon by the passers-by with indefinable awe; and, as noises unfamiliar sometimes reached the street, it was presumed that the piano made them, and the excitement rose higher than ever. In the midst of it, one or two old ladies, presuming upon their age and respectability, called upon the strangers and inquired after their health, and offered their services and friendship; meantime, everything in the house was eyed with great intensity, but, seeing nothing strange, a hint was given about the piano. One of the new family observed, carelessly, "that it had been much injured by bringing out, that the damp had affected its tones, and that one of its legs was so injured that it would not stand up, and for the present it would not ornament the parlor."

Here was an explanation indeed: injured in bringing out; damp affecting its tones; leg broken. "Poor thing!" ejaculated the old ladies, with real sympathy, as they proceeded homeward; "travelling has evidently fatigued it; the Mass-is-sip fogs has given it a cold, poor thing!" and they wished to see it with increased curiosity.

The "village" agreed that if Moses Mercer, familiarly called "Mo Mercer," was in town, they would have a description of the piano, and the uses to which it was put; and, fortunately, in the midst of the excitement "Mo" arrived, he having been temporarily absent on a hunting-expedition.

Moses Mercer was the only son of "old Mercer," who was, and had been, in the State Senate ever since Arkansas was admitted into the "Union." Mo from this fact received great glory, of course; his father's greatness alone would have stamped him with superiority; but his having been twice in the "Capitol" when the legislature was in session stamped his claims to pre-eminence over all competitors.

Mo Mercer was the oracle of the renowned village of Hardscrabble.

"Mo" knew everything; he had all the consequence and complacency of a man who had never seen his equal, and never expected to. "Mo" bragged extensively upon his having been to the "Capitol" twice,—of his there having been in the most "fashionable society,"—of having seen the world. His return to town was therefore received with a shout. The arrival of the piano was announced to him, and he alone of all the community was not astonished at the news.

His insensibility was considered wonderful. He treated the piano as a thing that he was used to, and went on, among other things, to say that he had seen more pianos

in the "Capitol," than he had ever seen woodchucks, and
that it was not an animal, but a musical instrument played
upon by the ladies; and he wound up his description by
saying that the way "the dear creeturs could pull music
out of it was a caution to hoarse owls."

The new turn given to the piano-excitement in Hardscrabble by Mo Mercer was like pouring oil on fire to ex-
tinguish it, for it blazed out with more vigor than ever.
That it was a musical instrument made it a rarer thing in
that wild country than if it had been an animal, and people
of all sizes, colors, and degrees were dying to see and hear it.

Jim Cash was Mo Mercer's right-hand man: in the language of refined society, he was "Mo's toady;" in the language of Hardscrabble, he was "Mo's wheel-horse." Cash
believed in Mo Mercer with an abandonment that was
perfectly ridiculous. Mr. Cash was dying to see the
piano, and the first opportunity he had alone with his
Quixote he expressed the desire that was consuming his
vitals.

"We'll go at once and see it," said Mercer.

"Strangers!" echoed the frightened Cash.

"Humbug! Do you think I have visited the 'Capitol'
twice, and don't know how to treat fashionable society?
Come along at once, Cash," said Mercer.

Off the pair started, Mercer all confidence, and Cash all
fears as to the propriety of the visit. These fears Cash
frankly expressed; but Mercer repeated for the thousandth
time his experience in the fashionable society of the "Capitol, and pianos," which he said "was synonymous;" and
he finally told Cash, to comfort him, that, however abashed
and ashamed he might be in the presence of the ladies, "he
needn't fear of sticking, for he would pull him through."

A few minutes' walk brought the parties on the broad
galleries of the house that contained the object of so much

curiosity. The doors and windows were closed, and a suspicious look was on everything.

"Do they always keep a house closed up this way that has a piano in it?" asked Cash, mysteriously.

"Certainly," replied Mercer: "the damp would destroy its tones."

Repeated knocks at the doors, and finally at the windows, satisfied both Cash and Mercer that nobody was at home. In the midst of their disappointment, Cash discovered a singular machine at the end of the gallery, crossed by bars and rollers and surmounted with an enormous crank. Cash approached it on tiptoe; he had a presentiment that he beheld the object of his curiosity, and, as its intricate character unfolded itself, he gazed with distended eyes, and asked Mercer, with breathless anxiety, what that strange and incomprehensible box was.

Mercer turned to the thing as coolly as a north wind to an icicle, and said, that was *it*.

"That *it*!" exclaimed Cash, opening his eyes still wider; and then, recovering himself, he asked to see "the tone."

Mercer pointed to the cross-bars and rollers. With trembling hands, with a resolution that would enable a man to be scalped without winking, Cash reached out his hand and seized the handle of the crank (Cash, at heart, was a brave and fearless man). He gave it a turn: the machinery grated harshly, and seemed to clamor for something to be put in its maw.

"What delicious sounds!" said Cash.

"Beautiful!" observed the complacent Mercer, at the same time seizing Cash's arm and asking him to desist, for fear of breaking the instrument or getting it out of tune.

The simple caution was sufficient; and Cash, in the joy of the moment at what he had done and seen, looked as conceited as Mo Mercer himself.

Busy indeed was Cash, from this time forward, in explaining to gaping crowds the exact appearance of the piano, how he had actually taken hold of it, and, as his friend Mo Mercer observed, "pulled music out of it."

The curiosity of the village was thus allayed, and consequently died comparatively away,—Cash, however, having risen to almost as much importance as Mo Mercer, for having seen and handled the thing.

Our "Northern family" knew little or nothing of all this excitement; they received meanwhile the visits and congratulations of the hospitable villagers, and resolved to give a grand party to return some of the kindness they had received, and the piano was, for the first time, moved into the parlor. No invitation on this occasion was neglected; early at the post was every visitor, for it was rumored that Miss Patience Doolittle would, in the course of the evening, "perform on the piano."

The excitement was immense. The supper was passed over with a contempt rivalling that which is cast upon an excellent farce played preparatory to a dull tragedy in which the star is to appear. The furniture was all critically examined, but nothing could be discovered answering Cash's description. An enormously thick-leafed table with a "spread" upon it, attracted little attention, timber being so very cheap in a new country, and so everybody expected soon to see the piano "brought in."

Mercer, of course, was the hero of the evening: he talked much and loudly. Cash, as well as several young ladies, went into hysterics at his wit. Mercer, as the evening wore away, grew exceedingly conceited, even for him; and he graciously asserted that the company present reminded him of his two visits to the "Capitol," and other associations equally exclusive and peculiar.

The evening wore on apace, and still—no piano. That

hope deferred which maketh the heart sick was felt by some elderly ladies and by a few younger ones; and Mercer was solicited to ask Miss Patience Doolittle to favor the company with the presence of the piano.

"Certainly," said Mercer, and with the grace of a city dandy he called upon the lady to gratify all present with a little music, prefacing his request with the remark that if she was fatigued "his friend Cash would give the machine a turn."

Miss Patience smiled, and looked at Cash.

Cash's knees trembled.

All eyes in the room turned upon him.

Cash trembled all over.

Miss Patience said she was gratified to hear that Mr. Cash was a musician: she admired people who had a musical taste. Whereupon Cash fell into a chair, as he afterwards observed, "chawed up."

Oh that Beau Brummel or any of his admirers could have seen Mo Mercer all this while! Calm as a summer morning, complacent as a newly-painted sign, he smiled and patronized, and was the only unexcited person in the room.

Miss Patience rose. A sigh escaped from all present: the piano was evidently to be brought in. She approached the thick-leafed table and removed the covering, throwing it carelessly and gracefully aside, opened the instrument, and presented the beautiful arrangement of dark and white keys.

Mo Mercer at this, for the first time in his life, looked confused: he was Cash's authority in his descriptions of the appearance of the piano; while Cash himself began to recover the moment that he ceased to be an object of attention. Many a whisper now ran through the room as to the "tones," and more particularly the "crank:" none could see them.

Miss Patience took her seat, ran her fingers over a few octaves, and if "Moses in Egypt" was not perfectly *executed*, Moses in Hardscrabble *was*. The dulcet sound ceased. "Miss," said Cash, the moment that he could express himself, so entranced was he by the music,—"Miss Doolittle, what was that instrument Mo Mercer showed me in your gallery once, that went by a crank and had rollers in it?"

It was now the time for Miss Patience to blush : so away went the blood from confusion to her cheeks. She hesitated, stammered, and said, if Mr. Cash must know, it was a—a—a— *Yankee washing-machine.*

The name grated on Mo Mercer's ears as if rusty nails had been thrust into them ; the heretofore invulnerable Mercer's knees trembled, the sweat started to his brow, as he heard the taunting whispers of "visiting the Capitol twice" and seeing pianos as plenty as woodchucks.

The fashionable vices of envy and maliciousness were that moment sown in the village of Hardscrabble ; and Mo Mercer, the great, the confident, the happy and self-possessed, surprising as it may seem, was the first victim sacrificed to their influence.

Time wore on, and pianos became common, and Mo Mercer less popular ; and he finally disappeared altogether on the evening of the day on which a Yankee peddler of notions sold to the highest bidder, "six patent, warranted, and improved Mo Mercer pianos."

MAIDENLY CULTURE.

ANONYMOUS.

[In the following poems girlish æstheticism and culture are satir-
ized by a brace of unfeeling and unsympathetic rhymesters,—whom
we shall not dignify with the name of poets. We can only say, " Go
on, girls: there is more in the universe than bread-and-butter, and
you are as well entitled to your share of the utterly utter as your
greedy and grasping brothers."]

A GIRL OF THE PERIOD.

OH, she was so utterly utter!
She couldn't eat plain bread-and-butter,
But a nibble she'd take
At a wafer of cake,
Or the wing of a quail for her supper:
Roast beef and plum-pudding she'd sneer at,
A boiled leg of mutton she'd jeer at,
But the limb of a frog
Might her appetite jog,
Or some delicate bit that came near that.
The consequence was, she grew paler,
And more wishy-washy, and frailer,
Ate less for her dinner,
Grew thinner and thinner,
Till I really think,
If you marked her with ink,
Put an envelope on her,
And stamped it upon her,
You could go to the office and mail her!
Her voice was so low and so thrilling,
Its cadence was perfectly killing;
And she talked with a lisp and a stutter,
For she was so utterly utter!

Oh, she was so very æsthetic!
Her face was quite long and pathetic;
    The ends of her hair
    Floated loose on the air,
And her eyes had a sadness prophetic;
The bangs she wore down on her forehead
Were straight and deliciously horrid;
    And a sad-colored gown
    Going straight up and down
She wore when the weather was torrid.
It was terrible hard to enthuse her,
But a bit of old china would fuse her;
And she'd glow like a coal or a candle
At the mention of Bach or of Handel.
At pinks and sweet-williams and roses
She'd make the most *retroussé* noses,
    But would swoon with delight
    At a sunflower bright
And use it in making her poses.
She moved with the sleepiest motion,
As if not quite used to the notion,
    And her manner was chill
    As a water-fowl's bill
When he's fresh from a dip in the ocean!
It was quite the reverse of magnetic,
But, oh, it was very æsthetic!

And if, with your old-fashioned notions,
You could wish that more cheerful emotions,
    More sunshine and grace,
    Should appear in her face,
More gladness should speak in her motions,—
If you heard with a homesick dejection
The changes in voice and inflection,

And sighed for smooth tresses,
And the plain, simple dresses,
That used to command your affection,—
Oh, hide your rash thoughts in your bosom!
Or, if you must speak out and use 'em,
Then under your breath you must mutter;
For *she* is *too* UTTERLY *utter!*

EDUCATIONAL COURTSHIP.

She was a Boston maiden, and she'd scarcely passed
    eighteen,
And as lovely as an houri, but of grave and sober mien,
A sweet encyclopædia of every kind of lore,
Though love looked coyly from behind the glasses that
    she wore.

She sat beside her lover, with her elbow on his knee,
And dreamily she gazed upon the slumbering summer sea,
Until he broke the silence, saying, "Pray, Minerva dear,
Inform me of the meaning of the Thingness of the Here?

"I know you're just from Concord, where the lights of
    wisdom be,
Your head crammed full to bursting, with their philoso-
    phy,—
Those hoary-headed sages and maids of hosiery blue:
Then solve me the conundrum, love, that I have put to
    you."

She smiled a dreamy smile, and said, "The Thingness of
    the Here
Is that which is not passed and hasn't yet arrived, my
    dear.

Indeed," the maid continued, with a calm, unruffled brow,
" The Thingness of the Here is just the Thisness of the
    Now."

A smile illumed the lover's face; then, without undue
    haste,
He slid a manly arm around the maiden's slender waist,
And on her cherry lips impressed a warm and loving kiss,
And said, " Love, this is what I call the Nowness of the
    This."

[To the above we add a prose contribution in the same vein, and
aimed, like the last, at the maidenly scion of the " hub of the universe."]

AWFULLY LOVELY PHILOSOPHY.

A few days ago a Boston girl, who had been attending
the School of Philosophy at Concord, arrived in Brooklyn,
on a visit to a seminary chum. After canvassing thoroughly the fun and gum-drops that made up their educa-
tion in the seat of learning at which their early scholastic
efforts were made, the Brooklyn girl began to inquire the
nature of the Concord entertainment.

" And so you are taking lessons in philosophy! How
do you like it?"

" Oh, it's perfectly lovely! It's about science, you know,
and we all just dote on science."

" It must be nice. What is it about?"

" It's about molecules as much as anything else, and
molecules are just too awfully nice for anything. If there's
anything I really enjoy, it's molecules."

" Tell me about them, my dear. What are molecules?"

" Oh, molecules! They are little wee things, and it takes
ever so many of them. They are splendid things. Do

you know, there ain't anything but what's got molecules in it? And Mr. Cook is just as sweet as he can be, and Mr. Emerson too. They explain everything so beautifully."

"How I'd like to go there!" said the Brooklyn girl, enviously.

"You'd enjoy it ever so much. They teach protoplasm, too; and if there is one thing perfectly heavenly its protoplasm. I really don't know which I like best, protoplasm or molecules."

"Tell me about protoplasm. I know I should adore it."

"'Deed you would. It's just too sweet to live. You know it's about how things get started, or something of that kind. You ought to hear Mr. Emerson tell about it. It would stir your very soul. The first time he explained about protoplasm there wasn't a dry eye in the house. We named our hats after him. This is an Emerson hat. You see, the ribbon is drawn over the crown and caught with a buckle and a bunch of flowers. Then you turn up the side with a spray of forget-me-nots. Ain't it just too sweet? All the girls in the school have them."

"How exquisitely lovely! Tell me some more science."

"Oh, I almost forgot about differentiation. I am really and truly positively in love with differentiation. It's different from molecules and protoplasm, but it's every bit as nice. And Mr. Cook! You should hear him go on about it. I really believe he's perfectly bound up in it. This scarf is the Cook scarf. All the girls wear them, and we named them after him, just on account of the interest he takes in differentiation."

"What is it, anyway?"

"This is mull, trimmed with Languedoc lace——"

"I don't mean that,—that other."

"Oh, differentiation! Ain't it sweet? It's got something to do with species. It's the way you tell one hat from another, so you'll know which is becoming. And we learn all about ascidians, too. They are the divinest things! I'm absolutely enraptured with ascidians. If I only had an ascidian of my own I wouldn't ask anything else in the world."

"What do they look like, dear? Did you ever see one?" asked the Brooklyn girl, deeply interested.

"Oh, no; nobody ever saw one except Mr. Cook and Mr. Emerson; but they are something like an oyster with a reticule hung on its belt. I think they are just heavenly."

"Do you learn anything else besides?"

"Oh, yes. We learn about common philosophy and logic, and those common things like metaphysics; but the girls don't care anything about those. We are just in ecstasies over differentiations and molecules, and Mr. Cook and protoplasms, and ascidians and Mr. Emerson, and I really don't see why they put in those vulgar branches. If anybody beside Mr. Cook and Mr. Emerson had done it, we should have told him to his face that he was too terribly, awfully mean."

And the Brooklyn girl went to bed that night in the dumps, because fortune had not vouchsafed her the advantages enjoyed by her friend.

ESSAY ON ANIMALS.

CHARLES F. BROWNE (ARTEMUS WARD).

[Charles Farrar Browne, who became a highly-popular writer and lecturer under the pen-name of " Artemus Ward," was born at Waterford, Maine, in 1834. His descriptions, in the *Cleveland Plaindealer*, of

his assumed natural-history and wax-figure show, attracted wide attention by their comical extravagance, and he soon became famous as a
humorist. In 1860 he became editor of *Vanity Fair*, in New York.
He went to England in 1866, and became very popular there, but died
in the following year. We append some illustrative selections.]

SCIENCE AND NATURAL HISTORY.

Mr. Punch: *My Dear Sir,*—I was a little disapinted at
not receivin a invitation to jine in the meetins of the
Social Science Congress. . . .

I prepared an Essy on Animals to read before the Social Science meetins. It is a subjeck I may troothfully say
I have successfully wrastled with. I tackled it when only
nineteen years old. At that tender age I writ a Essy for
a lit'ry Institoot entitled, "Is Cats to be trusted?" Of the
merits of that Essy it doesn't becum me to speak, but I
may be excoos'd for mentionin that the Institoot parsed a
resolution that " whether we look upon the length of this
Essy, or the manner in which it is written, we feel that
we will not express any opinion of it, and we hope it will
be read in other towns."

Of course the Essy I writ for the Social Science Society
is a more finisheder production than the one on Cats,
which was wroten when my mind was crood, and afore
I had masterd a graceful and ellygant stile of composition. I could not even punctooate my sentences proper at
that time, and I observe with pane, on lookin over this
effort of my youth, that its beauty is in one or two instances mar'd by ingrammaticisms. This was inexcusa-
ble, and I'm surprised I did it. A writer who can't write
in a grammerly manner better shut up shop.

You shall hear this Essy on Animals. Some day when
you have four hours to spare, I'll read it to you. I think
you'll enjoy it. Or—what will be much better, if I may

suggest—omit all picturs in next week's *Punch*, and do not let your contributors write eny thing whatever (let them have a holiday; they can go to the British Mooseum) and publish my Essy intire. It will fill all your collumes full, and create comment. Does this proposition strike you? Is it a go?

In case I had read the Essy to the Social Sciencers, I had intended it should be the closin attraction. I intended it should finish the proceedins. I think it would have finished them. I understand animals better than any other class of human creeturs. I have a very animal mind, and I've been identified with 'em doorin my entire perfessional career as a showman, more especial bears, wolves, leopards, and serpunts.

The leopard is as lively a animal as I ever came into contack with. It is troo he cannot change his spots, but you can change 'em for him with a paint-brush, as I once did in the case of a leopard who wasn't nat'rally spotted in a attractive manner. In exhibitin him I used to stir him up in his cage with a protracted pole, and for the purpuss of makin him yell and kick up in a leopardy manner I used to casionally whack him over the head. This would make the children inside the booth scream with fright, which would make fathers of families outside the booth very anxious to come in,—because there is a large class of parents who have a uncontrollable passion for takin their children to places where they will stand a chance of being frightened to death.

One day I whacked this leopard more than ushil, which elissited a remonstrance from a tall gentleman in spectacles, who said, "My good man, do not beat the poor caged animal. Rather fondle him."

"I'll fondle him with a club," I ansered, hitting him another whack.

"I prithy desist," said the gentleman; "stand aside and see the effeck of kindness. I understand the idiosyncracies of these creeturs better than you do."

With that he went up to the cage, and, thrustin his face in between the iron bars, he said, soothingly, "Come hither, pretty creetur."

The pretty creetur come-hithered rayther speedy, and seized the gentleman by the whiskers, which he tore off about enuff to stuff a small cushion with.

He said, "You vagabone, I'll have you indicted for exhibitin dangerous and immoral animals."

I replied, "Gentle sir, there isn't a animal here that hasn't a beautiful moral, but you musn't fondle 'em. You mustn't meddle with their idiotsyncracies."

The gentleman was a dramatic cricket, and he wrote a article for a paper, in which he said my entertainment wos a decided failure.

As regards bears, you can teach 'em to do interestin things, but they're onreliable. I had a very large grizzly bear once, who would dance, and larf, and lay down, and bow his head in grief, and give a mournful wale, etsetry. But he often annoyed me. It will be remembered that on the occasion of the first battle of Bull Run it suddenly occurd to the Fed'ral soldiers that they had business in Washington which ought not to be neglected, and they all started for that beautiful and romantic city, maintainin a rate of speed durin the entire distance that would have done credit to the celebrated French steed *Gladiateur*. Very nat'rally our Gov'ment was deeply grieved at this defeat; and I said to my bear shortly after, as I was givin a exhibition in Ohio,—I said, "Brewin, are you not sorry the national arms has sustained a defeat?" His business was to wale dismal, and bow his head down, the band (a barrel-origin and a wiolin) playing slow and melancholy

moosic. What did the grizzly old cuss do, however, but
commence darncin and larfin in the most joyous manner?
I had a narrer escape from being imprisoned for disloyalty.

*　　*　　*　　*　　*　　*　　*　　*

Some years ago I engaged a celebrated Living American
Skeleton for a tour through Australia. He was the thin-
nest man I ever saw. He was a splendid skeleton. He
didn't weigh anything, scarcely,—and I said to myself,—
the people of Australia will flock to see this tremendous
curiosity. It is a long voyage—as you know—from New
York to Melbourne—and to my utter surprise the skeleton
had no sooner got out to sea than he commenced eating
in the most horrible manner. He had never been on the
ocean before—and he said it agreed with him. I thought
so!—I never saw a man eat so much in my life. Beef—
mutton—pork—he swallowed them all like a shark—and
between meals he was often discovered behind barrels
eating hard-boiled eggs. The result was that when we
reached Melbourne this infamous skeleton weighed sixty-
four pounds more than I did!

I thought I was ruined; but I wasn't. I took him on
to California—another very long sea-voyage—and when I
got him to San Francisco I exhibited him as a fat man.

This story hasn't anything to do with my Entertainment, I know; but one of the principal features of my
Entertainment is that it contains so many things that
don't have anything to do with it.

A MORMON ROMANCE.—REGINALD GLOVERSON.

[We add the following pathetic story mainly on account of its being
in readable English, not in the Choctaw-like dialect of the bulk of
the Artemus Ward productions.]

The morning on which Reginald Gloverson was to leave
Great Salt Lake City with a mule-train dawned beautifully.

Reginald Gloverson was a young and thrifty Mormon, with an interesting family of twenty young and handsome wives. His unions had never been blessed with children. As often as once a year he used to go to Omaha, in Nebraska, with a mule-train for goods; but, although he had performed the rather perilous journey many times with entire safety, his heart was strangely sad on this particular morning, and filled with gloomy forebodings.

The time for his departure had arrived. The high-spirited mules were at the door, impatiently champing their bits. The Mormon stood sadly among his weeping wives.

"Dearest ones," he said, "I am singularly sad at heart this morning; but do not let this depress you. The journey is a perilous one, but—pshaw!—I have always come back safely heretofore, and why should I fear? Besides, I know that every night as I lie down on the broad starlit prairie, your bright faces will come to me in my dreams, and make my slumbers sweet and gentle. You, Emily, with your mild blue eyes, and you, Henrietta, with your splendid black hair, and you, Nelly, with your hair so brightly, beautifully golden, and you, Molly, with your cheeks so downy, and you, Betsy, with your wine-red lips,—far more delicious, though, than any wine I ever tasted,—and you, Maria, with your winsome voice, and you, Susan, with your—with your—that is to say, Susan, with your—and the other thirteen of you, each so good and beautiful, will come to me in sweet dreams, will you not, Dearestists?"

"Our own," they lovingly chimed, "we will!"

"And so farewell!" cried Reginald. "Come to my arms, my own!" he said, "that is, as many of you as can do it conveniently at once, for I must away."

He folded several of them to his throbbing breast, and drove sadly away.

But he had not gone far when the trace of the off-hind mule became unhitched. Dismounting, he essayed to adjust the trace; but, ere he had fairly commenced the task, the mule, a singularly refractory animal, snorted wildly, and kicked Reginald frightfully in the stomach. He arose with difficulty, and tottered feebly towards his mother's house, which was near by, falling dead in her yard with the remark, "Dear mother, I've come home to die!"

"So I see," she said. "Where's the mules?"

Alas! Reginald Gloverson could give no answer. In vain the heart-stricken mother threw herself upon his inanimate form, crying, "Oh, my son! my son! only tell me where the mules are, and then you may die if you want to."

In vain! in vain! Reginald had passed on.

The mules were never found.

Reginald's heart-broken mother took the body home to her unfortunate son's widows. But before her arrival she indiscreetly sent a boy to burst the news gently to the afflicted wives, which he did by informing them, in a hoarse whisper, that their "old man had gone in."

The wives felt very badly indeed.

"He was devoted to me," sobbed Emily.

"And to me," said Maria.

"Yes," said Emily, "he thought considerably of you, but not so much as he did of me."

"I say he did!"

"And I say he didn't!"

"He did!"

"He didn't!"

"Don't look at *me* with your squint eyes!"

"Don't shake your red head at *me!*"

"Sisters," said the black-haired Henrietta, "cease this

unseemly wrangling. I, as his first wife, shall strew flowers
on his grave."

"No, you *won't*," said Susan. "I, as his last wife, shall
strew flowers on his grave. It's *my* business to strew!"

"You shan't, so there!" said Henrietta.

"You bet I will!" said Susan, with a tear-suffused cheek.

"Well, as for me," said the practical Betsy, "I ain't on
the strew much; but I shall ride at the head of the funeral
procession."

"Not if I've been introduced to myself, you won't," said
the golden-haired Nelly; "that's my position. You bet
your bonnet-strings it is."

"Children," said Reginald's mother, "you must do some
crying, you know, on the day of the funeral; and how
many pocket-handkerchiefs will it take to go round?
Betsy, you and Nelly ought to make one do between
you."

"I'll tear her eyes out if she perpetuates a sob on my
handkercher!"

"Dear daughters-in-law," said Reginald's mother, "how
unseemly is this anger! Mules is five hundred dollars a
span, and every identical mule my poor boy had has been
gobbled up by the red man. I knew when my Reginald
staggered into the door-yard that he was on the die; but
if I'd only thunk to ask him about them mules ere his
gentle spirit took flight, it would have been four thousand
dollars in *our* pockets, and *no* mistake! Excuse these real
tears, but you've never felt a parent's feelin's."

"It's an oversight," sobbed Maria. "Don't blame us."

The funeral passed off in a very pleasant manner, nothing occurring to mar the harmony of the occasion. By a
happy thought of Reginald's mother, the wives walked to
the grave twenty abreast, which rendered that part of the
ceremony thoroughly impartial.

That night the twenty wives, with their heavy hearts, sought their twenty respective couches. But no Reginald occupied those twenty respective couches. Reginald would never more linger all night in blissful repose in those twenty respective couches; Reginald's head would never more press the twenty respective pillows of those twenty respective couches,—never, never more!

In another house, not many leagues from the house of mourning, a gray-haired woman was weeping passionately. "He died," she cried, "he died without signerfyin', in any respect, where them mules went to!"

Two years are supposed to elapse between the third and fourth chapters of this original American romance.

A manly Mormon, one evening as the sun was preparing to set among a select apartment of gold and crimson clouds in the western horizon,—although, for that matter, the sun has a right to "set" where it wants to, and so, I may add, has a hen,—a manly Mormon, I say, tapped gently at the door of the mansion of the late Reginald Gloverson.

The door was opened by Mrs. Susan Gloverson.

"Is this the house of the widow Gloverson?" the Mormon asked.

"It is," said Susan.

"And how many is there of she?" he inquired.

"There is about twenty of her, including me," courteously returned the fair Susan.

"Can I see her?"

"You can."

"Madam," he softly said, addressing the twenty disconsolate widows, "I have seen part of you before. And although I have already twenty-five wives, whom I respect and tenderly care for, I can truly say I never felt love's holy thrill till I saw thee! Be mine!—be mine!" he enthusiastically cried; "and we will show the world a striking illustration of the beauty and truth of the noble lines, only a good deal more so,—

> " Twenty-one souls with a single thought,
> Twenty-one hearts that beat as one."

They were united, they were.

Gentle reader, does not the moral of this romance show that—does it not, in fact, show that, however many there may be of a young widow woman—or, rather, does it not show that, whatever number of persons one woman may consist of—well, never mind what it *shows*. Only this writing Mormon romances is confusing to the intellect. You try it and see.

AUNT PEN'S FUNERAL.

HARRIET PRESCOTT SPOFFORD.

[Mrs. Spofford, who has written many interesting stories, occasionally indulges in humor. That she has the faculty well developed is evident from the following amusing contribution to *Harper's Magazine*. The author is a native of Calais, Maine, where she was born in 1835. In addition to her imaginative and humorous tales, she has written some excellent poetry.]

Poor Aunt Pen! I am sorry to say it, but for a person alive and well—tolerably well and very much alive, that is—she did use to make the greatest business of dying! Alive! why, when she was stretched out on the sofa, after an agony of asthma, or indigestion, or whatever, and had called us all about her with faltering and tears, and was apparently at her last gasp, she would suddenly rise, like her own ghost, at the sound of a second ringing of the

door-bell, which our little renegade Israel had failed to
answer, and declare if she could only once lay hands on
Israel she would box his ears till they heard!

For the door-bell was, perhaps, among many, one of
Aunt Pen's weakest points. She knew everybody in
town, as you might say. She was exceedingly entertaining to everybody outside the family. She was a great
favorite with everybody. Countless gossips came to see
her, tinkling at the door-bell, and hated individually by
Israel, brought her all the news, heard all the previous
ones had brought, admired her, praised her, pitied her,
listened to her, and went away leaving her in such satisfied mood that she did not die any more that day. And
as they went away they always paused at the door to say
to some one of us what a cheerful invalid Aunt Pen had
made herself, and what a nest of sunbeams her room always was, and what a lesson her patience and endurance
ought to be. But, oh, dear me, how very little they knew
about it all!

We all lived together, as it happened; for when we children were left alone with but a small income, Aunt Pen—
who was also alone, and only five years my senior—wrote
word that we might as well come to her house in the city,
for it wouldn't make expenses more, and might make them
less if we divided them; and then, too, she said, she would
always be sure of one out of three bright and reasonable
nurses. Poor Aunt Pen! perhaps she didn't find us either
so bright or so reasonable as she had expected, for we used
to think that in her less degree she went on the same principle with the crazy man who declared all the rest of the
world except himself insane.

In honest truth, as doctor after doctor was turned away
by the impatient and distempered woman up-stairs, each
one took occasion to say to us down-stairs that our aunt's

illness was of that nature that all the physic it required
was to have her fancies humored, and that we never need
give ourselves any uneasiness, for she would doubtless live
to a good old age, unless some acute disease should inter-
vene, as there was nothing at all the matter with her except a slight nervous sensitiveness, that never destroyed
anybody. I suppose we were a set of young heathen, for
really there were times, if you will believe it, when that
was not the most reassuring statement in the world.

However, sometimes Aunt Pen found a doctor, or a medicine, or a course of diet, or something, that gave her great
sensations of relief, and then she would come down, and
go about the house, and praise our administration, and say
everything went twice as far as it used to go before we
came, and tell us delightful stories of our mother's housewifely skill, and be quite herself again; and she would
make the table ring with laughing, and give charming
little tea-parties; and then we all did wish that Aunt Pen
would live forever,—and be down-stairs. But probably
the next day, after one of the tea-parties, oysters, or claret
punch, or hot cakes, or all together, had wrought their
diablerie, and the doctor was sent for, and the warming-
pan was brought out, and there was another six weeks'
siege, in which, obeyed by every one, and physicked by
herself, and sympathized with to her heart's content by
callers, and shut up in a hot room with the windows full
of flowering plants, and somebody reading endless novels
to her with the lights burning all night long,—if she
wasn't ill she had every inducement to be, and nothing
but an indomitable constitution hindered it. It was perfectly idle for us to tell her she was hurting herself; it only
made her very indignant with us, and more determined
than ever to persist in doing so. . . .

When at last Aunt Pen had had an alarm from nearly

every illness for which the pharmacopœia prescribes, and
she knew that neither we nor the doctors would listen to
the probability of their recurrence, she had an attack of
"sinking." No, there was no particular disease, she used
to say,—only sinking; she had been pulled down to an
extent from which she had no strength to recuperate;
she was only sinking, a little weaker to-day than she was
yesterday; only sinking. But Aunt Pen ate a very good
breakfast of broiled birds and toast and coffee, a very good
lunch of cold meats and dainties and a great goblet of
thick cream, a very good dinner of soup and roast and
vegetables and dessert, and perhaps a chicken-bone at
eleven o'clock in the evening. And when the saucy little
Israel, who carried up her tray, heard her say she was
sinking, he remarked that it was because of the load on
her stomach.

One day, I remember, Aunt Pen was very much worse
than usual. We were all in her room, a sunshiny place
which she had connected with the adjoining one by sliding-
doors, so that it might be big enough for us all to bring
our work on occasion and make it lively for her. She had
on a white-cashmere dressing-gown trimmed with swan's-
down, and she lay among the luxurious cushions of a blue
lounge, with a paler blue blanket, which she had had one
of us tricot for her, lying over her feet, and altogether she
looked very ideal and ethereal; for Aunt Pen always did
have such an eye to picturesque effect that I don't know
how she could ever consent to the idea of mouldering
away into dust like common clay.

She had sent Maria down for Mel and me to come up-
stairs with whatever occupied us, for she was convinced
that she was failing fast, and knew we should regret it if
we did not have the last of her. As we had received the
same message nearly every other day during the last three

or four weeks, we did not feel extraordinarily alarmed, but composedly took our baskets and scissors and trudged along after Maria.

[Of the conversation that ensued we omit the opening portions, and pass on to its close, in which Aunt Penn gives her final funeral directions.]

"By the way," said she, suddenly, sitting upright on the lounge, "I won't have the horses from Brown's livery——"

"The what, auntie?"

"The horses for the cortége. You know Brown puts that magnificent span of his in the hearse on account of their handsome action. I'm sure Mrs. Gaylard would have been frightened to death if she could only have seen the way they pranced at her funeral last fall. I was determined then that they should never draw me." And Aunt Pen shivered for herself beforehand. "And I can't have them from Timlins's, for the same reason," said she. "All his animals are skittish; and you remember when a pair of them took fright and dashed away from the procession and ran straight to the river, and there'd have been four other funerals if the schooner at the wharf hadn't stopped the runaways. And Timlins has a way, too, of letting white horses follow the hearse with the first mourning-coach, and it's very bad luck, very,—an ill omen, a prophecy of Death and the Pale Horse again, you know. And I won't have them from Shust's, either," said Aunt Pen, "for he is simply the greatest extortioner since old Isaac the Jew."

"Well, auntie," said Mel, forgetful of her late repentance, "I don't see but you'll have to go with Shank's mare."

Even Aunt Pen laughed then. "Don't you really think you are going to lose me, girls?" asked she.

"No, auntie," replied Maria. "We all think you are a hypo."

"A hypo?"

"Not a hypocrite," said Mel, "but a hypochondriac."

"I wish I were!" sighed Aunt Pen; "I wish I were! I should have some hope of myself then," said the poor inconsistent innocent. "Oh, no, no; I feel it only too well; I am going fast. You will all regret your disbelief when I am gone." And she lay back among her pillows. "That reminds me," she murmured, presently. "About my monument."

"Oh, Aunt Pen, do be still!" said Mel.

"No," said Aunt Pen, firmly, "it may be a disagreeable duty, but that is all the better reason for me to bring my mind to it. And if I don't attend to it now, it never will be attended to. I know what relatives are. They put down a slab of slate with a skull and cross-bones scratched on it, and think they've done their duty. Not that I mean any reflections on you: you're all well-meaning, but you're giddy. I shall haunt you if you do anything of the kind! No; you may send Mr. Mason up here this afternoon, and I will go over his designs with him. I am going to have carved Carrara marble, set in a base of polished Scotch granite, and the inscription is——Girls," cried Aunt Pen, rising and clasping her knees with unexpected energy, "I expressly forbid my age being printed in the paper, or on the lid, or on the stone! I won't gratify every gossip in town, that I won't! I shall take real pleasure in baffling their curiosity. And another thing, while I am about it: don't you ask Tom Maltby to my funeral, or let him come in, if he comes himself, on any account whatever. I should rise in my shroud if he approached me. Yes, I should! Tom Maltby may be all very well; I dare say he is; and I hope I die at peace

with him and all mankind, as a good Christian should.
I forgive him; yes, certainly, I forgive him; but it doesn't
follow that I need forget him; and, so long as I remember
him, the way he conducted in buying the pew over my
head I can't get over, dead or alive. And if I only do get
well we shall have a reckoning that will make his hair
stand on end,—that he may rely on!" And here Aunt
Pen took the fan from Maria, and moved it actively, till
she remembered herself, when she resigned it. "One
thing more," she said. "Whatever happens, Helen, don't
let me be kept over Sunday. There'll certainly be another
death in the family within the year if you do. If I die on
Saturday, there's no help for it. Common decency won't
let you shove me into the ground at once, and so you will
have to make up your minds for a second summons." And
Aunt Pen, contemplating the suttee of some one of us with
great philosophy, lay down and closed her eyes again.
"You might have it by torchlight on Sunday night,
though," said she, half opening them. "That would be
very pretty." And then she dropped off to sleep with
such a satisfied expression of countenance that we judged
her to be welcoming in imagination the guests at her last
rites herself.

Whatever the dream was, she was rudely roused from
it by the wretched little Israel, who came bounding up
the stairs, and, without word or warning, burst into the
room, almost white with horror. Why Israel was afraid I
can't conjecture, but, at any rate, a permanent fright
would have been of great personal advantage to him.
"Oh, ma'am! oh, miss! dere's a pusson down-stairs, a
cullud woman, wid der small-pox!" he almost whistled in
his alarm.

"With the small-pox!" cried Aunt Pen, springing into
the middle of the floor, regardless of her late repose *in*

articulo mortis. "Go away, Israel! Have you been near her? Put her out immediately! How on earth did she get there?"

"You allus telled me to let everybody in," chattered Israel.

"Put her out! put her out!" cried Aunt Pen, half dancing with impatience.

"We can't get her out. She's right acrost der door-step. We's feard ter tech her."

But Aunt Pen's head was out of the window, and she was shouting, "Police! fire! murder! thieves!" possibly in the order of importance of the four calamities, but quite as if she had a plenty of breath left; and, for a wonder, the police came to the rescue, and directly afterward an ambulance took the victim of the frightful epidemic to the hospital. I believe it turned out to be only measles after all, though.

"Run, Israel," screamed Aunt Pen then, "run instantly and bring home a couple of pounds of roll-brimstone, and tell the maids to riddle the furnace fire and make it as bright and hot as possible, and to light fires in the parlor grates, and in the old Latrobe, and in every room in the house, without losing a minute. We'll make this house too warm for it!"

And, to our amazement, as soon as Israel came darting back with the impish material, Aunt Pen took a piece in each hand, directed us to do the same, and, wrapping the blue afghan round her shoulders, descended to the lower rooms three steps at a time, sent for the doctor to come and vaccinate us, and, having set a chair precisely over the register, where a red-hot stream of air was pouring up, she placed herself upon it and issued her orders.

Every window was closed, every grate from basement to attic had a fire lighted in it, and little pans of brimstone were burning in every room and hall in the house, while we, astonished, indignant, frightened, and amused, sat enduring the torments of vapor and sulphur baths to the point of suffocation.

"I can't bear this another moment," wheezed Mel.

"It's the only way," replied Aunt Pen, serenely, with a rivulet trickling down her nose. "You kill the germs by heat, and, since we can't bake ourselves quite to death, we make sure of the work by the fumes."

And as she sat there, her face rubicund, her swan's-down straight, drops on her cheeks, her chin, her forehead, and wherever drops could cling, her eyes watering, her curls limp, and an atmosphere of unbearable odor enveloping her in its cloud, the front door opened, and a footstep rung on the tiles.

"Jess you keep out o' yer!" yelled Israel to the intruder, seeing it wasn't the doctor. "We's got der small-pox, and am a-killin' de gemmens——"

"Pen!" cried a man's voice through the smoke,—a deep, melodious voice.

"What!" exclaimed Aunt Pen, starting up, and then pausing as if she fancied the horrid fumes might have befogged her brain.

"Pen!" the voice cried again.

"Chauncey! Chauncey Read!" she shrieked. "Where do you come from? Am I dreaming?"

"From the North Pacific," answered the voice; and we dimly discerned its owner groping his way forward. "From the five years' whaling-voyage into which I was gagged and dragged,—shanghaied, they call it. Oh, Pen, I didn't dare to hope I should find——"

"Oh, Chauncey, is it you?" she cried, and fell fainting at his feet.

The draught from the open door after him was blowing

away the smoke, and we saw what a great, sunburned, handsome fellow it was that had caught her in his arms and was bearing her out to the back balcony and the fresh air there, used in the course of his whaling voyage, perhaps, to odors no more belonging to Araby the Blest than those of burning brimstone do; and, seeing the movement, we divined that he knew as much about the resources of the house as we did, and so we discreetly withdrew, Israel's head being twisted behind him as he went to such extent that you might have supposed he had had his neck wrung.

Well, we put the white silk and the tulle on Aunt Pen after all; yellow as it was, she would have no other,— only fresh, natural orange-blossoms in place of the false wreath. And, if we had not so often had her word for it in past times, we never should have taken her for anything but the gayest bride, the most alive and happy woman, in the world. They returned to the old house from their wedding journey, and we all live together in great peace and pleasantness. But, though three years are passed and gone since Chauncey Read came home and brought a new atmosphere with him into our lives, Aunt Pen has never had a sick day yet; and we find that any allusion to her funeral gives her such a superstitious trembling that we are pleased to believe it indefinitely postponed, and by tacit and mutual consent we never say anything about it.

THE LIBERTY-POLE.

JOHN TRUMBULL.

[John Trumbull, the satirical poet of the Revolutionary period, was born at Waterbury, Connecticut, in 1750. He studied law under John Adams, and practised at New Haven and Hartford. In 1772

appeared "The Progress of Dulness," a humorous poem, which he
followed in 1782 by "McFingal," a satirical poem which reached the
highest popularity and passed through thirty editions.   In the words
of Griswold, "It is much the best imitation of the great satire of
Butler that has been written."   The author died in 1831.   We give
that portion describing McFingal's attack on the liberty-pole and its
disastrous consequences, stopping short, however, of the tarring and
feathering of the hero which followed his suspension in mid-air.]

Now, warm with ministerial ire,
Fierce sallied forth our loyal 'Squire,
And on his striding steps attends
His desperate clan of Tory friends.
When sudden met his wrathful eye
A pole ascending through the sky,
Which numerous throngs of Whiggish race
Were raising in the market-place.
Not higher school-boys' kites aspire,
Or royal masts, or country spire;
Like spears at Brobdingnagian tilting,
Or Satan's walking-staff in Milton,
And on its top, the flag unfurled,
Waved triumph o'er the gazing world,
Inscribed with inconsistent types
Of *Liberty* and *thirteen stripes.*
Beneath, the crowd without delay
The dedication rites essay,
And gladly pay, in ancient fashion,
The ceremonies of libation,
While briskly to each patriot lip
Walks eager round the inspiring flip,
Delicious draught! whose powers inherit
The quintessence of public spirit,
Which whoso tastes perceives his mind
To noble politics refined,

Or roused to martial controversy,
As from transforming cups of Circe,
Or warmed with Homer's nectared liquor,
That filled the veins of gods with ichor.
At hand for new supplies in store,
The tavern opes its friendly door,
Whence to and fro the waiters run,
Like bucket-men at fires in town.
Then, with three shouts that tore the sky,
'Tis consecrate to Liberty.
To guard it from the attacks of Tories,
A grand committee called of four is,
Who foremost on the patriot spot
Had brought the flip and paid the shot.
   By this McFingal with his train
Advanced upon th' adjacent plain,
And, full with loyalty possest,
Poured forth the zeal that fired his breast:
   " What mad-brained rebel gave commission
To raise this May-pole of sedition?
Like Babel, reared by bawling throngs,
With like confusion too of tongues,
To point at heaven and summon down
The thunders of the British crown?
Say, will this paltry pole secure
Your forfeit heads from Gage's power?
Attacked by heroes brave and crafty,
Is this to stand your ark of safety?
Or, driven by Scottish laird and laddie,
Think you to rest beneath its shadow?
When bombs like fiery serpents fly,
And balls rush hissing through the sky,
Will this vile pole, devote to freedom,
Save, like the Jewish pole in Edom,

Or, like the brazen snake of Moses,
Cure your cracked skulls and battered noses?

*   *   *   *   *   *   *

Rise, then, my friends, in terror rise,
And sweep this scandal from the skies.
You'll see their Dagon, though well jointed,
Will shrink before the Lord's anointed,
And, like old Jericho's proud wall,
Before our rams' horns prostrate fall."
      This said, our 'Squire, yet undismayed,
Called forth the constable to aid,
And bade him read, in nearest station,
The Riot-Act and Proclamation.
He, swift advancing to the ring,
Began, " Our Sovereign Lord the King——"
When thousand clam'rous tongues he hears,
And clubs and stones assail his ears.
To fly was vain ; to fight was idle ;
By foes encompassed in the middle,
His hope in stratagems he found,
And fell right craftily to ground,
Then crept to seek a hiding-place,
'Twas all he could, beneath a brace,
When soon the conquering crew espied him,
And where he lurked they caught and tied him.
      At once, with resolution fatal,
Both Whigs and Tories rushed to battle.
Instead of weapons, either band
Seized on such arms as came to hand.
And famed as Ovid paints th' adventures
Of wrangling Lapithæ and Centaurs,
Who at their feast, by Bacchus led,
Threw bottles at each other's head,

And, these arms failing in their scuffles,
Attacked with andirons, tongs, and shovels,
So clubs and billets, staves and stones,
Met fierce, encountering every sconce,
And covered o'er with knobs and pains
Each void receptacle for brains;
Their clamors rend the skies around,
The hills rebellow to the sound,
And many a groan increased the din
From battered nose and broken shin.
McFingal, rising at the word,
Drew forth his old militia-sword,
Thrice cried, " King George!" as erst in distress
Knights of romance invoked a mistress,
And, brandishing the blade in air,
Struck terror through th' opposing war.
The Whigs, unsafe within the wind
Of such commotion, shrunk behind;
With whirling steel around addressed,
Fierce through their thickest throng he pressed
(Who rolled on either side in arch,
Like Red Sea waves in Israel's march),
And, like a meteor rushing through,
Struck on their pole a vengeful blow.
Around the Whigs, of clubs and stones
Discharged whole volleys, in platoons,
That o'er in whistling fury fly;
But not a foe dares venture nigh.
And now perhaps, with glory crowned,
Our 'Squire had felled the pole to ground,
Had not some power, a Whig at heart,
Descended down and took their part
(Whether 'twere Pallas, Mars, or Iris,
'Tis scarce worth while to make inquiries),

Who at the nick of time alarming
Assumed the solemn form of Chairman,
Addressed a Whig, in every scene
The stoutest wrestler on the green,
And pointed where the spade was found
Late used to set their pole in ground,
And urged with equal arms and might
To dare our 'Squire to single fight.
The Whig, thus armed, untaught to yield,
Advanced tremendous to the field;
Nor did McFingal shun the foe,
But stood to brave the desperate blow,
While all the party gazed suspended
To see the deadly combat ended,
And Jove in equal balance weighed
The sword against the brandished spade.
He weighed; but, lighter than a dream,
The sword flew up and kicked the beam.
Our 'Squire, on tiptoe rising fair,
Lifts high a noble stroke in air,
Which hung not, but, like dreadful engines,
Descended on his foe in vengeance.
But, ah! in danger, with dishonor,
The sword perfidious fails its owner;
That sword, which oft had stood its ground
By huge train-bands encircled round,
And on the bench, with blade right loyal,
Had won the day at many a trial,
Of stones and clubs had braved th' alarms,
Shrunk from these new Vulcanian arms.
The spade so tempered from the sledge,
Nor keen nor solid harmed its edge,
Now met it, from his arm of might,
Descending with steep force to smite;

The blade snapt short, and from his hand
With rust embrowned the glittering sand.
Swift turned McFingal at the view,
And called to aid the attendant crew.
In vain ; the Tories all had run
When scarce the fight had well begun ;
Their setting wigs he saw decreased
Far in th' horizon towards the west.
Amazed he viewed the shameful sight,
And saw no refuge but in flight :
But age unwieldy checked his pace,
Though fear had winged his flying race ;
For not a trifling prize at stake,—
No less than great McFingal's back.
With legs and arms he worked his course,
Like rider that outgoes his horse,
And labored hard to get away, as
Old Satan struggling on through chaos,
Till, looking back, he spied in rear
The spade-armed chief advanced too near,
Then stopt and seized a stone that lay
An ancient landmark near the way ;
Nor shall we, as old bards have done,
Affirm it weighed a hundred ton ;
But such a stone as at a shift
A madman might suffice to lift,
Since men, to credit their enigmas,
Are dwindled down to dwarfs and pigmies,
And giants exiled with their cronies
To Brobdingnags and Patagonias.
But, while our hero turned him round,
And tugged to raise it from the ground,
The fatal spade discharged a blow
Tremendous on his rear below ;

II.   5*

His bent knees failed, and void of strength
Stretched on the ground his manly length.
Like ancient oak o'erturned, he lay,
Or tower to tempests fall'n a prey,
Or mountain sunk with all his pines,
Or flower the plough to dust consigns,
And more things else,—but all men know 'em,
If slightly versed in epic poem.
At once the crew, at this dread crisis,
Fall on, and bind him, ere he rises,
And with loud shouts and joyful soul
Conduct him prisoner to the pole,
Where now the mob, in lucky hour,
Had got their enemies in their power.
They first proceed, by grave command,
To take the constable in hand.
Then from the pole's sublimest top
The active crew let down a rope,
At once its other end in haste bind,
And make it fast upon his waistband,
Till, like the earth, as stretched on tenter,
He hung self-balanced on his centre.*
Then upwards, all hands hoisting sail,
They swung him like a keg of ale,
Till to the pinnacle in height
He vaulted, like balloon or kite,
As Socrates of old at first did,
To aid philosophy, get hoisted,
And found his thoughts flow strangely clear,
Swung in a basket in mid-air :
Our culprit thus, in purer sky,
With like advantage raised his eye,

---

* " And earth self-balanced on her centre hung."—MILTON.

And, looking forth in prospect wide,
His Tory errors clearly spied,
And from his elevated station
With bawling voice began addressing:
  " Good gentlemen and friends and kin,
For heaven's sake hear, if not for mine !
I here renounce the Pope, the Turks,
The King, the Devil, and all their works,
And will, set me but once at ease,
Turn Whig or Christian, what you please,
And always mind your rules so justly,
Should I live long as old Methus'lah.
I'll never join the British rage,
Nor help Lord North, nor General Gage,
Nor lift my gun in future fights,
Nor take away your charter rights,
Nor overcome your new-raised levies,
Destroy your towns, nor burn your navies,
Nor cut your poles down while I've breath,
Though raised more thick than hatchel-teeth,
But leave King George and all his elves
To do their conquering work themselves."
  This said, they lowered him down in state,
Spread at all points, like falling cat,
But took a vote first on the question
That they'd accept his full confession,
And to their fellowship and favor,
Restore him on his good behavior.

THE HIGH-ROAD TO FAME.

DAVID R. LOCKE ("PETROLEUM V. NASBY").

[The most amusing writings of the humorist from whom our present selection is taken are to be found in the political diatribes emanating from the "Confedrit Cross Roads" during the civil war period. His "Swingin' Round the Cirkle" and similar sketches are full of humorous satire, but have the defect of being one-sided politically and of referring to passing circumstances. From a work less amusing, yet at the same time less localized in interest, "The Morals of Abou Ben Adhem," we select a chapter in which the crude form of fun native to weak intellects and unfeeling dispositions known as practical joking is sarcastically handled. The author was born at Vestal, New York, in 1833, and became a journalist in Ohio.]

THERE came to Abou Ben Adhem one day a young man who insisted on being put in the way to the achievement of distinction. Abou looked the young man over with great care, and proceeded to give him a prescription at once.

"There are various kinds of fame, my son," said the sage, "but to attain any one of them requires an adaptability to that particular one, and much labor. It takes a great many years to attain eminence at the bar,—that is, as a lawyer; political distinction is attained only by years of labor; and the same may be said of the pulpit and the tripod. From the size and peculiar shape of your head, I should say that your shortest cut to fame is *via* the practical joke. It is not the best reputation to have and to hold, but it will answer you, because it strikes me you are fitted for it. The practical joker may, in a year's time, become sufficiently famous to have the town all speaking of "Jones's last good thing," if Jones gives his whole mind to it and has nothing else to take his attention.

"A few plain directions are all that are necessary.

"In the first place, a practical joker should have a good income; indeed, he ought to be rich. If he is rich enough to be always able to order and pay for wine, dinners, and carriages, he can always be sure of having in his train a regiment of 'good fellows,' who will repeat his good things, and who will frown down the sober people who, if left to themselves, would howl down the fountain of all their joys as an unmitigated nuisance and a pest only a trifle less terrible than a mad dog.

"Secondly, the practical joker must give his entire attention to the pursuit, for one effort, though it be successful, will not hold permanent distinction. It must be repeated daily, till the public shall hear as regularly of 'Jones's (we shall say) last' as they do of bank-defalcations.

"Thirdly, the practical joker must have no weak scruples. The feelings of others must not affect him, nor must any earthly consideration turn him from his purpose.

"He need not have wit or originality; all that is necessary is stolidity, and money enough to keep his corps of followers to applaud and repeat.

"Having designated the qualities necessary for success in this pursuit, I shall suggest a few practical jokes which have done good service in their day, and will do to use again.

"We will suppose that A., the practical joker, has a friend, B., who lives during the summer at Staten Island. B. has a brother in Chicago. What more exquisite piece of fun could there be than to have A. forge a telegram to B., in the name of the clerk of, say the Fifth Avenue Hotel, to the effect that his brother fell with a stroke of paralysis in the corridor of the hotel, just as he was registering his name, and was at the point of death? B., seeing the name all right, and not suspecting that that funny dog

A. had anything to do with it, would be greatly distressed. He would tear away from table, throw himself on the ferry-boat, frantically call a carriage, ride like a madman to the Fifth Avenue, and rush to the office and excitedly demand the room where his brother was dying. At this point A. and his crowd should appear, and, laughing till their sides ache at the blank wonderment of the clerk and the distressed expression of B., should shout, 'Sold!' Nothing could be more exquisitely humorous than this. Every practical joker should thank me for the suggestion. I do not say that it is above the average of practical jokes, but it is a trifle different from the usual run. Then it is capable of infinite variety. A man has many relatives, and it could be run on him for all of them. Thus, it might be telegraphed that his wife was dying, his father, his mother, his son at West Point, his daughter in Vassar, and so forth.

"If a man has a maiden aunt, from whom he has expectations, what would be better than to telegraph him of her death, and let things go to the length of ordering mourning? How glorious it would be to have the pleasure of poking him in the ribs for a month, with the query, 'How is your aunt? Ha! ha! ha!'

"Another good thing is to issue tickets of invitation to an amateur performance at some hall for the benefit of a charity, and to prescribe full dress for the occasion. It is better always to select for such a 'rig' a rainy season, that the victims of the 'sell' may be put to as much trouble and expense as possible. If three thousand invitations are issued, and the printing is well done, it is safe to assume that two thousand five hundred will attend. What rare sport to see two thousand five hundred ladies and gentlemen get out of carriages only to find a dark hall! This was done in New York once, but the joke was not carried half far enough. The joker was a poor one, and did not extract half the juice from it that was possible. To have made it complete he should have employed boys to stand in the dark and bespatter the ladies' dresses with mud as they alighted from their carriages and got back into them. To have armed the boys with squirt-guns, that they might shower the ladies with water from the gutters, would have been a positive triumph of genius. But to have simply thrown the mud would have been a proper and sufficiently humorous finish.

"The trick of advertising a 'dog wanted' at the house of a friend is very good. But few things can be funnier than the perplexity of the lady of the house indicated in the advertisement, as the regiments of ragamuffins come with dogs in their arms. So, likewise, is the advertising that a man will fly from the top of Trinity Church, particularly if you designate the man funnily, as, for instance, 'Herr Sellemall,' or 'Monsieur Foolemall,' or any appellation of the kind. These names are easy of construction, as will be seen, and when the fact works through the heads of the expectant crowd that the German 'Herr Sellemall' is in English 'sell-'em-all,' the way they shout, 'Sold, by Jove!' is a reward that practical jokers always appreciate.

"Another exceedingly pleasant practical joke is to stretch a cord across a gateway to a church, Sunday night, at an elevation of say five feet eight inches. As the congregation pass out under the cord, it neatly takes off and ruins the hats of all under that height, and rasps the faces of all over that altitude. The fright of an ancient maiden lady of attenuated proportions, as the cord strikes her face and breaks the skin on her nose and cheeks, is very amusing. The effect of this is immensely heightened by stretching another stout cord across the gateway at an elevation from the ground of say a foot, just high enough to trip them as they pass. Nothing can be more exquisitely funny than to see their consternation at the first cord, unless it is to see them sprawling in the mud over the second.

"There are other jokes fitted to all, but there is a class on which only medical students should venture. For instance, it is a 'big thing' to invite a party of friends to drink, and dexterously to get into their glasses a few drops of croton oil, or to substitute tartar emetic for cream of tartar in the kitchen of a friend, that it may get into the cake served for refreshments at a party. One rare wag, whom I knew once, in the most dexterous manner put some coal-oil in the lemonade, at a little gathering given by a clergyman's wife, and he and the few choice spirits who were 'in it' got no end of fun out of the distress of the hostess and the disgust of the guests. The circumstance created trouble in the parish, which resulted in the dismissal of the minister; but that was nothing: the faces of the people who got a taste of that coal-oil were ludicrous beyond description.

"A pin stuck in the bottom of a chair, in which a precise old lady is to sit down, is a good thing, as is also the tying of two cats and slinging them across your neighbor's fence, under his window.

"In fact, there is no limit to the amusement that can be got out of this kind of thing. Sewing up the sleeves of a friend's coat, when he is in a hurry to get to a train, is a most exquisite performance; and to blacken the face of a sleeping man is a piece of humor that always affords the liveliest satisfaction.

"And the beauty of this kind of humor, the great advantage in it, is, it is as applicable to animals as to men. A dog may be made the source of much amusement. It is the nature of dogs when they approach each other to put their noses together, which is equivalent, we presume, to the hand-shaking of humans. Now, the practical joker who inserts a pin in the muzzle of his dog does a very bright thing. The dog will run the pin into the noses of all the dogs who salute him, and the howls of the punctured canines, and the look of blank astonishment on the face of the innocent cause of the trouble, afford amusement beyond expression. Tying a tin kettle to a dog's tail is another good thing. The frightened dog, at full speed, will charge into a crowd of persons and scatter them in a highly amusing manner. I have known ladies to faint, and horses to be frightened so that they ran away, and an immense number of exceedingly ludicrous incidents to happen in consequence.

"Another amusing trick may be played with a dog. Buy a large Newfoundland,—a very shaggy one, whose coat of hair will hold a barrel of water; then invite a party of friends to the water-side. The ladies should be dressed in white, and the gentlemen, also, in light pantaloons. Throw a stick into the water, and say, 'Get it, Nero!' Then get into the centre of the group. The sagacious dog will swim out and get the stick, and will rush back to you, and rub against all who stand in his way; and when he gets to you he will shake himself, and completely drench the whole party, and soil their clothes. If the water is muddy the effect of the joke will be heightened very much.

"In short, there are a thousand ways of doing this sort of thing, and the advantage is that anybody can do it. And it is safe, too ; for you do not practise it on anybody but your friends. If you should 'get off' a practical joke on a stranger he might knock you down ; but your friend, no matter how much annoyed he might be, would never do it. He will swear and howl about it; but you laugh at him, and get mirth even out of his anger.

"Some people are unreasonable enough to speak of practical jokers as 'nuisances', as 'pests,' and so forth, and possibly they are right. There are those so utterly devoid of the sense of fun that they object to be put to serious inconvenience, or to bodily hurt, or to be made to appear ridiculous, for the sake of making amusement for others. But such people should not be regarded. The practical joker has his point to make,—he wants to rise a little above the level, and this is the only way in which he can do it. Therefore it should not be barred to him, and those who growl should be frowned down. But one who has nothing else to do can well afford to bear this stigma for the amusement and reputation he gets.

"I have shown you, my ambitious young friend, how you may attain distinction. Go and attain it! Be bold and merciless. The few who have sought to climb to eminence and have failed have fallen because they were not bold and had scruples. Go, my son, go!"

The young man left the presence, and Abou reclined on his divan and laughed heartily.

"By the bones of the Prophet!" he chuckled to himself, "this morn have I done humanity some service. That young man will attempt this kind of thing in his native State of New Jersey, whose people will refuse to see anything good in it. His eyes will be blackened on his first attempt, his second will procure his being dragged through a horse-pond, and his third will be the means of his dying prematurely. Then will the world be the better for my advice. Bismillah, it is good!"

And the Sage laughed himself to sleep.

AUNT ANNIKY'S TEETH.

KATHARINE S. McDOWELL.

[We have already given a selection from the " Dialect Tales" of
Mrs. McDowell.   They are worthy of a second presentation.]

AUNT ANNIKY was an African dame, fifty years old, and
of an imposing presence.   As a waffle-maker she possessed
a gift beyond the common, but her unapproachable talent
lay in the province of nursing.   She seemed born for the
benefit of sick people.   She should have been painted with
the apple of healing in her hand.   For the rest, she was
a funny, illiterate old darky, vain, affable, and neat as a
pin.

On one occasion my mother had a dangerous illness.
Aunt Anniky nursed her through it, giving herself no
rest, night nor day, until her patient had come " back to
de walks an' ways ob life," as she expressed the dear
mother's recovery.   My father, overjoyed and grateful,
felt that we owed this result quite as much to Aunt Anniky as to our family doctor, so he announced his intention of making her a handsome present, and, like King
Herod, left her free to choose what it should be.   I shall
never forget how Aunt Anniky looked as she stood there
smiling and bowing, and bobbing the funniest little cour-
tesies all the way down to the ground.

And you would never guess what it was the old woman
asked for.

" Well, Mars' Charles," said she (she had been one of
our old servants, and she always called my father " Mars'
Charles"), " to tell you de livin' trufe, my soul an' body
is a-yearnin' fur a han'sum chany set o' teef."

"A set of teeth!" said father, surprised enough. "And have you none left of your own?"

"I has gummed it fur a good many ye'rs," said Aunt Anniky, with a sigh, "but, not wishin' ter be ongrateful ter my obligations, I owns ter havin' five natural teef. But dey is po' sojers; dey shirks battle. One ob dem's got a little somethin' in it as lively as a speared worm, an' I tell you when anything teches it, hot or cold, it jest makes me *dance!* An' anudder is in my top jaw, an' ain't got no match fur it in de bottom one; an' one is broke off nearly to de root; an' de las' two is so yaller dat I's ashamed ter show 'em in company, an' so I lif's my turkey-tail ter my mouf every time I laughs or speaks."

Father turned to mother with a musing air. "The curious student of humanity," he remarked, "traces resemblances where they are not obviously conspicuous. Now, at the first blush, one would not think of any common ground of meeting for our Aunt Anniky and the Empress Josephine. Yet that fine French lady introduced the fashion of handkerchiefs by continually raising delicate lace *mouchoirs* to her lips to hide her bad teeth. Aunt Anniky lifts her turkey-tail. It really seems as if human beings should be classed by *strata*, as if they were metals in the earth. Instead of dividing by nations, let us class by qualities. So we might find Turk, Jew, Christian, fashionable lady and washerwoman, master and slave, hanging together like cats on a clothes-line by some connecting cord of affinity——"

"In the mean time," said my mother, mildly, "Aunt Anniky is waiting to know if she is to have her teeth."

"Oh, surely, surely!" cried father, coming out of the clouds with a start. "I am going to the village to-morrow, Anniky, in the spring wagon. I will take you with me, and we will see what the dentist can do for you."

"Bless yo' heart, Mars' Charles!" said the delighted Anniky; "you're jest as good as yo' blood and yo' name, and mo' I *couldn't* say."

[We may pass over Anniky's visit to the dentist as of secondary importance to the startling and momentous consequences.]

After a few weeks of sore gums, Aunt Anniky appeared, radiant with her new teeth. The effect was certainly funny. In the first place blackness itself was not so black as Aunt Anniky. She looked as if she had been dipped in ink and polished off with lamp-black. Her very eyes showed but the faintest rim of white. But those teeth were white enough to make up for everything. She had selected them herself, and the little ridiculous milk-white things were more fitted for the mouth of a Titania than for the great cavern in which Aunt Anniky's tongue moved and had its being. The gums above them were black, and when she spread her wide mouth in a laugh, it always reminded me of a piano-lid opening suddenly and showing all the black and white ivories at a glance. Aunt Anniky laughed a good deal, too, after getting her teeth in, and declared she had never been so happy in her life. It was observed, to her credit, that she put on no airs of pride, but was as sociable as ever, and made nothing of taking out her teeth and handing them around for inspection among her curious and admiring visitors. On that principle of human nature which glories in calling attention to the weakest part, she delighted in tough meat, stale bread, green fruits, and all other eatables that test the biting quality of the teeth. But finally destruction came upon them in a way that no one could have foreseen. Uncle Ned was an old colored man who lived alone in a cabin not very far from Aunt Anniky's, but very different from hers in point of cleanliness and order. In fact, Uncle Ned's wealth, apart from a little corn-crop, consisted in a lot of fine young pigs, that ran in and out of the house at all times and were treated by their owner as tenderly as if they had been his children. One fine day the old man fell sick of a fever, and he sent in haste for Aunt Anniky to come and nurse him. He agreed to give her a pig in case she brought him through; should she fail to do so, she was to receive no pay. Well, Uncle Ned got well, and the next thing we heard was that he refused to pay the pig. My father was usually called on to settle all the disputes in the neighborhood; so one morning Anniky and Ned appeared before him, both looking very indignant.

"I'd jes' like ter tell yer, Mars' Charles," began Uncle Ned, "ob de trick dis miser'ble ole nigger played on me."

"Go on, Ned," said my father, with a resigned air.

"Well, it wuz de fift night o' de fever," said Uncle Ned, "an' I wuz a-tossin' and a-moanin', an' old Anniky jes' lay back in her cheer an' snored as ef a dozen frogs wuz in her throat. I wuz a-perishin' an' a-burnin' wid thirst, an' I hollered to Anniky; but, Lor'! I might as well 'a' hollered to a tombstone! It wuz ice I wanted; an' I knowed dar wuz a glass somewhar on my table wid cracked ice in it. Lor'! Lor'! how dry I wuz! I neber longed fer whiskey in my born days ez I panted fur dat ice. It wuz powerful dark, fur de grease wuz low in de lamp, an' de wick spluttered wid a dyin' flame. But I felt aroun' feeble-like an' slow, till my fingers touched a glass. I pulled it to me, an' I run my han' in an' grabbed de ice, as I s'posed, an' flung it in my mouf, an' crunched, an' crunched——"

Here there was an awful pause. Uncle Ned pointed his thumb at Anniky, looked wildly at my father, and said, in a hollow voice, "*It was Anniky's teef!*"

My father threw back his head and laughed as I had never heard him laugh. Mother from her sofa joined in.

I was doubled up like a jack-knife in the corner. But as
for the principals in the affair, neither of their faces moved
a muscle. They saw no joke. Aunt Anniky, in a dreadful, muffled, squashy sort of voice, took up the tale:

"Nexsh ting I knowed, Marsh Sharles, somebody's
sheizin' me by the head, a-jammin' it up ag'in' de wall,
a-jawin' at me like de Angel Gabriel at de rish ole sinners
in de bad plashe; an' dar wash ole Ned a-spittin' like a
black cat, an' a-howlin' so dreadful dat I tought he wash
de debil; an' when I got de light, dar wash my beautiful
chany teef a-flung aroun', like scattered seed-corn, on de
flo', an' Ned a-swearin' he'd have de law o' me."

"An' arter all dat," broke in Uncle Ned, "she pretends
to lay a claim fur my pig. But I says no, sir; I don't pay
nobody nothin' who's played me a trick like dat."

"Trick!" said Aunt Anniky, scornfully, "whar's de
trick? Tink I wanter yer ter eat my teef? An' furder-
mo,' Marsh Sharles, dar's jes' dis about it: when dat night
set in dar warn't no mo' hope for old Ned dan fur a
foundered sheep. Laws-a-massy! dat's why I went ter
sleep. I wanter ter hev strengt ter put on his burial-
clo'es in de mornin'. But don' yer see, Marsh Sharles, dat
when he got so mad it brought on a sweat dat *broke de
fever!* It saved him! But for all dat, arter munchin' an'
manglin' my chany teef, he had de imperdence ob tryin'
to 'prive me ob de pig I honestly 'arned."

It was a hard case. Uncle Ned sat there a very image
of injured dignity, while Aunt Anniky bound a red handkerchief around her mouth and fanned herself with her
turkey-tail.

"I am sure I don't know how to settle the matter," said
father, helplessly. "Ned, I don't see but you'll have to
pay up."

"Neber, Mars' Charles, neber."

"Well, suppose you get married?" suggested father, brilliantly. "That will unite your interests, you know."

Aunt Anniky tossed her head. Uncle Ned was old, wizened, wrinkled as a raisin, but he eyed Anniky over with a supercilious gaze, and said, with dignity, "Ef I wanted ter marry, I could git a likely young gal."

All the four points of Anniky's turban shook with indignation. "Pay me fur dem chany teef!" she hissed.

Some visitors interrupted the dispute at this time, and the two old darkies went away.

A week later Uncle Ned appeared, with rather a sheepish look.

"Well, Mars' Charles," he said, "I's about concluded dat I'll marry Anniky."

"Ah! is that so?"

"'Pears like it's de onliest way I can save my pig," said Uncle Ned, with a sigh. "When she's married she boun' ter *'bey* me. Women, 'bey your husbands; dat's what de good Book says."

"Yes, she will *bay* you, I don't doubt," said my father, making a pun that Uncle Ned could not appreciate.

"An' ef ever she opens her jaw ter me 'bout dem 'ar teef," he went on, "I'll *mash* her."

Uncle Ned tottered on his legs like an unscrewed fruit-stand, and I had my own opinion as to his "mashing" Aunt Anniky. This opinion was confirmed the next day when father offered her his congratulations. "You are old enough to know your own mind," he remarked.

"I's ole, maybe," said Anniky, "but so is a oak-tree, an' it's vigorous, I reckon. I's a purty vigorous sort o' growth myself, an' I reckon I'll have my own way with Ned. I'm gwine to fatten dem pigs o' hisn, an' you see ef I don't sell 'em nex' Christmas fur money 'nough ter git a new string o' chany teef."

"Look here, Anniky," said father, with a burst of generosity, "you and Ned will quarrel about those teeth till the day of doom; so I will make you a wedding-present of another set, that you may begin married life in harmony."

Aunt Anniky expressed her gratitude. "An' *dis* time," she said, with sudden fury, "I sleeps wid 'em *in*."

The teeth were presented, and the wedding-preparations began. The expectant bride went over to Ned's cabin and gave it such a clearing up as it had never had. But Ned did not seem happy. He devoted himself entirely to his pigs, and wandered about looking more wizened every day. Finally he came to our gate and beckoned to me mysteriously.

"Come over to my house, honey," he whispered, "an' bring a pen an' ink an' a piece o' paper wid yer. I wants yer ter write me a letter."

I ran into the house for my little writing-desk, and followed Uncle Ned to his cabin.

"Now, honey," he said, after barring the door carefully, "don't you ax me no questions, but jes' put down de words dat comes out o' my mouf on dat ar paper."

"Very well, Uncle Ned; go on."

"Anniky Hobbleston," he began, "dat weddin' ain't a-gwine ter come off. You cleans up too much ter suit me. I ain't used ter so much water splashin' aroun'. Dirt is warmin'. 'Spec' I'd freez dis winter if you wuz here. An' you got too much tongue. Besides, I's got another wife over in Tipper. An' I ain't a-gwine ter marry. As fur havin' de law, I's a leaving dese parts, an' I takes der pigs wid me. Yer can't fin' *dem*, an' yer can't fin' *me*. *Fur I ain't a-gwine ter marry.* I wuz born a bachelor, an' a bachelor will I represent myself befo' de judgment-seat.

If you gives yer promise ter say no mo' 'bout dis marryin' business, p'r'aps I'll come back some day. So no mo' at present, from your humble worshipper,

" NED CUDDY."

"Isn't that last part rather inconsistent?" said I, greatly amused.

"Yes, honey, if yer says so; an' it's kind o' soothin' to de feelin's ob a woman, yer know."

I wrote it all down and read it aloud to Uncle Ned.

"Now, my chile," he said, "I'm a-gwine ter git on my mule as soon as der moon rises, an' drive my pigs ter Col' Water Gap, whar I'll stay an' fish. Soon as I'm well gone, you take dis letter ter Anniky; but, *min'*, don't tell whar I's gone. An' if she takes it all right, an' promises ter let me alone, you write me a letter, an' I'll git de fust Methodis' preacher I run across in der woods ter read it ter me. Den, if it's all right, I'll come back an' weed yer flower-garden fur yer as purty as preachin'."

I agreed to do all Uncle Ned asked, and we parted like conspirators. The next morning Uncle Ned was missing, and, after waiting a reasonable time, I explained the matter to my parents, and went over with his letter to Aunt Anniky.

"Powers above!" was her only comment as I got through the remarkable epistle. Then, after a pause to collect her thoughts, she seized me by the shoulder, saying, "Run to yo' pappy, honey, quick, an' ax him if he's goin' ter stick to his bargain 'bout de teef. Yer know he p'intedly said dey wuz a *weddin'*-gif'."

Of course my father sent word that she must keep the teeth, and my mother added a message of sympathy, with a present of a pocket-handkerchief to dry Aunt Anniky's tears.

"But it's all right," said that sensible old soul, opening her piano-lid with a cheerful laugh. "Bless you, chile, it was de teef I wanted, not de man! An', honey, you jes' sen' word to dat shif'less old nigger, ef you know whar he's gone, to come back home and get his crap in de groun'; an', as far as *I'm* consarned, yer jes' let him know dat I wouldn't pick him up wid a ten-foot pole, not ef he wuz to beg me on his knees till de millennial day."

THE BOOK-CANVASSER.

ANONYMOUS.

[The unfortunate book-agent is one of the butts of modern humorists, as he is one of the torments of modern families. But those who know him best will have no apprehension of his going into a decline, either in numbers or in importunity, in consequence of the sarcasm of his enemies. We give the following stories without fear of hurting the feelings of any agent. The genuine book-agent has no feelings to be hurt, except when some victim, on whom he has wasted half an hour's eloquence, declines to take his book. It may be news to some that the marvellous erudition displayed by the agent is second-hand knowledge. He is loaded and primed by his publisher, to be discharged on the innocent and suffering public. The hero of our first sketch had got his story somewhat mixed.]

HE came into my office with a portfolio under his arm. Placing it upon the table, removing a ruined hat, and wiping his nose upon a ragged handkerchief that had been so long out of the wash that it was positively gloomy, he said,—

"Mr. ——, I'm canvassing for the National Portrait Gallery; very valuable work; comes in numbers, fifty cents apiece; contains pictures of all the great American

heroes from the earliest times down to the present day.
Everybody subscribing for it, and I want to see if I can't
take your name.

"Now, just cast your eyes over that," he said, opening
his book and pointing to an engraving. "That's—lemme
see—yes, that's Columbus. Perhaps you've heard sumfin'
about him? The publisher was telling me to-day before
I started out that he discovered—no; was it Columbus
that dis—oh, yes, Columbus he discovered America,—was
the first man here. He came over in a ship, the publisher
said, and it took fire, and he stayed on deck because his
father told him to, if I remember right, and when the old
thing busted to pieces he was killed. Handsome picture,
ain't it? Taken from a photograph; all of 'em are; done
especially for this work. His clothes are kinder odd, but
they say that's the way they dressed in them days.

"Look at this one. Now, isn't that splendid? That's
William Penn, one of the early settlers. I was reading
t'other day about him. When he first arrived he got a
lot of Indians up a tree, and when they shook some apples
down he set one on top of his son's head and shot an arrow
plump through it and never fazed him. They say it struck
them Indians cold, he was such a terrific shooter. Fine
countenance, hasn't he? Face shaved clean; he didn't
wear a moustache, I believe, but he seems to have let himself out on hair. Now, my view is that every man ought
to have a picture of that patriarch, so's to see how the fust
settlers looked and what kind of weskets they used to
wear. See his legs, too! Trousers a little short, maybe,
as if he was going to wade in a creek; but he's all there.
Got some kind of a paper in his hand, I see. Subscription-
list, I reckon. Now, how does that strike you?

"There's something nice. That, I think is—is—that—
a—a—yes, to be sure, Washington: you recollect him,

of course? Some people call him Father of his Country.
George—Washington. Had no middle name, I believe.
He lived about two hundred years ago, and he was a
fighter. I heard the publisher telling a man about him
crossing the Delaware River up yer at Trenton, and seems
to me, if I recollect right, I've read about it myself. He
was courting some girl on the Jersey side, and he used to
swim over at nights to see her when the old man was
asleep. The girl's family were down on him, I reckon.
He looks like a man to do that, don't he? He's got it in
his eye. If it'd been me I'd gone over on a bridge; but
he probably wanted to show off afore her; some men are
so reckless, you know. Now, if you'll conclude to take
this I'll get the publisher to write out some more stories,
and bring 'em round to you, so's you can study up on him.
I know he did ever so many other things, but I've forgot
'em; my memory's so awful poor.

"Less see! Who have we next? Ah, Franklin! Ben-
jamin Franklin! He was one of the old original pioneers,
I think. I disremember exactly what he is celebrated for,
but I think it was a flying a—oh, yes, flying a kite, that's
it. The publisher mentioned it. He was out one day
flying a kite, you know, like boys do nowadays, and while
she was a-flickering up in the sky, and he was giving her
more string, an apple fell off a tree and hit him on the
head; then he discovered the attraction of gravitation, I
think they call it. Smart, wasn't it? Now, if you or
me'd 'a' been hit, it'd just 'a' made us mad, like as not, and
set us a-ravin'. But men are so different. One man's
meat's another man's pison. See what a double chin he's
got. No beard on him, either, though a goatee would
have been becoming to such a round face. He hasn't got
on a sword, and I reckon he was no soldier; fit some when
he was a boy, maybe, or went out with the home-guard,

but not a regular warrior. I ain't one myself, and I think all the better of him for it.

"Ah, here we are! Look at that! Smith and Poca-hontas! John Smith! Isn't that gorgeous? See how she kneels over him, and sticks out her hands while he lays on the ground and that big fellow with a club tries to hammer him up. Talk about woman's love! There it is for you. Modocs, I believe; anyway, some Indians out West there, somewheres; and the publisher tells me that Captain Shackanasty, or whatever his name is, there, was going to bang old Smith over the head with a log of wood, and this here girl she was sweet on Smith, it appears, and she broke loose, and jumped forward, and says to the man with a stick, 'Why don't you let John alone? Me and him are going to marry, and if you kill him I'll never speak to you as long as I live,' or words like them, and so the man he give it up, and both of them hunted up a preacher and were married and lived happy ever after-ward. Beautiful story, isn't it? A good wife she made him, too, I'll bet, if she was a little copper-colored. And don't she look just lovely in that picture? But Smith appears kinder sick; evidently thinks his goose is cooked; and I don't wonder, with that Modoc swooping down on him with such a discouraging club.

"And now we come to—to—ah—to—Putnam,—General Putnam: he fought in the war, too; and one day a lot of 'em caught him when he was off his guard, and they tied him flat on his back on a horse and then licked the horse like the very mischief. And what does that horse do but go pitching down about four hundred stone steps in front of the house, with General Putnam lying there nearly skeered to death! Leastways, the publisher said some-how that way, and I once read about it myself. But he came out safe, and I reckon sold the horse and made a pretty good thing of it. What surprises me is he didn't break his neck; but maybe it was a mule, for they're pretty sure-footed, you know. Surprising what some of these men have gone through, ain't it?

"Turn over a couple of leaves. That's General Jackson. My father shook hands with him once. He was a fighter, I know. He fit down in New Orleans. Broke up the rebel Legislature, and then when the Ku-Kluxes got after him he fought 'em behind cotton breastworks and licked 'em till they couldn't stand. They say he was terrific when he got real mad,—hit straight from the shoulder, and fetched his man every time. Andrew his fust name was; and look how his hair stands up.

"And then here's John Adams, and Daniel Boone, and two or three pirates, and a whole lot more pictures; so you see it's cheap as dirt. Lemme have your name, won't you?"

[The agent next to be considered knew his business better.]

THE MERCHANT AND THE BOOK-AGENT.

A book-agent importuned James Watson, a rich merchant living a few miles out of the city, until he bought a book,—the "Early Christian Martyrs." Mr. Watson didn't want the book, but he bought it to get rid of the agent; then, taking it under his arm, he started for the train which takes him to his office in the city.

Mr. Watson hadn't been gone long before Mrs. Watson came home from a neighbor's. The book-agent saw her, and went in and persuaded the wife to buy a copy of the book. She was ignorant of the fact that her husband had bought the same book in the morning. When Mr. Watson came back in the evening, he met his wife with a cheery smile as he said, "Well, my dear, how have you enjoyed yourself to-day? Well, I hope?"

"Oh, yes! had an early caller this morning."

"Ah, and who was she?"

"It wasn't a 'she' at all; it was a gentleman,—a book-agent"

"A what?"

"A book-agent; and to get rid of his importuning I bought his book,—the 'Early Christian Martyrs.' See, here it is," she exclaimed, advancing towards her husband.

"I don't want to see it," said Watson, frowning terribly.

"Why, husband?" asked his wife.

"Because that rascally book-agent sold me the same book this morning. Now we've got two copies of the same book,—two copies of the 'Early Christian Martyrs,' and——"

"But, husband, we can——"

"No, we can't, either!" interrupted Mr. Watson. "The man is off on the train before this. Confound it! I could kill the fellow. I——"

"Why, there he goes to the dépôt now," said Mrs. Watson, pointing out of the window at the retreating form of the book-agent making for the train.

"But it's too late to catch him, and I'm not dressed. I've taken off my boots, and——"

Just then Mr. Stevens, a neighbor of Mr. Watson, drove by, when Mr. Watson pounded on the window-pane in a frantic manner, almost frightening the horse.

"Here, Stevens!" he shouted, "you're hitched up! Won't you run your horse down to the train and hold that book-agent till I come? Run! Catch 'im now!"

"All right," said Mr. Stevens, whipping up his horse and tearing down the road.

Mr. Stevens reached the train just as the conductor shouted, "All aboard!"

"Book-agent!" he yelled, as the book-agent stepped on the train. "Book-agent! hold on! Mr. Watson wants to see you."

"Watson? Watson wants to see me?" repeated the seemingly puzzled book-agent. "Oh, I know what he wants: he wants to buy one of my books; but I can't miss the train to sell it to him."

"If that is all he wants, I can pay for it and take it back to him. How much is it?"

"Two dollars, for the 'Early Christian Martyrs,'" said the book-agent, as he reached for the money and passed the book out the car-window.

Just then Mr. Watson arrived, puffing and blowing, in his shirt-sleeves. As he saw the train pull out he was too full for utterance.

"Well, I got it for you," said Stevens,—"just got it, and that's all."

"Got what?" yelled Watson.

"Why, I got the book,—'Early Christian Martyrs,'—and paid——"

"By—the—great—guns!" moaned Watson, as he placed his hand to his brow and swooned right in the middle of the street.

BRER RABBIT AND THE TAR-BABY.

JOEL CHANDLER HARRIS.

[The fable, which has been a favorite form of literature with all nations at a certain stage of intellectual progress, is well developed among the negroes of the South, who possess a plentiful stock of animal-stories of the same general character as the "Reynard the Fox" of early European literature. It is of interest to find that in these narratives the fox, the exemplar of cunning in Aryan fable, is constantly outwitted by the rabbit, a creature usually considered a type of stupidity. Of the renditions of these stories, that of Joel Chandler Harris is much the best, and his "Uncle Remus" is an original of much merit in himself. We append the introduction to Uncle Remus's narrations, and the "Tar-Baby" story, the favorite fable of the negro folk-lore. Mr. Harris was born at Eatonton, Georgia, in 1848, became a journalist of Atlanta, and has industriously gathered from the colored population of that vicinity the large stock of popular fables which he has so skilfully rendered into dialectic English.]

ONE evening recently, the lady whom Uncle Remus calls "Miss Sally" missed her little seven-year-old. Making search for him through the house and through the yard, she heard the sound of voices in the old man's cabin, and, looking through the window, saw the child sitting by Uncle Remus. His head rested against the old man's arm, and he was gazing with an expression of the most intense interest into the rough, weather-beaten face that beamed so kindly upon him. This is what "Miss Sally" heard:

"Bimeby, one day, arter Brer Fox bin doin' all dat he could fer ter ketch Brer Rabbit, en Brer Rabbit bin doin' all he could fer ter keep 'im fum it, Brer Fox say to hisse'f dat he'd put up a game on Brer Rabbit, en he ain't mo'n got de wuds out'n his mouf twel Brer Rabbit come a-lopin' up de big road, lookin' des ez plump en ez fat en ez sassy ez a Moggin hoss in a barley-patch.

"'Hol' on dar, Brer Rabbit,' sez Brer Fox, sezee.

"'I ain't got time, Brer Fox,' sez Brer Rabbit, sezee, sorter mendin' his licks.

"'I wanter have some confab wid you, Brer Rabbit,' sez Brer Fox, sezee.

"'All right, Brer Fox, but you better holler fum whar

you stan': I'm monstus full er fleas dis mawnin',' sez Brer
Rabbit, sezee.

" ' I seed Brer B'ar yistiddy,' sez Brer Fox, sezee, ' en he
sorter raked me over de coals kaze you en me ain't make
frens en live naberly, en I told him dat I'd see you.'

" Den Brer Rabbit scratch one year wid his off hine-foot
sorter jub'usly, en den he ups en sez, sezee,—

" ' All a-settin', Brer Fox. S'posen you drap roun' ter-
morrer en take dinner wid me. We ain't got no great
doin's at our house, but I speck de ole 'oman en de chilluns
kin sort o' scramble roun' en git up sump'n fer ter stay yo'
stummuck.'

" ' I'm 'gree'ble, Brer Rabbit,' sez Brer Fox, sezee.

" ' Den I'll 'pen' on you,' says Brer Rabbit, sezee.

" Nex' day, Mr. Rabbit an' Miss Rabbit got up soon, 'fo'
day, en raided on a gyarden like Miss Sally's out dar, en
got some cabbiges, en some roas'n-years, en some sparrer-
grass, en dey fix up a smashin' dinner. Bimeby one er de
little Rabbits, playin' out in de back-yard, come runnin' in
hollerin', ' Oh, ma! oh, ma! I seed Mr. Fox a-comin'!' En
den Brer Rabbit he tuck de chilluns by der years en make
um set down, and den him en Miss Rabbit sorter dally
roun' waitin' for Brer Fox. En dey keep on waitin', but
no Brer Fox ain't come. Atter while Brer Rabbit goes to
de do', easy like, en peep out, en dar, stickin' out fum behime de cornder, wuz de tip-een' er Brer Fox's tail. Den
Brer Rabbit shot de do' en sot down, en put his paws behime his years, en begin fer ter sing :

> " ' De place wharbouts you spill de grease,
>   Right dar youer boun' ter slide,
>   An' whar you fine a bunch er ha'r,
>   You'll sholy fine de hide !' "

" Nex' day Brer Fox sont word by Mr. Mink en skuze
hisse'f kaze he wuz too sick fer ter come, en he ax Brer

Rabbit fer ter come en take dinner wid him, en Brer Rabbit say he wuz 'gree'ble.

"Bimeby, w'en de shadders wuz at der shortes', Brer Rabbit he sorter brush up en santer down ter Brer Fox's house, en w'en he got dar he yer somebody groanin', en he look in de do', en dar he see Brer Fox settin' up in a rockin'-cheer all wrop up wid flannil, en he look mighty weak. Brer Rabbit look all 'roun', he did, but he ain't see no dinner. De dish-pan wuz settin' on de table, en close by wuz a kyarvin'-knife.

"'Look like you gwineter have chicken fer dinner, Brer Fox,' sez Brer Rabbit, sezee.

"'Yes, Brer Rabbit, deyer nice en fresh en tender,' sez Brer Fox, sezee.

"Den Brer Rabbit sorter pull his mustarsh, en say, 'You ain't got no' calamus-root, is you, Brer Fox? I done got so now dat I can't eat no' chicken 'ceppin' she's seasoned up wid calamus-root.' En wid dat Brer Rabbit lipt out er de do' and dodge 'mong de bushes, en sot dar watchin' fer Brer Fox; en he ain't watch long, nudder, kaze Brer Fox flung off de flannil en crope out er de house en got whar he could close in on Brer Rabbit, en bimeby Brer Rabbit holler out, 'Oh, Brer Fox! I'll des put yo' calamus-root out yer on dis yer stump. Better come git it while hit's fresh.' And wid dat Brer Rabbit gallop off home. En Brer Fox ain't never kotch 'im yit, en w'at's mo', honey, he ain't gwineter."

"Didn't the fox *never* catch the rabbit, Uncle Remus?" asked the little boy the next evening.

"He come mighty nigh it, honey, sho's you bawn,— Brer Fox did. One day atter Brer Rabbit fool 'im wid dat calamus-root, Brer Fox went ter wuk en got 'im some tar, en mix it wid some turkentime, en fix up a contrapshun what he call a Tar-Baby, en he tuck dish yer Tar-

Baby en he sot 'er in de big road, en den he lay off in de bushes fer ter see wat de news wuz gwineter be. En he didn't hatter wait long, nudder, kaze bimeby here come Brer Rabbit pacin' down de road,—lippity-clippity, clippity-lippity,—des ez sassy ez a jay-bird. Brer Fox he lay low. Brer Rabbit come prancin' 'long twel he spy de Tar-Baby, en den he fotch up on his behime legs like he was 'stonished. De Tar-Baby she sot dar, she did, en Brer Fox he lay low.

" 'Mawnin' !' sez Brer Rabbit, sezee; 'nice wedder dis mawnin',' sezee.

" Tar-Baby ain't sayin' nuthin', en Brer Fox he lay low.

" 'How duz yo' sym'tums seem ter segashuate?' sez Brer Rabbit, sezee.

" Brer Fox he wink his eye slow, en lay low, en de Tar-Baby she ain't sayin' nuthin'.

" 'How you come on, den? Is you deaf?' sez Brer Rabbit, sezee. 'Kase if you is I kin holler louder,' sezee.

" Tar-baby lay still, en Brer Fox he lay low.

" ' Youer stuck up, dat's w'at you is,' says Brer Rabbit, sezee, ' en I'm gwineter kyore you, dat's w'at I'm a-gwineter do,' sezee.

" Brer Fox he sorter chuckle in his stummuck, he did, but Tar-Baby ain't sayin' nuthin'.

" ' I'm gwineter larn you howter talk ter 'specttubble fokes ef hit's de las' ack,' sez Brer Rabbit, sezee. ' Ef you don't take off dat hat en tell me howdy, I'm gwineter bus' you wide open,' sezee.

" Tar-Baby stay still, en Brer Fox he lay low.

" Brer Rabbit keep on axin' 'im, en de Tar-Baby she keep on sayin' nuthin', twel present'y Brer Rabbit draw back wid his fis', he did, en blip he tuck er side er de head. Right dar's whar he broke his merlasses-jug. His fis' stuck,

II.—*f*

en he can't pull loose. De tar hilt him. But Tar-Baby she stay still, en Brer Fox he lay low.

" 'Ef you don't lemme loose, I'll knock you ag'in,' sez Brer Rabbit, sezee ; en wid dat he fotch 'er a wipe wid de udder han', en dat stuck. Tar-Baby she ain't sayin' nuthin', en Brer Fox he lay low.

" 'Tu'n me loose, fo' I kick de natal stuffin' outen you,' sez Brer Rabbit, sezee; but de Tar-Baby she ain't sayin' nuthin'. She des hilt on, en den Brer Rabbit lose de use er his feet in de same way. Brer Fox he lay low. Den Brer Rabbit squall out dat ef de Tar-Baby don't tu'n 'im loose he butt 'er crank-sided. En den he butted, en his head got stuck. Den Brer Fox he santered fort', lookin' des ez innercent ez wunner yo' mammy's mockin'-birds.

" 'Howdy, Brer Rabbit?' sez Brer Fox, sezee. 'You look sorter stuck up dis mawnin',' sezee ; en den he rolled on de groun', en laft en laft twel he couldn't laff no mo'. 'I speck you'll take dinner wid me dis time, Brer Rabbit. I done laid in some calamus-root, en I ain't gwineter take no skuse,' sez Brer Fox, sezee."

Here uncle Remus paused, and drew a two-pound yam out of the ashes.

"Did the fox eat the rabbit?" asked the little boy to whom the story had been told.

"Dat's all de fur de tale goes," replied the old man. "He mout, en den ag'in he moutent. Some say Jedge B'ar come 'long en loosed 'im; some say he didn't. I hear Miss Sally callin'. You better run 'long." . . .

"Uncle Remus," said the little boy one evening, when he had found the old man with little or nothing to do, "did the fox kill and eat the rabbit when he caught him with the Tar-Baby?"

"Law, honey, ain't I tell you 'bout dat?" replied the old darky, chuckling slyly. "I 'clar ter grashus I ought er tole you dat; but ole man Nod wuz ridin' on my eyelids twel a leetle mo'n I'd 'a' dis'member'd my own name, en den on to dat here come yo' mammy hollerin' atter you.

"W'at I tell you w'en I fus' begin? I tole you Brer Rabbit wuz a monstus soon beas'; leas'ways dat's w'at I laid out fer ter tell you. Well, den, honey, don't you go en make no udder kalkalashuns, kaze in dem days Brer Rabbit en his family wuz at de head er de gang w'en enny racket wuz on han', en dar dey stayed. 'Fo' you begins fer ter wipe yo' eyes 'bout Brer Rabbit, you wait en see whar'bouts Brer Rabbit gwineter fetch up at. But dat's needer yer ner dar.

"W'en Brer Fox fine Brer Rabbit mixt up wid de Tar-Baby, he feel mighty good, en he roll on de groun' en laff. Bimeby he up 'n' say, sezee,—

"'Well, I speck I got you dis time, Brer Rabbit,' sezee; 'maybe I ain't, but I speck I is. You been runnin' roun' here sassin' atter me a mighty long time, but I speck you done come ter de een' er de row. You bin cuttin' up yo' capers en bouncin' roun' in dis naberhood ontwel you come ter b'leeve yo'se'f de boss er de whole gang. En den youer allers some'rs whar you got no bizness,' sez Brer Fox, sezee. 'Who ax you fer ter come en strike up a 'quaintence wid dish yer Tar-Baby? En who stuck you up dar whar you iz? Nobody in de roun' worril. You des tuck en jam yo'se'f on dat Tar-Baby widout waitin' fer enny invite,' sez Brer Fox, sezee, 'en dar you is, en dar you'll stay twel I fixes up a bresh-pile and fires her up, kase I'm gwineter bobbycue you dis day, sho,' sez Brer Fox, sezee.

"Den Brer Rabbit talk mighty 'umble.

"'I don't keer w'at you do wid me, Brer Fox,' sezee, 'so you don't fling me in dat brier-patch. Roas' me, Brer Fox,' sezee, 'but don't fling me in dat brier-patch,' sezee.

"'Hit's so much trouble fer ter kindle a fier,' sez Brer Fox, sezee, 'dat I speck I'll hatter hang you,' sezee.

"'Hang me des ez high ez you please, Brer Fox,' sez Brer Rabbit, sezee, 'but do fer de Lord's sake don't fling me in dat brier-patch,' sezee.

"'I ain't got no string,' sez Brer Fox, sezee, 'en now I speck I'll hatter drown you,' sezee.

"'Drown me ez deep ez you please, Brer Fox,' sez Brer Rabbit, sezee, 'but do don't fling me in dat brier-patch,' sezee.

"'Dey ain't no water nigh,' sez Brer Fox, sezee, 'en now I speck I'll hatter skin you,' sezee.

"'Skin me, Brer Fox,' sez Brer Rabbit, sezee, 'snatch out my eyeballs, t'ar out my years by de roots, en cut off my legs,' sezee, 'but do please, Brer Fox, don't fling me in dat brier-patch,' sezee.

"Co'se Brer Fox wanter hurt Brer Rabbit bad ez he kin, so he cotch him by de behime legs en slung 'im right in de middle er de brier-patch. Dar wuz a considerbul flutter whar Brer Rabbit struck de bushes, en Brer Fox sorter hang roun' fer ter see what wuz gwineter happen. Bimeby he hear somebody call 'im, en way up de hill he see Brer Rabbit settin' cross-legged on a chinkapin log koamin' de pitch outen his har wid a chip. Den Brer Fox know dat he bin swop off mighty bad. Brer Rabbit wuz bleedzed fer ter fling back some er his sass, en he holler out,—

"'Bred en bawn in a brier-patch, Brer Fox,—bred en bawn in a brier-patch!' en wid dat he skip out des ez lively ez a cricket in de embers."

THE MARRIAGE OF BAPTISTE.

TIMOTHY FLINT.

[Timothy Flint, the author of "Ten Years in the Valley of the Mississippi" and "Geography of the Mississippi Valley," was born in Massachusetts in 1780, and died in the same State in 1840. He travelled considerably in the then almost unknown regions described in his works, whither he went as a missionary in 1815. He was the author also of "Arthur Clenning" and other novels. His Western experiences are often told in a lively manner, as in the following story from "The Shoshonee Valley."]

BAPTISTE, always a standing lover and gallant for all the undistinguished Indian girls of the nation, had been observed in earnest dialogue with T'selle'nee, or the *Peony*, the pretty daughter of Mon-son-sah, or the *Spotted Panther*, a proud and fine Shienne warrior, who doted on this his only child. What injury or insult was offered the belle of round and vermilion-rouged cheek does not appear; but next morning it was the current gossip among the fair of the nation that T'selle'nee had had a "medicine-dream." At any rate, she was reported to be in tears, shut up under the customary and severest interdiction of Indian usage. . . . There was a great trouble in the wigwam. The fierce father forced his daughter to confession. The smooth-tongued and voluble Canadian had vague intimations that this affair was likely to bring no good to him. Truth was, as a general lover, he had the reputation of being particularly slippery and unworthy of confidence. Various girls had made calculation upon him for a husband. But Baptiste had a manifest preference for being a general lover, and a specific aversion to matrimony in particular.

Whoever among this people has had a dream of sufficient

II.   8

import to cause the dreamer to wear black paint and to proclaim an interdict becomes for the time a subject of universal speculation and remark. The general whisper, especially among the women, was, What has Baptiste done? and, What has caused the interdict of T'selle'nee?

Mon-son-sah, meanwhile, was not idle. The deepest indignation of his burning spirit was called forth. The frequent amours and infidelities of Baptiste were circulated, and generally not at all to his advantage. An affair of his, touching a Shoshonee girl, was blazoned with many a minute circumstance of wanton cruelty. "What right," they said, "had the proud and babbling pale-face to conduct himself after this fashion toward the red-skin girls? They would teach him to repent such courses." The cunning young T'selle'nee, though interdicted, and of course supposed to be unable to see or converse with any one, was in fact at the bottom of all this.

The result of the long-brooded mischief was at length disclosed. Hatch was the envoy of Mon-son-sah to Baptiste Dettier, to make known to him the purposes that were settled in respect to his case. Hatch, Dutch though he was, enjoyed a comfortable broad joke. . . . Baptiste in passing heard him call him to stop, with a pale face and palpitating heart. He seemed disposed to walk on.

"Will you stop, Mynheer Baptiste?" said the Dutchman, with a visage of mysterious importance. "Perhaps you will find it to your interest to hear what I have to say to you?"

"Vell, sare," said Baptiste, stopping and squaring himself, "suppose you tell me vat for you stop me from mine promenade. Is it von mighty dem big ting dat you hab to tell me?"

"Oh, no, Mynheer Baptiste, it is no great matter. It only concerns your life."

"Sacre! Monsieur Dutchman," cried Baptiste, shrugging and turning pale, "s'pose you tink it von mighty dem leet ting to concern my life. Monsieur Dutchman, vat for make you look so dem big? I pray you, sare, speak out vat for you stop me."

The Dutchman continued to economize the luxury of his joke as long as possible, and proceeded in his customary dialect, and with the most perfect *sang-froid*, to ask him if he had ever known such an Indian demoiselle as T'selle'nee.

"Sare, vat for you ax me dat? 'Tis mine own affair, sare."

"Well, Baptiste, they say she has had a dream, and that her face is painted as black as a thunder-cloud. It is common report that the matter closely concerns you. At any rate, the Spotted Panther is not to be trifled with, and he takes a deep interest in the business. You know the Spotted Panther?"

"Yes, sare, dat garçon is one dem farouche villain."

"Perhaps you like his daughter better?"

"Sacre! no. She is von dem—what you call him in Hinglees?"

"Never mind. She will make you the better wife for that. I have an errand to you from the Spotted Panther."

"You make me frissonne all over my body," said Baptiste, looking deadly pale.

"I have it in charge from the Spotted Panther to ask you, Baptiste, if you are disposed to marry T'selle'nee as soon as she is out of her black paint and her dream. They say she loves you to distraction."

"Sez bien," replied Baptiste, giving his wonted shrug of self-complacency; "so do twenty oder demoiselles of dese dem sauvages. Dat all for vat you stop me?"

"No. I am commissioned only to propose to you the

simple question, Do you choose to marry T'selle'nee, or not? And you are to let me report an immediate answer."

"Parbleu, Monsieur Dutchman. S'pose I say no?"

"You will hear the consequences, and then I will say him no, if you wish it."

"Vell, sare, what are de big consequence if I say no? 'Tis von dem farouche affair, ça!"

"He proposes to you one of two alternatives,—to marry his daughter, or be roasted alive at a slow fire. It is no great matter, after all. The beautiful T'selle'nee, or a roasting,—that's the alternative."

"'Tis von dem—what you call him, alternateeve? O mon Dieu! mon Dieu!" cried Baptiste, crossing himself, and seeming in an agony. "You dem Dutchman have no heart on your body, or you no tell me dat dem word and half grin your teeth all the time, sacre! You call him leet matter to roast von Christian like a pig, sacre!"

"Why, certainly, you don't think it so great a thing to be roasted? You know, Baptiste, that an Indian smokes his pipe, and sings songs, and tells stories, and provokes his roasters, and thinks it little more than a comfort to be roasted."

"O ciel!" cried the Canadian, apparently feeling faint at the horror of the idea. "You are von dem hard-heart Dutchman, to make sport of dis farouche affair!"

"Still, Baptiste, something must be done. You know the Spotted Panther is not a personage to be trifled with. Have you made up your mind for your answer?"

"'Tis von dem sommaire business, ça! O mon Dieu, aidez-moi! Oui, oui. I vill marree dis dem crapeau. S'pose—how like dem fool you talk!—that it be von leet ting to be roast? Certainement, me no make experimong."

"Very good," answered Hatch, with the same unmoved calmness. "Then we need not discuss the matter of roasting at all. I thought you would prefer the wife. But you will please tell me the very words I am to report to the Spotted Panther."

"O mon Dieu! 'Tis trop dur, a ting très-misérable. Me love all de demoiselles. Dey all love me. 'Tis ver hard affair, to tie me up to von dem crapeau, like un chien in a string."

"Are these the words you wish me to carry back to the Spotted Panther?"

"No, certainement, no. You tell that savage gentilhomme, vid my best complimens, that I am trop sensible of de great honneur which his belle fille have done me. S'pose his belle fille no say that word to me fuss, den I tell her I offer my love and my devotions and my heart wid von satisfaction infini, and dat I lead her to de altare with great plaisir, sacre!"

Hatch omitted the last word, and reported all the rest with great fidelity. The invincible solemnity of the Dutchman's narrative gave greater zest to the enjoyment of the Indians, who all knew, amid these forced compliments, what a bitter pill matrimony was to such an indiscriminate gallant.

PAN IN WALL STREET.

A.D. 1867.

EDMUND CLARENCE STEDMAN.

[Edmund Clarence Stedman, born at Hartford, Connecticut, in 1833, ranks high in our present generation of poets, while as a critical essayist on modern poets and poetry he has no superior. His "Victorian Poets" and other critical essays, with his several volumes of poetry, are productions of high merit and much popularity. Though

II.   8*

not often indulging in humor, he leans strongly in that direction in the following example, which, while "caviare to the general," will have a fine flavor for the lovers of classical literature.]

JUST where the Treasury's marble front
  Looks over Wall Street's mingled nations,
Where Jews and Gentiles most are wont
  To throng for trade and last quotations,—
Where, hour by hour, the rates of gold
  Outrival, in the ears of people,
The quarter-chimes, serenely tolled
  From Trinity's undaunted steeple,—

Even there I heard a strange, wild strain
  Sound high above the modern clamor,
Above the cries of greed and gain,
  The curbstone war, the auction's hammer;
And swift, on music's misty ways,
  It led, from all this strife for millions,
To ancient, sweet-do-nothing days
  Among the kirtle-robed Sicilians.

And as it stilled the multitude,
  And yet more joyous rose, and shriller,
I saw the minstrel where he stood
  At ease against a Doric pillar;
One hand a droning organ played,
  The other held a Pan's pipe (fashioned
Like those of old) to lips that made
  The reeds give out that strain impassioned.

'Twas Pan himself that wandered here,—
  A-strolling through this sordid city,
And piping to the civic ear
  The prelude of some pastoral ditty!

The demi-god had crossed the seas—
  From haunts of shepherd, nymph, and satyr,
And Syracusan times—to these
  Far shores and twenty centuries later.

A ragged cap was on his head;
  But—hidden thus—there was no doubting
That, all with crispy locks o'erspread,
  His gnarléd horns were somewhere sprouting;
His club-feet, cased in rusty shoes,
  Were crossed, as on some frieze you see them,
And trousers, patched of divers hues,
  Concealed his crooked shanks beneath them.

He filled the quivering reeds with sound,
  And o'er his mouth their changes shifted,
And with his goat's-eyes looked around
  Where'er the passing current drifted;
And soon, as on Trinacrian hills
  The nymphs and herdsmen ran to hear him,
Even now the tradesmen from their tills,
  With clerks and porters, crowded near him.

The bulls and bears together drew
  From Jauncey Court and New Street Alley,
As erst, if pastorals be true,
  Came beasts from every wooded valley;
The random passers stayed to list,—
  A boxer Ægon, rough and merry;
A Broadway Daphnis, on his tryst
  With Nais at the Brooklyn Ferry;

A one-eyed Cyclops halted long
  In tattered cloak of army pattern;
And Galatea joined the throng,—
  A blowsy, apple-vending slattern;

While old Silenus staggered out
  From some new-fangled lunch-house handy,
And bade the piper, with a shout,
  To strike up Yankee Doodle Dandy.

A newsboy and a peanut-girl
  Like little fawns began to caper,—
His hair was all in tangled curl,
  Her tawny legs were bare and taper;
And still the gathering larger grew,
  And gave its pence and crowded nigher,
While aye the shepherd-minstrel blew
  His pipe, and struck the gamut higher.

O heart of Nature, beating still
  With throbs her vernal passion taught her,
Even here as on the vine-clad hill
  Or by the Arethusan water!
New forms may fold the speech, new lands
  Arise within these ocean portals,
But music waves eternal wands,
  Enchantress of the souls of mortals!

So thought I; but among us trod
  A man in blue, with legal baton,
And scoffed the vagrant demi-god,
  And pushed him from the steps I sat on;
Doubting, I mused upon the cry,
  "Great Pan is dead!"—and all the people
Went on their ways; and clear and high
  The quarter sounded from the steeple.

EPIGRAMS.

Among the humorous productions of mankind the epigram ranks
high, yielding sparkling fragments of versified wit that seem to glitter
from every word as the diamond from every facet.   The world's literary museum is well stored with specimens of this condensed wisdom,
of which we offer a few anonymous examples.   What an epigram is,
or should be, can be best told by an epigram:

> THE qualities all in a bee that we meet
>   In an epigram never should fail:
> The body should always be little and sweet,
>   And a sting should be felt in the tail.

Or, as still more briefly photographed,—

> What is an epigram?   A dwarfish whole;
> Its body brevity, and wit its soul.

The following on wit has the same application:

> True wit is like the brilliant stone
>   Dug from the Indian mine,
> Which boasts two various powers in one,—
>   To cut as well as shine.
> Genius, like that, if polished right
>   With the same gift abounds;
> Appears at once both keen and bright,
>   And sparkles while it wounds.

With these introductory examples we give a series of epigrams
selected from the multitude afloat upon the stream of literature.

> A fool does never change his mind;
>   But who can think that strange?
> The reason's clear, for fools, my friends,
>   Have not a mind to change.

Your comedy I've read, my friend,
 And like the half you pilfered best;
But sure the piece you yet may mend:
 Take courage, man, and steal the rest.

I cannot praise the doctor's eyes,
 I never saw his glance divine;
For when he prays he shuts his eyes,
 And when he preaches he shuts mine.

May never lady press his lips,
 His proffered love returning,
Who makes a furnace of his mouth
 And keeps its chimney burning.
May each true woman shun his sight
 For fear the fumes might choke her,
And none but those who smoke themselves
 Have kisses for a smoker.

With whiskers thick upon my face
 I went my fair to see;
She told me she could never love
 A bear-faced chap like me.
I shaved them clean, and called again,
 And thought my trouble o'er;
She laughed outright, and said I was
 More bare-faced than before.

"I cannot conceive," said a lady one day,
"Why my hair all at once should be growing so gray;
Perhaps," she continued, "the change may be due
To my daily cosmetic, the essence of rue."
"That may be," said a wag, "but I'll really protest
The essence of Time (thyme) will account for it best."

An album, prythee, what is it?
A book I always shun;
Kept to be filled with others' wit
By people that have none.

What is the reason—can you guess?—
Why men are poor, and women thinner?
So much do they for dinner dress,
There's nothing left to dress for dinner.

Vanity Fair is responsible for the following:

"Old dog Tray's ever faithful," they say,
But the dog who is faithful can never be-Tray.

As Pat, an old joker, and Yankee more sly,
Once, riding together, a gallows passed by,
Said the Yankee to Pat, "If I don't make too free,
Give the gallows its due, and pray where would you be?"
"Why, honey," said Pat, "'faith that's easily known:
I'd be riding to town by myself all alone."

He who a watch would keep,
This he must do,
Pocket his watch
And watch his pocket too.

The earliest incident in the history of the human race, as represented by Father Adam, is thus wittily epitomized:

He laid him down and slept, and from his side
A woman in her magic beauty rose:
Dazzled and charmed, he called the woman bride,
And his first sleep became his last repose.

"Is my wife out of spirits?" said Jones, with a sigh,
   As her voice of a tempest gave warning.
"Quite out, sir, indeed," was the servant's reply,
   "For she finished the bottle this morning."

"Friend Ass," said the Fox, as he met him one day,
"What can people mean? Do you know what they say?"
"No, I don't," said the Ass; "nor I don't care, not I."
"Why, they say you're a genius," was Reynard's reply.
"My stars!" muttered Jack, quite appalled by the word,
"What can I have done that's so very absurd?"

   A long way off Lucinda strikes the men;
      As she draws near,
      And one sees clear,
   A long way off one wishes her again.

On a wife who beat her husband:

"Come hither, Sir George, my picture is here;
   What think you, my love; does it strike you?"
"I can't say it does just at present, my dear,
   But I think it soon will, it's so like you."

RECIPE FOR A MODERN BONNET.

Two scraps of foundation, some fragments of lace,
A shower of French rose-buds to droop o'er the face;
Fine ribbons and feathers, with crape and illusion,
Then mix and *de*range them in graceful confusion;
Inveigle some fairy, out roaming for pleasure,
And beg the slight favor of taking her measure,
The length and the breadth of her dear little pate,
And hasten a miniature frame to create;
Then pour, as above, the bright mixture upon it,
And, lo! you possess " such a love of a bonnet!"

MY WIFE AND I.

As my wife and I at the window one day
   Stood watching a man with a monkey,
A cart came by, with a " broth of a boy,"
   Who was driving a stout little donkey.
To my wife I then spoke, by way of a joke,
   " There's a relation of yours in that carriage ;"
To which she replied, as the donkey she spied,
   " Ah, yes,—a relation *by marriage.*"

REQUEST AND REPLY.

How comes it, this delightful weather,
That U and I can't dine together ?

My worthy friend, it cannot B :
U cannot come till after T.

THE RHEUMATISM MOVEMENT-CURE.

ROBERT J. BURDETTE.

[Robert Jones Burdette was born at Greensborough, Pennsylvania, in 1844, but has resided during most of his life in the West, becoming an editor of the *Hawkeye* of Burlington, Iowa, about 1873. He has written much humorous prose and poetry, and is a lecturer of great popularity. As an example of his productions we submit the following, premising that the man who can read it without laughter is " fit for treason, stratagems, and spoils."]

ONE day, not a great while ago, Mr. Middlerib read in his favorite paper a paragraph stating that the sting of a bee was a sure cure for rheumatism, and citing several remarkable instances in which people had been perfectly cured by this abrupt remedy. Mr. Middlerib thought of the rheumatic twinges that grappled his knees once in a while and made his life a burden to him.

He read the article several times, and pondered over it. He understood that the stinging must be done scientifically and thoroughly. The bee, as he understood the article, was to be gripped by the ears and set down upon the rheumatic joint and held there until it stung itself stingless. He had some misgivings about the matter. He knew it would hurt. He hardly thought it could hurt any worse than the rheumatism, and it had been so many years since he was stung by a bee that he had almost forgotten what it felt like. He had, however, a general feeling that it would hurt some. But desperate diseases require desperate remedies, and Mr. Middlerib was willing to undergo any amount of suffering if it would cure his rheumatism.

He contracted with Master Middlerib for a limited supply of bees: humming and buzzing about in the summer air, Mr. Middlerib did not know how to get them. He felt, however, that he could safely depend upon the instincts and methods of boyhood. He knew that if there was any way in heaven whereby the shyest bee that ever lifted a two-hundred-pound man off the clover could be induced to enter a wide-mouthed glass bottle, his son knew that way.

For the small sum of one dime Master Middlerib agreed to procure several, to wit, six bees, sex and age not specified; but, as Mr. Middlerib was left in uncertainty as to the race, it was made obligatory upon the contractor to have three of them honey- and three humble-, or, in the generally-accepted vernacular, bumble-bees. Mr. M. did not tell his son what he wanted those bees for, and the boy went off on his mission with his head so full of astonishment that it fairly whirled. Evening brings all home, and the last rays of the declining sun fell upon Master Middlerib with a short, wide-mouthed bottle comfortably populated with hot, ill-natured bees, and Mr. Middlerib and a dime. The dime and the bottle changed hands. Mr. Middlerib put the bottle in his coat-pocket and went into the house, eying everybody he met very suspiciously, as though he had made up his mind to sting to death the first person who said "bee" to him. He confided his guilty secret to none of his family. He hid his bees in his bedroom, and as he looked at them just before putting them away he half wished the experiment was safely over. He wished the imprisoned bees did not look so hot and cross. With exquisite care he submerged the bottle in a basin of water and let a few drops in on the heated inmates to cool them off.

At the tea-table he had a great fright. Miss Middlerib, in the artless simplicity of her romantic nature, said,—

"I smell bees. How the odor brings up——"

But her father glared at her, and said, with superfluous harshness and execrable grammar,—

"Hush up! You don't smell nothing."

Whereupon Mrs. Middlerib asked him if he had eaten anything that disagreed with him, and Miss Middlerib said, "Why, pa!" and Master Middlerib smiled as he wondered.

Bedtime at last, and the night was warm and sultry. Under various false pretences, Mr. Middlerib strolled about the house until everybody else was in bed, and then he sought his room. He turned the lamp down until its feeble ray shone dimly as a death-light.

Mr. Middlerib disrobed slowly,—very slowly. When at last he was ready to go lumbering into his peaceful couch, he heaved a profound sigh, so full of apprehension and grief that Mrs. Middlerib, who was awakened by it, said if it gave him so much pain to come to bed perhaps he had better sit up all night. Mr. Middlerib choked another sigh, but said nothing and crept into bed. After lying still a few moments he reached out and got his bottle of bees.

It was not an easy thing to do to pick one bee out of the bottleful with his fingers and not get into trouble. The first bee Mr. Middlerib got was a little brown honey-bee, that wouldn't weigh half an ounce if you picked him up by the ears, but if you lifted him by the hind leg would weigh as much as the last end of a bay mule. Mr. Middlerib could not repress a groan.

"What's the matter with you?" sleepily asked his wife.

It was very hard for Mr. Middlerib to say he only felt hot, but he did it. He didn't have to lie about it, either. He did feel very hot indeed, about eighty-six all over, and one hundred and ninety-seven on the end of his thumb. He reversed the bee, and pressed the warlike terminus of it firmly against the rheumatic knee.

It didn't hurt so badly as he thought it would.

It didn't hurt at all.

Then Mr. Middlerib remembered that when the honey-bee stabs a human foe it generally leaves its harpoon in the wound, and the invalid knew that the only thing this bee had to sting with was doing its work at the end of his thumb. He reached his arm out from under the sheets and dropped this disabled atom of rheumatism liniment on the carpet. Then, after a second of blank wonder, he began to feel round for the bottle, and wished he knew what he did with it.

In the mean time strange things had been going on. When he caught hold of the first bee, Mr. Middlerib, for reasons, drew it out in such haste that for the time he forgot all about the bottle and its remedial contents, and left it lying uncorked in the bed, between himself and his innocent wife. In the darkness there had been a quiet but general emigration from that bottle. The bees, their wings clogged with the water Mr. Middlerib had poured upon them to cool and tranquillize them, were crawling aimlessly about over the sheet. While Mr. Middlerib was feeling around for it, his ears were suddenly thrilled and his heart frozen by a wild, piercing scream from his wife.

"Murder!" she screamed, "murder! Oh, help me! Help! help!"

Mr. Middlerib sat bolt upright in bed. His hair stood on end. The night was warm, but he turned to ice in a minute.

"Where in thunder," he said, with pallid lips, as he felt all over the bed in frenzied haste,—"where in thunder are them infernal bees?"

And a large "bumble," with a sting as pitiless as the finger of scorn, just then climbed up the inside of Mr. Middlerib's night-shirt, until it got squarely between his shoulders, and then it felt for his marrow, and he said, calmly,—

"Here is one of them."

And Mrs. Middlerib felt ashamed of her feeble screams when Mr. Middlerib threw up both arms, and, with a howl that made the windows rattle, roared,—

"Take him off! Oh, land of Scott, somebody take him off!"

And when a little honey-bee began tickling the sole of Mrs. Middlerib's foot, she so shrieked that the house was bewitched, and immediately went into spasms.

The household was aroused by this time. Miss Middlerib and Master Middlerib and the servants were pouring into the room, adding to the general confusion by howling at random and asking irrelevant questions, while they gazed at the figure of a man a little on in years, arrayed in a long night-shirt, pawing fiercely at the unattainable spot in the middle of his back, while he danced an unnatural, weird, wicked-looking jig by the dim, religious light of the night-lamp. And while he danced and howled, and while they gazed and shouted, a navy-blue wasp, that Master Middlerib had put in the bottle for good measure and variety and to keep the menagerie stirred up, had dried his legs and wings with a corner of the sheet, and, after a preliminary circle or two around the bed to get up his motion and settle down to a working gait, he fired himself across the room, and to his dying day Mr. Middlerib will always believe that one of the servants mistook him for a burglar and shot him.

No one, not even Mr. Middlerib himself, could doubt that he was, at least for the time, most thoroughly cured of rheumatism. His own boy could not have carried himself more lightly or with greater agility. But the cure was not permanent, and Mr. Middlerib does not like to talk about it.

THE HORSE-SWAP.

AUGUSTUS B. LONGSTREET.

[Of Southern humor we have no better examples than those in Longstreet's " Georgia Scenes, Characters, Incidents," etc., originally published as newspaper sketches, and afterwards gathered into a highly-popular volume. The author was born at Augusta, Georgia, in 1790, was for a while a Methodist minister, and afterwards at the head of several institutions of learning, being for many years President of the University of Mississippi. He died in 1870. We select one of the most amusing brief sketches in the work.]

DURING the session of the Supreme Court, in the village of ——, about three weeks ago, when a number of people

were collected in the principal street of the village, I observed a young man riding up and down the street, as I
supposed, in a violent passion. He galloped this way, then
that, and then the other ; spurred his horse to one group of
citizens, then to another ; then dashed off at half speed, as
if fleeing from danger ; and, suddenly checking his horse,
returned first in a pace, then in a trot, and then in a
canter. While he was performing these various evolutions, he cursed, swore, whooped, screamed, and tossed
himself in every attitude which man could assume on
horseback. In short, he *cavorted* most magnanimously (a
term which, in our tongue, expresses all that I have described, and a little more), and seemed to be setting all
creation at defiance. As I like to see all that is passing, I
determined to take a position a little nearer to him, and to
ascertain, if possible, what it was that affected him so sen-
sibly. Accordingly, I approached a crowd before which
he had stopped for a moment, and examined it with the
strictest scrutiny. But I could see nothing in it which
seemed to have anything to do with the cavorter. Every
man appeared to be in good humor, and all minding their
own business. Not one so much as noticed the principal
figure. Still he went on. After a semicolon pause, which
my appearance seemed to produce (for he eyed me closely
as I approached), he fetched a whoop, and swore that " he
could out-swap any live man, woman, or child that ever
walked those hills, or that ever straddled horseflesh since
the days of old daddy Adam. Stranger," said he to me,
" did you ever see the *Yallow* Blossom from Jasper ?"

" No," said I ; " but I have often heard of him."

" I'm the boy," continued he, " perhaps a *leetle*, jist a
leetle, of the best man at a hoss-swap that ever trod shoe-
leather."

I began to feel my situation a little awkward, when I

was relieved by a man somewhat advanced in years, who stepped up and began to survey the "Yallow Blossom's" horse with much apparent interest. This drew the rider's attention, and he turned the conversation from me to the stranger.

"Well, my old coon," said he, "do you want to swap hosses?"

"Why, I don't know," replied the stranger; "I believe I've got a beast I'd trade with you for that one, if you like him."

"Well, fetch up your nag, my old cock: you're jist the lark I wanted to get hold of. I am perhaps a *leetle*, jist a *leetle*, of the best man at a hoss-swap that ever stole *cracklin's* out of his mammy's fat-gourd. Where's your hoss?"

"I'll bring him presently; but I want to examine your horse a little."

"Oh, look at him," said the Blossom, alighting and hitting him a cut; "look at him. He's the best piece of hoss-flesh in the thirteen united univarsal worlds. There's no sort o' mistake in little Bullet. He can pick up miles on his feet and fling 'em behind him as fast as the next man's hoss, I don't care where he comes from. And he can keep at it as long as the sun can shine without resting."

During this harangue, little Bullet looked as if he understood it all, believed it, and was ready at any moment to verify it. He was a horse of goodly countenance, rather expressive of vigilance than fire; though an unnatural appearance of fierceness was thrown into it by the loss of his ears, which had been cropped pretty close to his head. Nature had done but little for Bullet's head and neck; but he managed, in a great measure, to hide their defects by bowing perpetually. He had obviously suffered severely for corn; but if his ribs and hip-bones had not disclosed the fact, *he* never would have done it; for he was

in all respects as cheerful and happy as if he commanded
all the corn-cribs and fodder-stacks in Georgia. His height
was about twelve hands; but, as his shape partook somewhat of that of the giraffe, his haunches stood much lower.
They were short, straight, peaked, and concave. Bullet's
tail, however, made amends for all his defects. All that
the artist could do to beautify it had been done; and all
that horse could do to compliment the artist Bullet did.
His tail was nicked in superior style, and exhibited the
line of beauty in so many directions that it could not fail
to hit the most fastidious taste in some of them. From
the root it drooped into a graceful festoon, then rose in a
handsome curve, then resumed its first direction, and then
mounted suddenly upward like a cypress knee to a perpendicular of about two and a half inches. The whole had
a careless and bewitching inclination to the right. Bullet
obviously knew where his beauty lay, and took all occasions
to display it to the best advantage. If a stick cracked,
or if any one moved suddenly about him, or coughed, or
hawked, or spoke a little louder than common, up went
Bullet's tail like lightning; and if the *going up* did not
please, the *coming down* must of necessity, for it was as
different from the other movement as was its direction.
The first was a bold and rapid flight upward, usually to
an angle of forty-five degrees. In this position he kept
his interesting appendage until he satisfied himself that
nothing in particular was to be done; when he commenced
dropping it by half-inches, in second beats, then in triple
time, then faster and shorter, and faster and shorter still,
until it finally died away imperceptibly into its natural
position. If I might compare sights to sounds, I should
say its *settling* was more like the note of a locust than
anything else in nature.

Either from native sprightliness of disposition, from uncontrollable activity, or from an unconquerable habit of removing flies by the stamping of the feet, Bullet never stood still, but always kept up a gentle fly-scaring movement of his limbs, which was peculiarly interesting.

"I tell you, man," proceeded the Yellow Blossom, "he's the best live hoss that ever trod the grit of Georgia. Bob Smart knows the hoss. Come here, Bob, and mount this hoss, and show Bullet's motions." Here Bullet bristled up, and looked as if he had been hunting for Bob all day long and had just found him. Bob sprang on his back.

"Boo-oo-oo!" said Bob, with a fluttering noise of the lips; and away went Bullet, as if in a quarter-race, with all his beauties spread in handsome style.

"Now fetch him back," said Blossom. Bullet turned, and came in pretty much as he went out.

"Now trot him by." Bullet reduced his tail to "customary," sidled to the right and left airily, and exhibited at least three varieties of trot in the short space of fifty yards.

"Make him pace." Bob commenced twitching the bridle and kicking at the same time. These inconsistent movements obviously (and most naturally) disconcerted Bullet; for it was impossible for him to learn from them whether he was to proceed or stand still. He started to trot, and was told that wouldn't do. He attempted a canter, and was checked again. He stopped, and was urged to go on. Bullet now rushed into the wild field of experiment, and struck out a gait of his own, that completely turned the tables upon his rider, and certainly deserved a patent. It seemed to have derived its elements from the jig, the minuet, and the cotillion. If it was not a pace, it certainly had *pace* in it, and no man would venture to call it anything else: so it passed off to the satisfaction of the owner.

"Walk him." Bullet was now at home again; and he walked as if money was staked on him.

The stranger, whose name, I afterwards learned, was Peter Ketch, having examined Bullet to his heart's content, ordered his son Neddy to go and bring up Kit. Neddy soon appeared upon Kit,—a well-formed sorrel of the middle size, and in good order. His *tout ensemble* threw Bullet entirely in the shade, though a glance was sufficient to satisfy any one that Bullet had the decided advantage of him in point of intellect.

"Why, man," said Blossom, "do you bring such a hoss as that to trade for Bullet? Oh, I see you've no notion of trading."

"Ride him off, Neddy," said Peter. Kit put off at a handsome lope. "Trot him back!" Kit came in at a long, sweeping trot, and stopped suddenly at the crowd.

"Well," said Blossom," "let me look at him: maybe he'll do to plough."

"Examine him!" said Peter, taking hold of the bridle close to the mouth. "He's nothing but a tacky. "He ain't as *pretty* a horse as Bullet, I know; but he'll do. Start 'em together for a hundred and fifty mile, and if Kit ain't twenty mile ahead of him at the coming out, any man may take Kit for nothing. But he's a monstrous mean horse, gentlemen; any man may see that. He's the scariest horse, too, you ever saw. He won't do to hunt on, nohow. Stranger, will you let Neddy have your rifle to shoot off him? Lay the rifle between his ears, Neddy, and shoot at the blaze in that stump. Tell me when his head is high enough."

Ned fired, and hit the blaze; and Kit did not move a hair's breadth.

"Neddy, take a couple of sticks and beat on that hogshead at Kit's tail."

Ned made a tremendous rattling, at which Bullet took fright, broke his bridle, and dashed off in grand style, and would have stopped all further negotiations by going home in disgust, had not a traveller arrested him and brought him back; but Kit did not move.

"I tell you, gentlemen," continued Peter, "he's the scariest horse you ever saw. He ain't as gentle as Bullet, but he won't do any harm if you watch him. Shall I put him in a cart, gig, or wagon for you, stranger? He'll cut the same capers there he does here. He's a monstrous mean horse."

During all this time Blossom was examining him with the nicest scrutiny. Having examined his frame and limbs, he now looked at his eyes.

"He's got a curious look out of his eyes," said Blossom.

"Oh, yes, sir," said Peter, "just as blind as a bat. Blind horses always have clear eyes. Make a motion at his eyes, if you please, sir."

Blossom did so, and Kit threw up his head rather if something pricked him under the chin than as if fearing a blow. Blossom repeated the experiment, and Kit jerked back in considerable astonishment.

"Stone-blind, you see, gentlemen," proceeded Peter; "but he's just as good to travel of a dark night as if he had eyes."

"Blame my buttons," said Blossom, "if I like them eyes."

"No," said Peter, "nor I neither. I'd rather have 'em made of diamonds; but they'll do, if they don't show as much white as Bullet's."

"Well," said Blossom, "make a pass at me."

"No: you made the banter, now make your pass."

"Well, I'm never afraid to price my horses. You must give me twenty-five dollars boot."

"Oh, certainly; say fifty, and my saddle and bridle in. Here, Neddy, my son, take away daddy's horse."

"Well," said Blossom, "I've made my pass, now make yours."

"I'm for short talk in a horse-swap, and therefore always tell a gentleman at once what I mean to do. You must give me ten dollars."

Blossom swore absolutely, roundly, and profanely that he never would give boot.

"Well," said Peter, "I didn't care about trading; but you cut such high shines that I thought I'd like to back you out, and I've done it. Gentlemen, you see I've brought him to a back."

"Come, old man," said Blossom, "I've been joking with you. I begin to think you do want to trade: therefore, give me five dollars and take Bullet. I'd rather lose ten dollars any time than not make a trade, though I hate to fling away a good hoss."

"Well," said Peter, "I'll be as clever as you are. Just put the five dollars on Bullet's back, and hand him over: it's a trade."

Blossom swore again, as roundly as before, that he would not give boot; "and," said he, "Bullet wouldn't hold five dollars on his back, nohow. But, as I bantered you, if you say an even swap, here's at you."

"I told you," said Peter, "I'd be as clever as you: therefore, here goes two dollars more, just for trade sake. Give me three dollars, and it's a bargain."

Blossom repeated his former assertion; and here the parties stood for a long time, and the by-standers (for many were now collected) began to taunt both parties. After some time, however, it was pretty unanimously decided that the old man had backed Blossom out.

At length Blossom swore he "never would be backed

out for three dollars after bantering a man ;" and, accordingly, they closed the trade.

"Now," said Blossom, as he handed Peter the three dollars, "I'm a man that when he makes a bad trade makes the most of it until he can make a better. I'm for no rues and after-claps."

"That's just my way," said Peter. "I never goes to law to mend my bargains."

"Ah, you're the kind of boy I love to trade with. Here's your hoss, old man. Take the saddle and bridle off him, and I'll strip yours; but lift up the blanket easy from Bullet's back, for he's a mighty tender-backed hoss."

The old man removed the saddle, but the blanket stuck fast. He attempted to raise it, and Bullet bowed himself, switched his tail, danced a little, and gave signs of biting.

"Don't hurt him, old man," said Blossom, archly; "take it off easy. I am, perhaps, a leetle of the best man at a hoss-swap that ever catched a coon."

Peter continued to pull at the blanket more and more roughly, and Bullet became more and more *cavortish*, insomuch that when the blanket came off he had reached the kicking-point in good earnest.

The removal of the blanket disclosed a sore on Bullet's backbone that seemed to have defied all medical skill. It measured six full inches in length and four in breadth, and had as many features as Bullet had motions. My heart sickened at the sight; and I felt that the brute who had been riding him in that situation deserved the halter.

The prevailing feeling, however, was that of mirth. The laugh became loud and general at the old man's expense, and rustic witticisms were liberally bestowed upon him and his late purchase. These Blossom continued to provoke by various remarks. He asked the old man "if

he thought Bullet would let five dollars lie on his back."
He declared most seriously that he had owned that horse
three months, and had never discovered before that he had
a sore back, "or he should never have thought of trading
him," etc., etc.

The old man bore it all with the most philosophic composure. He evinced no astonishment at his late discovery,
and made no replies. But his son Neddy had not disci-
plined his feelings quite so well. His eyes opened wider
and wider from the first to the last pull of the blanket;
and when the whole sore burst upon his view, astonishment
and fright seemed to contend for the mastery of his countenance. As the blanket disappeared, he stuck his hands in
his breeches-pockets, heaved a deep sigh, and lapsed into a
profound revery, from which he was only roused by the
cuts at his father. He bore them as long as he could; and,
when he could contain himself no longer, he began, with a
certain wildness of expression which gave a peculiar interest to what he uttered: "His back's mighty bad off;
but dod drot my soul if he's put it to daddy as bad as he
thinks he has, for old Kit's both blind and deef, I'll be dod
drot if he ein't!"

"The devil he is!" said Blossom.

"Yes, dod drot my soul if he ein't. You walk him, and
see if he ein't. His eyes don't look like it; but he'd jist
as lieve go ag'in' the house with you, or in a ditch, as anyhow. Now you go try him."

The laugh was now turned on Blossom; and many
rushed to test the fidelity of the little boy's report. A
few experiments established its truth beyond controversy.

"Neddy," said the old man, "you oughn't to try and
make people discontented with their things. Stranger,
don't mind what the little boy says. If you can only get
Kit rid of them little failings, you'll find him all sorts of a

horse.   You are a *leetle* the best man at a horse-swap that
ever I got hold of; but don't fool away Kit.   Come, Neddy,
my son, let's be moving: the stranger seems to be getting
snappish."

AUNT PATIENCE'S DOUGH-NUTS.

ANONYMOUS.

[We do not know the author of the following sketch, yet, like the
dough-nuts which it celebrates, it is far too palatable to be floating
around without a name.   We should be glad to give the writer credit
for his or her amusing story, as also to give the authorship of that
which follows it.]

"WELL, you've got back, hev you?   S'pose you and
that Lancaster feller hed a fine time out a-ridin', didn't
you?"

"Yes, indeed, Aunt Patience?   It's so lovely out of
doors, and it has been such a perfect day!   Don't you
think so?"

"Well, yes, I dunno but it hez," acknowledged Aunt
Patience, reluctantly; "but, as I was a-tellin' your ma jest
now, it's a weather-breeder, 'nd I shouldn't be a mite surprised if we hed a regular northeaster in a day or two,—
mebbe a freshet.   'Twas jest sich weather before we hed
thet dreadful freshet twenty years ago this fall, jest after
the equinoxal,—awful storm!   Jonas was laid up with a
sore toe.   Dear me! what a time I hed with thet man.
Ef any little thing ailed him, there wa'n't no livin' with
him.   Then the freshet came on, 'nd carried off bridges,
'nd washed the roads, 'nd I was shet up with thet man fur
two mortal weeks.   But then they're 'bout all alike: they
can't bear nothin', none of 'em."

"You don't think much of the men, do you, Aunt Patience?" asked Bessie, smiling.

"Lor' sakes! no! I don't take no stock in 'em. It's always ben a wonderment to me what they was made for; but, like musketoes 'nd lice, I s'pose 'twas fur some good purpose. Yes, I've often thought what a peaceable time we should hev of it, if 'twa'n't for the men."

"Why, Aunt Patience," laughed Bessie, "I am sure I don't see what we could do without them. I think they are just splendid! But what did induce you to marry, if you hate the men so?"

"I never should, child, ef I hedn't ben so tender-hearted. It always was my worse fault. I hed beaux a plenty when I was your age, jest because I was so sarsy 'nd aggravatin'; but I wouldn't hev none of 'em, 'nd when I got nigh on to thirty they give it up."

"What a relief it must have been, aunt!"

"Yes, 'twas. I calculated then I could hev a little peace; but, law sakes! it didn't last long, for jest about thet time who should buy the Deacon Sikes place, and move inter the neighborhood, but Jonas Pettybone!"

"Did *he* fall in love at first sight?" laughed saucy Bessie.

"Goodness, no! I reckon he didn't know much about love. I never thought he was over and above smart, 'nd he was dredful shif'less. But there was one thing that he was a master-hand at, 'nd that was eatin'. You hain't no idee what a sight of victuals it took to do him. Why, I've seen him set down 'nd eat a hull panful of dough-nuts, 'nd a half a pie besides, fur lunch, 'nd then git up 'nd say he felt as holler as a punkin."

"How did you happen to marry him, Aunt Patience? Do tell me about it," persisted Bessie.

"'Tain't no use to revive that old story; it's too redikilous; besides, you hain't ready to die, are you?"

"What do you mean, Aunt Patience," asked Bessie.

"You might die laughin' ef I should tell you; I didn't but just survive it, 'nd, besides, the poor man's dead 'nd gone, 'nd long's I don't hev to provide fur him I hadn't ought to grudge him the pleasure he got out o' my dough-nuts. No, I hain't a-goin' to bring up anything ag'in' him now; 'tain't right; you needn't ask me."

"Oh, please do tell me why you married him, Aunt Patience, that's a darling," urged Bessie.

"He was a dreadful moderate man," resumed Aunt Patience. "I used to tell him an earthquake wouldn't start him. I never seed him in a hurry but once. Oh, dear! 'twas enough to kill anybody,—the way he shot round thet kitchen."

"Please tell me——" began Bessie.

"Well, well, do wait till I get to it," interrupted Aunt Patience, impatiently. "I ain't no talker, an' it takes some time to git ready to begin. But I'm comin' to the main point right away. You see, he come in one day to borrow somethin',—them Pettybones was allus a-borrowin', shif'less set,—'nd I was a-fryin' dough-nuts, 'nd he got a taste of 'em. Of course I hed to offer him one, when he sot there lookin' so wishful like. But I wish, for the land's sake, I hedn't, fur it created a hankerin' for 'em which lasted as long as he lived. And I hain't no idee but what 'twas them that carried him off at last."

"Dough-nuts? Aunt Patience, how could they?" asked Bessie.

"He was took down in hayin' time, you see,—he hedn't no more calc'lation than that,—with a fever. If it hed ben me, I shouldn't have minded nothin' about it; but he was so lazy he'd give right up to any little thing 'nd think he was a-goin' to die; 'nd finally he did worry himself into a regular fever. Goodness! how I did work over that

man! I sweat him and give him arbs enough to cure
a sick cow, 'nd after a while he begun to pick up.   The
first thing he begun to think about, of course, was eatin'.
I made him gruel 'nd beef tea by the bucketful, but Jonas
said they didn't begin to make no impression on him.   One
day I was a-fryin' dough-nuts, 'nd Jonas smelt 'em, 'nd
says he, ' Patience, I can't stand this no longer; I've got to
have some dough-nuts, whether or no.'   ' Jonas Pettybone,'
says I, ' be you crazy ?   You hain't a-goin' to hev no sign
of no dough-nuts.'   Then I took my bonnet and went up
in the garden to git some sass for dinner, 'nd when I come
back the first thing I heard was Jonas a-groanin'.   I sot
down my sass and went into the pantry, and—what do
you think ?—out o' that hull pan of dough-nuts that I'd
fried, there wa'n't *one* left."

"You don't mean——" gasped Bessie.

"Yes, I see in a minute there wa'n't no chance fur him ;
but 'twa'n't my way to keep throwin' folks' sins in their
faces, and I thought to myself I would never say nothin'
'bout it to Jonas ef he didn't to me; and he didn't.   But
then I hain't no kind of doubt but what 'twas them dough-
nuts that killed the poor creeter."

"You must have felt dreadfully, Aunt Patience," said
sympathizing Bessie.

"Yes; 'twas enough to make me down sick, fur, you
see, I hed to go and make another batch of dough-nuts
before dinner.   It did seem as if thet man hedn't no com-
passion on me."   And the dear woman laid down her
knitting with a sigh.

"But, Aunt Patience, you haven't told me why you
married him," broke in Bessie.

"I'm a-comin' to it bimeby: you don't give me no chance.
Lemme see.   I've dropped a stitch somewhere,—oh, here
'tis.   Wall, as I was sayin', 'twas in hayin'-time, 'nd we hed

a lot of men-folks, 'nd mother says to me, 'Patience,' says
she, 'what air we goin' to do? We hain't but one pie in
the house.' And says I, 'Never mind, ma: I'll stir up a
batch o' my dough-nuts. The men-folks 'drether hev 'em
than pie any time.' 'Wall,' says she, 'I wish you would,
and I'll jest run over and carry Widder Spinney a bowl o'
my jell': she don't hev no appetite 'nd it may give her a
start.' So I sot on the kittle,—'twas one o' them big, round,
shaller ones,—and I got a hull pan of cakes made ready to
fry, when I happened to look out, and I saw Jonas's shadder turnin' the corner of the house, 'nd says I to myself,
'Now, I hain't a-goin' to fry up a lot o' dough-nuts this hot
day for thet feller to gobble down, no such a thing.' So I
grabbed off the kittle of bilin' fat 'nd set it down on an old
stool I kep' to set the stove-leds on when I was a cookin',
'nd I'd jest clapped a newspaper over the top as Jonas
opened the door. 'Good-mornin',' says I, quite cheerful
like; I allus was blessed with a cheerful disposition by
natur'. 'Won't you take a cheer?' says I. 'No, thank ye,'
says he, 'I can't stop. I was jest a-goin' by, en I thought
I'd drop in a minnit and see how your folks all was.'"

"Did he propose, Aunt Patience?" asked irrepressible
Bessie.

"He 'peared dreadful frustrated," continued Aunt
Patience, not heeding the interruption except by a severe
look at Bessie, "'nd I knew in a minute he'd got somethin' on his mind: so I kep' a-talkin' an' he kep' fidgitin'
round, till after a while he broke out sort of discouraged
like. Says he,—

"'Patience, you hain't no idee how lonesome 'tis over
to our house with no wimmen-folks round to talk to: seems
like livin' in a tomb.'

"'Hain't your aunt Marandy a-keepin' house for you?'
says I.

" ' Yes,' says he, ' but she's so pesky cross a feller can't take no comfort with her. Besides, she dunno how to make dough-nuts; she can't make no doughnuts that wouldn't give you the dyspepsy. There ain't nobody that ken come up nigh to you,' says he, ' a-makin' them delicious compounds. They make my mouth water every time I think of 'em. Won't you come over and make dough-nuts for me? You hain't no idee how much I set by ye, Patience.' And, jest as he said thet, he edged along and sot down square into that kittle of bilin' fat!

" There hain't no pen that could describe the look of despair and mortification that came over his countenance as he popped up ag'in! It's come across me, time and again, at funerals and sich-like solemn places, and I've hed to stuff my handkerchief in my mouth and put my head down on the seat in front and shake all over to keep in from laughin' right out. I've allus hoped mourners would think I was a-cryin'; but I dunno, I couldn't 'a' helped it if it hed saved me from the gallus, any more'n I could at the time on't.

" I laughed till there wa'nt no more strength in me then there is in skim-milk. I laughed till I cried; the tears was just a-streamin' down my face; 'nd all the time he was a-tearin' round thet kitchen 'nd cuttin' up more antics than you ever see a clown do at a circus. After all, I couldn't help pityin' him,—I allus was tender-hearted,— 'nd, besides, I kinder blamed myself for gittin' the poor creeter into such a fix. So, as soon as I could git myself together 'nd git breath enough, I says to him, says I, ' For goodness' sake, Jonas Pettybone! the neighbors will think that I'm murderin' you. Ef you'll hush up and go home peaceably, and not make no more fuss, I dunno,— mebbe I may in time be persuaded to marry ye. Mind, I don't say *sartin*,' says I, ' but I'll think about it.'

"You ought to see what an effect it had on the feller! He stopped his prancin' in a minute, 'nd quieted down as meek as a lamb, 'nd he even tried to smile, as he clapped on his hat 'nd sneaked out the door without another word. Pretty quick ma came in, 'nd says she to me,—

"'What on arth *is* the matter, Patience? You look as if you'd ben through a coffee-mill!' Says I to her, 'That's jest the way I feel.' Then I told her about Jonas, but, instid of goin' inter convulsions of laughter as I expected, she sot down with a sigh, and says she, 'Well, 'tis a pity, that's a fact; but you've no need to cry your eyes out; tain't a dead loss: we ken use it for soap-grease.''

"'Oh,' says I, 'I hain't a-goin' to waste all thet fat, I can tell ye: I'm jest a-goin' to fry them dough-nuts in it.' Well, I never made no sich dough-nuts in all my born days, before or sence. They was light as a feather, and the men-folks praised 'em up, 'nd said I was the beateree for makin' dough-nuts of anybody they ever see."

"So you concluded to marry him, did you?" asked Bessie.

"Yes, I *hed* to," answered Aunt Patience, with a sigh, "Jonas said if I didn't he'd sue me for damages. So I tell you, child, gittin' married is all a humbug."

And, having freed her mind, Aunt Patience rolled up her knitting and betook herself to bed.

A FAMILY JAR.

Philemon Hayes and Fanny Ray had been just three weeks married.

They sat at breakfast in their cosey dining-room one fine morning in summer, totally infatuated with each other. Never such happiness as theirs before! The felicity of Adam and his lady before they made the acquaintance of the serpent was not to be mentioned in the same breath.

They kissed each other between every cup of coffee, and embraced twice—sometimes thrice—during every meal. Just now they were speaking of disagreements. Some friends of theirs had fallen out and refused to fall in again.

"We will never disagree, will we, Phil, dear?" asked Mrs. Fanny.

"Disagree! will the heavens fall?" returned Phil.

"I sincerely hope not. It would be decidedly disagreeable," laughed Fanny; "but if I thought we should ever quarrel and have harsh thoughts towards each other, I should be tempted to terminate my existence."

"My precious Fanny!" cried Phil, springing up and upsetting the toast-plate on the carpet, of which he was perfectly oblivious in his eagerness to get his arms around Fanny. "My foolish little darling! as if we should ever be so absurd! [a kiss]. May I be quartered [another kiss] if I ever speak one word that shall cause a tear to fill the divine eyes of my dearest [a third explosion] Fanny!"

"Oh, how happy you make me, Phil! I shall try so hard to be just the faithful, loving wife you deserve. Now finish your breakfast, deary. The toast will be growing cold. And oh, Phil! did you notice Mrs. Smith's horrid new bonnet last night? I declare, it destroyed all my pleasure in the music. I do wish people who wear such untasteful bonnets would stay at home from these delightful concerts!"

"So do I, Fanny. I noticed the ugly thing the moment we entered the hall. Blue flowers and pink ribbons, and she is as dark as a Creole!"

"No, my love, the flowers were green. Green and blue look so much alike by gas-light."

"I know they do, but I noticed it so particularly that I could not be deceived. Blue—especially light blue—looks fearfully on a dark-complected woman."

"So it does, Phil; I quite agree with you, dear. But the flowers were not blue: they were green. I saw them at Mrs. Gray's shop before they were purchased."

"My dearest Fanny, of course you think yourself right, love, but I have a very good eye for color, and noticed those flowers with great attention. Blue anemones with yellow centres."

"Green hibiscus with white centres, my dear Phil. Very pretty for a light-skinned woman, but horrid for a brunette."

"Why, Fanny, how absurd! As if I could not determine a color, when I studied it half the evening!"

"But it was by gas-light, my love. It would look altogether different by daylight. It was such a pale green."

"It was such a pale blue. I remember, I thought of the sky before a storm."

"And I thought of the sea. It was nearly sea-green."

"Why, Fanny, ridiculous! It was sky-blue."

"How you do contradict me, my Philemon! It was a very light green."

"And I insist it was blue."

"Do you mean to tell me I lie?"

"I mean to tell you you are mistaken."

"Which amounts to the same thing."

"You make the application, Mrs. Fanny Hayes."

"Mr. Philemon Hayes."

"Fanny!"

"I say it was green, sir."

"I say it was blue, so there!"

"You are a wretch, Phil, a real mean, heartless wretch!" And Fanny pushed back her plate angrily.

"And you are an opinionated, self-willed woman!" And Phil, in his agitation, upset the coffee, scalding the cat's back and himself at the same time. "The deuce!" cried he, rubbing his red hands with his handkerchief. "I wish I had never seen a woman!"

"What's that, sir? You brute!" cried Mrs. Hayes, now thoroughly incensed; "take that." And, seizing the plate of muffins, she took aim at Phil's head, but, being a woman, her aim was not so accurate as it might have been, and the plate went through the window, smashing the tile of Fitz-James Jones, who was passing, and the muffins were scattered in wild confusion about the room.

Phil was indignant. He laid his hand on the poker.

"Oh, strike!" exclaimed Fanny. "It will be in place with your other conduct. Don't let any notions of honor restrain you, because you never had any."

"Fanny, beware: you try me too far."

"I'll go home to pa, that I will. You inhuman monster, you, I'll be divorced from you this very day. So there!" And the platter of ham made a journey after the muffins.

Just at that moment Phil's uncle John, a shrewd old fellow, appeared on the scene. He surveyed the group with an anxious twinkle of the eye.

"What's the matter, Fanny? Anything gone wrong?" he inquired.

"Gone wrong! Matter enough! Oh, Uncle John, he's a wretch, and set out to strike me with a poker."

"And she threw a plate of muffins and the ham at me."

"He's a monster, Uncle John. I'll be divorced from him this very day. He is worse than a savage."

"So he is," cried Uncle John, entering warmly into the spirit of the thing, "so he is,"—stripping off his coat,—"and I'll settle the matter at once. You stand back, Fanny; I'll give him such a thrashing as he'll be likely to remember. Striking his wife with a poker, indeed! I'll rectify matters." And Uncle John grasped the long-handled duster and flourished it threateningly around the head of his

nephew. " There, sir, take that! and that! and that!" exclaimed he, bringing down the feathers on the shoulders
of the amazed Phil. "Fanny, my dear, I'll not leave a
bone of him whole."

Fanny's round blue eyes had been growing larger and
larger, and now her indignation broke.

"John Hayes," she cried, "you're a heathen and an old
meddling vagabond! Let Phil alone! He's my dear, dear
husband, and you've no right to touch him. He's an angel.
He never intended to strike me. Be still striking him, or
you'll be sorry." And Fanny seized the broom from behind
the door, and prepared to do battle.

"Stand back!" cried Uncle John: "he's a monster, and
deserves death. The man who would threaten to strike a
woman ought to be hung."

Fanny's eyes blazed. She flew at Uncle John with the
spite of a tigress, and the way the trio went round the
room was worth witnessing,—Uncle John after Phil with
the duster, and Fanny after Uncle John with the broom.

Phil made a spring for the window, but there was a
whatnot in the way, and, getting his leg entangled in that,
he brought the whole concern to the floor. Ambrotypes,
books, vases, rare china, and a hundred cherished curiosi-
ties, all were involved in direst ruin.

Phil went down with the other things, Uncle John
stumbled over him, and Fanny only saved herself by
seizing the bell-rope, which brought her two servants to
the spot.

Of course they took Phil and Uncle John for house-
breakers, and if Fanny's explanation had not been en-
forced by sundry touches of her broomstick the consequences might have been serious.

The first moment of calm was seized upon by the young
couple to embrace each other.

"My angel Fanny!"

"My precious Phil!"

And then followed an explanation like the bursting of beer-bottles.

Uncle John left the house during this interesting performance, still firmly of the opinion that the surest way of reconciling a wife to her husband is to get a third person to help abuse him.

THE RESULTS OF PHRENOLOGY.

JAMES K. PAULDING.

[James Kirke Paulding (born in the State of New York in 1779, died in 1860) was in his day a novelist and humorist of great popularity, though at present very little read. His most admired novel was "The Dutchman's Fireside," and of his humorous productions, the "Salmagundi" papers, which he issued in conjunction with Washington Irving, "John Bull and Brother Jonathan," "John Bull in America," and "Merry Tales of the Three Wise Men of Gotham," from which last we make a brief selection. It cannot be claimed that Paulding's style of humor ranks very high; and we select from him simply as a tribute to his former reputation as a humorist.]

THE lecture with which Dr. Gallgotha commenced his course in Paris was the same that frightened the sovereign princess and her court into fits; but I will do the ladies of Paris the justice to say that they stood the display of our phrenological specimens like heroines,—whether it be that the French women are naturally bolder than the German, or that a certain fashionable philosopher had in some degree prepared them for scientific horrors by his exhibition of fossil remains. The thing took amazingly: there was something new in the idea of looking at the back of the head, instead of the face, to ascertain the peculiarities of human character, and novelty is indispensable to the existence of people who have exhausted all other pleasures. There were, indeed, some ladies belonging to the coteries of the old lecturers who affected to laugh at the doctor's theory, but even they were effectually silenced by a discovery of my master that the organ of tune was developed in the head of the famous composer Rossini to such a degree that it had actually monopolized nearly the whole of his cerebellum. There was no resisting this proof not only that Rossini was a great composer of tunes, but likewise that the doctor's science was infallible. The fiddler and the doctor accordingly were the two greatest men in Paris. The rage for cerebral developments became intense, and thenceforward every lady of the least pretensions to fashion or science procured a skull, marked and mapped conformably with the principles of the sublime science, which she placed on her toilet, in order that she might dress and study at the same time. Two or three of the most zealous female devotees actually fell in love with the doctor, being deeply smitten with his cerebral development. The fashionable gentlemen, whose sole business is to make love, began to grow jealous of Varus and his legions, and one or two ludicrous anecdotes occurred which set all Paris tittering. I will relate them, although I cannot vouch for their truth any farther than to say that everybody believed them.

A young nobleman was deeply enamoured of a beautiful lady of high rank, and particularly jealous of one of his rivals who wore powder in his hair. He had been absent some weeks on military duty, and, returning to town one evening, proceeded directly to the house of his mistress, intending to surprise her with a visit. Finding a servant at the door, he inquired for the lady, and was told that she was so deeply engaged that she could see nobody. The jealousy of the lover was alarmed, and, pushing the servant aside, he proceeded silently towards the lady's boudoir, the door of which he found shut. Pausing a moment, he heard, as he imagined, two voices within exchanging words of most particular endearment, and something in the pause that sounded like kissing. Human nature could stand it no longer. He peeped through the key-hole, where he saw a sight that drove him to madness. The lady was sitting by the light of a fire which was fast going out, caressing and fondling a figure the whiteness of whose head too well indicated his detestable powdered rival. From time to time he heard the words amativeness, adhesiveness, hope, secretiveness, and elopement, or something that sounded very like it. The thing was perfectly plain: they were exchanging professions of love and planning an elopement. The sight and the conviction were no longer to be borne. He burst open the door furiously, and, being in full uniform as an officer of the guards, drew his sword, and, making a desperate blow at the powdered head, it flew off the shoulders and rolled upon the floor. The lady shrieked and sunk from her seat; and the jealous lover, hearing a noise in the outward apartments, and supposing he had done the gentleman's business pretty effectually, bethought himself that it was high time to take care of himself. He accordingly made the best of his way out of the house, towards the gate St.-Honoré, through which he hurried into the country, nor stopped till he had safely lodged himself within his castle of Normandy.

From thence he wrote a letter filled with the most cutting reproaches, charging his mistress with falsehood, cruelty, deceit, and all sorts of villany, and vowing on the cross of his sword never to see her more. The lady laughed two full hours on the receipt of this defiance.

When she had done laughing, as she really had a regard for her admirer, she sat down and wrote him the following reply:

"GOOD MONSIEUR JEALOUSY,—

"You are welcome to call me what you will, except it be old or ugly. However, I forgive you, and so does the formidable rival whose head you so dexterously severed from his body, and who I give you my honor is not the least the worse for the accident. I solemnly assure you, you may come back to Paris without the least danger of being prosecuted by the family of Monsieur M——, or being received by me with ill humor, for I shall laugh at you terribly.   Your friend,   N. N."

This epistle puzzled the lover not a little, and caused him fifty sensations in a minute. First he would return to Paris, and then he would not; then he resolved never to see his mistress again, and next to mount his horse, return immediately, look her stone-dead, and then set out on his travels to the interior of Africa. This last resolution carried the day, and he forthwith returned to Paris in as great a hurry as he had left it. When the lady saw him, she was as good as her word: she laughed herself out of breath, and the more he reproached her the louder she laughed. However, as anger and laughter can't last forever, a truce took place in good time, and the lady addressed her lover as follows:

"Cease thy reproaches, my good friend, and hear me. I am determined to give you the most convincing proof in the world of my truth and attachment, by delivering your rival into your hands, to be dealt with as you think proper. Know that he is now concealed in this very room."

"Is he?" replied the other, in a rage. "Then, by

heaven, he has not long to live. I shall take care to cut off his head so effectually this time that the most expert surgeon in Paris shall not put it on again. Where is the lurking caitiff? But I need not ask: I see his infernal powdered head peeping from under the sofa. Come out, villain, and receive the reward of thy insolence in rivalling me."

So saying, he seized the treacherous powdered head, and, to his astonishment, drew it forth without any body to it. He stood aghast; and the lady threw herself on the sofa, and laughed ten times louder than before.

"What in the name of woman," cried he, at last, "is the meaning of all this mummery?"

"It means that I am innocent, and that your worship is jealous of the skull, or, what is worse, the plaster counterfeit of the skull, of your great-grandmother, the immortal author of the 'Grand Cyrus.' I was but admiring the beautiful indication of the amative organ, from which it plainly appears impossible that any other person could have written such prodigiously long developments of the tender passion."

"But why did you kiss the filthy representation of mortality?"

"You were mistaken," answered the lady. "As the room was rather dark, I placed my face close to it in order the better to see and admire its beautiful cerebral development."

"Its what?" replied the lover, impatiently.

"Its phrenological indications."

"And what in the name of heaven are these?" cried the lover, in some alarm for the intellect of his fair mistress. The lady then proceeded to explain to him the revolution in science which had taken place during his absence; and, a reconciliation being the consequence, that night took him to the doctor's lecture, that he might no longer be an age behind the rest of the world. The story got abroad,—indeed, the lady could not resist telling it herself to a friend, with strict injunctions of secrecy,— and all Paris became still more devoted to the sublime science for having afforded such an excellent subject for a joke.

The other story relates to a young nobleman, whose situation near the king, and orthodox ultraism, made him a very distinguished person in the *beau-monde*. But he was distinguished only in a certain way; that is, he was a sort of butt, on whose shoulders every ridiculous incident was regularly fathered, whether it owed its paternity to him or not. As Pasquin stands sponsor for all the wise sayings of Rome, so M. the Viscount came in for all the foolish actions of Paris. He was, as it were, residuary legatee to all the posthumous follies of his ancestors, as well as the living absurdities of his noble contemporaries. He was one of those people who fancy themselves most eminently qualified for that for which they are most peculiarly unfit, and whom folly and vanity combined are perpetually stimulating to act in direct opposition to nature or destiny. He was contemptible in his person, yet he set up for a beau and Adonis; he was still more contemptible in mind, yet he never rested till he had bought the title of Mæcenas and a *savan* of an industrious manufacturer of ultra-doggerel rhymes whom he had got into the National Institute. He was, moreover, born for a valet, or at best a pastry-cook, yet he aspired to the lofty chivalry and inflexible honor of a feudal baron; and he became a soldier only, as it would seem, because he was the greatest coward in all Paris. It was well known that he gave five hundred francs to a noted bully to let him beat him at a public coffee-house, and afterwards allowed his brother, a tall grenadier, a pension not to kill him for it.

The viscount had likewise been absent some months at a small town in one of the northern departments, whither he had gone to suppress an insurrection begun by two or three fishwomen, stimulated, as was shrewdly suspected, by an old gardener, who had, as was confidently asserted, been one of Napoleon's trumpeters. On his return, he for the first time heard of the sublime science and its progress among the *beau-monde*. The viscount hated all innovations in science, or indeed anything else. He aspired to be a second Joshua, and to make the sun of intellect at least stand still, if he could not make it go backwards, as he had good hopes of doing. Without waiting to hear any of the particulars of our exhibition, he hastened, armed and in uniform as he was, to the hotel where the doctor was at that moment just commencing a lecture.

The valiant viscount advanced with great intrepidity close to the table, and, leaning gracefully on his sword, listened in silence to discover whether there was anything that smacked of democracy or heterodoxy. At the proper moment I put my hand into our Golgotha, and leisurely drew forth the far-famed skull of Varus, who I have always considered the most fortunate man of all antiquity, in having been surprised and slain in the now more memorable than ever forest of Teutoburgium. As we scientific gentlemen have a hawk's eye for a new-comer, one of whom is worth a host of old faces at a lecture, I took care, in bringing the cerebral development forth, to thrust it directly towards the face of the viscount with the teeth foremost. The viscount fell back, fainted, and lay insensible for some minutes. But the moment he revived he started upon his legs in a frenzy of terror, and began to lay about him with his good sword so valiantly that nobody dared to come near him. First he attacked the doctor and myself, whom he charged with the massacre of the eleven thousand vir-

II.—*i*

gins, and the introduction of infidel skulls into France, which was tantamount to preaching infidelity. The innocent cerebellum of poor Varus next felt the effects of his terror-inspired valor. He hacked it until the cerebral development was entirely destroyed, and then proceeded in like manner to make an example of the contents of the bag, which he shivered without mercy with his invincible sword. In short, before he fairly came to his senses, the worthy gentleman had demolished almost everything in the room, put out the lights, and frightened every soul from the lecture. The solitude and darkness which succeeded brought him gradually to his recollection, when, finding himself thus left alone with the ruins of so many pagan skulls, he gave a great shriek, scampered out of the room, and did not stop until he had sheltered himself in the very centre of a corporal and his guard, belonging to his regiment, who all swore they would stand by him to the last drop of their blood.

DARIUS GREEN AND HIS FLYING-MACHINE.

J. T. TROWBRIDGE.

[We have elsewhere given an example of Trowbridge's prose humor. As a poetical humorist he is equally able, in illustration of which we offer the following rendition of the feats and fate of a Yankee Icarus.]

If ever there lived a Yankee lad,
Wise or otherwise, good or bad,
Who, seeing the birds fly, didn't jump
With flapping arms from stake or stump,

Or, spreading the tail
Of his coat for a sail,
Take a soaring leap from post or rail,
And wonder why
He couldn't fly,
And flap, and flutter, and wish, and try,—
If ever you knew a country dunce
Who didn't try that as often as once,
All I can say is, that's a sign
He never would do for a hero of mine.

An aspiring genius was D. Green:
The son of a farmer, age fourteen;
His body was long and lank and lean,—
Just right for flying, as will be seen;
He had two eyes as bright as a bean,
And a freckled nose that grew between,
A little awry,—for I must mention
That he had riveted his attention
Upon his wonderful invention,
Twisting his tongue as he twisted the strings,
And working his face as he worked the wings,
And with every turn of gimlet and screw
Turning and screwing his mouth round too,
Till his nose seemed bent
To catch the scent,
Around some corner, of new-baked pies,
And his wrinkled cheeks and his squinting eyes
Grew puckered into a queer grimace,
That made him look very droll in the face,
And also very wise.
And wise he must have been, to do more
Than ever a genius did before,

Excepting Dædalus of yore
And his son Icarus, who wore
    Upon their backs
    Those wings of wax
He had read of in the old almanacs.
Darius was clearly of the opinion
That the air is also man's dominion,
And that, with paddle or fin or pinion,
    We soon or late shall navigate
The azure as now we sail the sea.
The thing looks simple enough to me;
    And, if you doubt it,
Hear how Darius reasoned about it.

    "The birds can fly, an' why can't I?
    Must we give in," says he, with a grin,
    "That the bluebird an' phœbe
    Are smarter'n we be?
Jest fold our hands an' see the swaller
An' blackbird an' catbird beat us holler?
Doos the little, chatterin', sassy wren,
No bigger'n my thumb, know more than men?
    Jest show me that!
    Ur prove 't the bat
Hez got more brains than's in my hat,
An' I'll back down, an' not till then!"
He argued further, "Nur I can't see
What's the use o' wings to a bumble-bee,
Fur to git a livin' with, more'n to me;
    Ain't my business
    Important's his'n is?
    That Icarus
    Made a perty muss:
Him an' his daddy Dædalus

They might 'a' knowed wings made o' wax
Wouldn't stand sun-heat an' hard whacks.
> I'll make mine o' luther,
> Ur suthin' ur other."

And he said to himself, as he tinkered and planned,
" But I ain't goin' to show my hand
To nummies that never can understand
The fust idee that's big an' grand."
So he kept his secret from all the rest,
Safely buttoned within his vest;
And in the loft above the shed
Himself he locks, with thimble and thread
And wax and hammer and buckles and screws,
And all such things as geniuses use ;
Two bats for patterns, curious fellows!
A charcoal-pot and a pair of bellows;
Some wire, and several old umbrellas;
A carriage-cover, for tail and wings;
A piece of harness; and straps and strings;
> And a big strong box,
> In which he locks
These and a hundred other things.
His grinning brothers, Reuben and Burke
And Nathan and Jotham and Solomon, lurk
Around the corner to see him work,—
Sitting cross-legged, like a Turk,
Drawing the wax-end through with a jerk,
And boring the holes with a comical quirk
Of his wise old head, and a knowing smirk.
But vainly they mounted each other's backs,
And poked through knot-holes and pried through cracks ;
With wood from the pile and straw from the stacks
He plugged the knot-holes and calked the cracks ;

And a dipper of water, which one would think
He had brought up into the loft to drink
When he chanced to be dry,
Stood always nigh,
For Darius was sly!
And whenever at work he happened to spy
At chink or crevice a blinking eye,
He let the dipper of water fly.
"Take that! an' ef ever ye git a peep,
Guess ye'll ketch a weasel asleep!"
And he sings as he locks
His big strong box,—

"The weasel's head is small an' trim,
An' he is little an' long an' slim,
An' quick of motion an' nimble of limb,
An', ef you'll be
Advised by me,
Keep wide awake when ye're ketchin' him!"

So day after day
He stitched and tinkered and hammered away,
Till at last 'twas done,—
The greatest invention under the sun!
"An' now," says Darius, "hooray for some fun!"

'Twas the Fourth of July,
And the weather was dry,
And not a cloud was on all the sky,
Save a few light fleeces, which here and there,
Half mist, half air,
Like foam on the ocean went floating by,—
Just as lovely a morning as ever was seen
For a nice little trip in a flying-machine.
Thought cunning Darius, "Now, I shan't go
Along 'ith the fellers to see the show.

I'll say I've got sich a terrible cough!
An' then, when the folks 'ave all gone off,
I'll hev full swing fur to try the thing
An' practise a little on the wing."

" Ain't goin' to see the celebration ?"
Says brother Nate.   " No ; botheration !
I've got sich a cold—a toothache—I—
My gracious !—feel's though I should fly !"
            Said Jotham, " Sho !
            Guess ye better go."
            But Darius said, " No !
Shouldn't wonder 'f you might see me, though,
'Long 'bout noon, ef I git red
O' this jumpin', thumpin' pain 'n my head."
For all the while to himself he said,—

            " I tell ye what !
I'll fly a few times around the lot,
To see how 't seems, then soon 's I've got
The hang o' the thing, ez likely 's not
            I'll astonish the nation,
            An' all creation,
By flyin' over the celebration !
Over their heads I'll sail like an eagle ;
I'll balance myself on my wings like a sea-gull ;
I'll dance on the chimbleys ; I'll stand on the steeple ;
I'll flop up to winders an' scare the people !
I'll light on the liberty-pole, an' crow ;
An' I'll say to the gawpin' fools below,
            ' What world 's this 'ere
            That I've come near ?'
Fur I'll make 'em b'lieve I'm a chap f'm the moon ;
An' I'll try a race 'ith their ol' balloon !"

He crept from his bed ;
And, seeing the others were gone, he said,
"I'm gittin' over the cold 'n my head."
          And away he sped,
To open the wonderful box in the shed.

His brothers had walked but a little way,
When Jotham to Nathan chanced to say,
"What is the feller up to, hey ?"
"Do'no' : the 's suthin' ur other to pay,
Ur he wouldn't 'a' stayed to hum to-day."
Says Burke, " His toothache's all 'n his eye !
He never 'd miss a Fo'th-o'-July,
Ef he hedn't got some machine to try."
Then Sol, the little one, spoke : " By darn !
Le's hurry back an' hide 'n the barn,
An' pay him fur tellin' us that yarn !"
"Agreed !"   Through the orchard they creep back,
Along by the fences, behind the stack,
And one by one, through a hole in the wall,
In under the dusty barn they crawl,
Dressed in their Sunday garments all ;
And a very astonishing sight was that,
When each in his cobwebbed coat and hat
Came up through the floor like an ancient rat.
          And there they hid ;
          And Reuben slid
The fastenings back, and the door undid.
          "Keep dark !" said he,
"While I squint an' see what the' is to see."

As knights of old put on their mail,—
          From head to foot an iron suit,
          Iron jacket and iron boot,

Iron breeches, and on the head
No hat, but an iron pot instead,
  And under the chin the bail
(I believe they called the thing a helm),
Then sallied forth to overwhelm
The dragons and pagans that plagued the realm,—
  So this *modern* knight
  Prepared for flight,
Put on his wings and strapped them tight,
Jointed and jaunty, strong and light,—
Buckled them fast to shoulder and hip;
Ten feet they measured from tip to tip!
And a helm had he, but that he wore,
Not on his head, like those of yore,
  But more like the helm of a ship.

  " Hush!" Reuben said,
  " He's up in the shed!
He's opened the winder,—I see his head!
He stretches it out, an' pokes it about,
Lookin' to see 'f the coast is clear
  An' nobody near:
Guess he do'no' who's hid in here!
He's riggin' a spring-board over the sill!
Stop laffin', Solomon! Burke, keep still!
He's a climbin' out now—— Of all the things!
What's he got on? I van, it's wings!
An' that t'other thing? I vum, it's a tail!
An' there he sets, like a hawk on a rail!
Steppin' careful, he travels the length
Of his spring-board, and teeters to try its strength.
Now he stretches his wings, like a monstrous bat,
Peeps over his shoulder, this way an' that,
Fur to see 'f the' 's any one passin' by;

But the' 's on'y a ca'f an' a goslin' nigh.
They turn up at him a wonderin' eye,
To see——   The dragon! he's goin' to fly!
Away he goes!   Jimminy! what a jump!
        Flop—flop—an' plump
          To the ground with a thump!
Flutt'rin' an' flound'rin', all 'n a lump!"

As a demon is hurled by an angel's spear,
Heels over head, to his proper sphere,—
Heels over head and head over heels,
Dizzily down the abyss he wheels,—
So fell Darius.   Upon his crown,
In the midst of the barn-yard, he came down,
In a wonderful whirl of tangled strings,
Broken braces and broken springs,
Broken tail and broken wings,
Shooting-stars, and various things,
Barn-yard litter of straw and chaff,
And much that wasn't so sweet by half.
Away with a bellow fled the calf;
And what was that?   Did the gosling laugh?
'Tis a merry roar from the old barn door,
And he hears the voice of Jotham crying,
"Say, D'rius! how do you like flyin'?"
Slowly, ruefully, where he lay,
Darius just turned and looked that way,
As he stanched his sorrowful nose with his cuff.
"Wal, I like flyin' well enough,"
He said; "but the' ain't sich a thunderin' sight
O' fun in 't when ye come to light."

I just have room for the MORAL here:
And this is the moral: Stick to your sphere.

Or, if you insist, as you have the right,
On spreading your wings for a loftier flight,
The moral is, Take care how you light.

THAT MAN.

ANONYMOUS.

[The story here given was originally published in *Lippincott's Magazine.* It is a good example of a certain class of American humorous sketches.]

Two little notes are necessary by way of introduction. The first is as follows, to Curtis Marston, Esq.:

"DEAR MARSTON,—Dine with me next Thursday, at six P.M., *precisely.* You *must* come. Monkhouse is to be there, and two others, and we want you to be on hand to put the said M. under an extinguisher. He tells such awful romances that he must be suppressed, and you are the man to do it.

"Yours truly,

"F. SIMMONS."

No. 2, to Frederick Simmons, Esq.:

"DEAR FRED,—I don't know why you select me. I never had a gift at telling crams, especially against such a superior artist in that line as Monkhouse. However, I will come and do what occurs to me on the spur of the moment.

"Yours truly,

"C. MARSTON."

The rest of the story Mr. Monkhouse shall tell himself.

" Come and dine with me, next Thursday. Bachelors'
dinner,—six precisely, and mean it : so don't come dropping
in at half-past." This was what Fred Simmons said to me.
What I said to Fred was, " Thanks ! I believe I will."
I always dine with Fred when he asks me. First,
because he was my classmate in college, and roomed in
the same entry with me. Fred then was poor, and I was
not. Now Fred is not, and I am. He used to dine with
me then ; now I dine with him. I figured up the account
between us the other day, and I make it that Fred still
owes me twenty-eight dinners and seventeen teas. The
teas were coffee and cakes, you know, at Marm Haven's,
in School Street, before walking out on Saturday nights.
And then interest, during twenty years. It only makes
Fred's conduct the more unprincipled.

Reason Number Two is, that Fred gives good dinners,
—perhaps better than I used to give him. But then, in
those days, our appetites were better, especially after the
long walk over Williams River bridge, from Yalehaven to
Botolphsville. At least, Fred's was. He boarded in commons then, and college commons were—well, apt to induce
a disregard of expense when we dined in the city on Satur-
days. Now my appetite is the better of the two. I board
at Mrs. McSkinner's, and dine down town in Maiden Lane
or thereabouts. I have no more money than before the
war, but dinners are twice as dear.

Reason Three is, that I meet queer people at Fred's.
Others who dine there say the same thing, so that I know
it is not prejudice on my part. It was only a month ago,
after dining with Fred, when there was but one guest besides myself,—a man who writes for the papers. I heard
of his saying the next day that Fred Simmons cultivated

more eccentricities in his kitchen-garden than any other man in —— Will it do for me to tell the city's name? No, I think not: we will say, "in Chicago Atlanticensis." I thought it was candid in the fellow to say so, for a queerer fish than he was *I* never met.

One thing I do not fancy about Fred. He lets men tell such extravagant stories. I suppose he thinks them brilliant, and all that, but I never could see the wit or the humor. Fiction is my abomination. I would not send this paper to any magazine in which all the stories were not strictly true. I don't mean "founded on fact,"—a compromised title which always reminds me of Mrs. McSkinner's coffee,—but all fact, as I am assured by the editor all the stories in *this* periodical are.

I hate lying. When I was a little boy I once was guilty of a trifling inaccuracy of statement,—I now think, unintentionally. I was in consequence shut up in a dark closet for a whole week, until I had read through—and in fact learnt by heart—Amelia Opie's "Illustrations of Lying," a book which in my youth was deemed efficacious for reforming juvenile Ananiases and Sapphiræ. The horror of that experience has always since kept me from the least deviation.

But to return to my story. I read the other day in a newspaper, "Truth is stranger than fiction." The man who wrote that must have dined frequently with Fred. Truth at his dinner-table is the greatest stranger possible.

I went to Fred's last Thursday. Of course I did not dine down town that day. And I was not late.

There were six of us at table,—four others, Fred, and me. It was a good dinner. But there was too much talking. And too much space between the courses. The time might have been filled up better, and where there are these delays men will drink more wine than they otherwise would.

The consequence is, they tell too long and too marvellous stories.

Fred calls this the "Feast of Reason, etc." He should be ashamed of such a trite and absurd quotation. If he boarded at Mrs. McSkinner's and dined at Fulton Market, he would know better than to talk when he should be eating.

One of the four guests (I don't consider myself a guest at Fred's, but *l'ami de la maison*,—at least I used to be) was an Irishman,—an Irish gentleman, Fred called him. To my taste, *gentlemen* should be less prosy. *He* was full of his stories,—could not wait for dinner to be done, and the proper time for story-telling, if such a thing must be, to come. I was just getting ready—it was after the soup— to mention a little adventure of mine at Naples,—in the crater of Vesuvius, in fact,—because I really thought it might interest the company. Fred *may* have heard it before, but they had not, and it was suggested very neatly by the vermicelli. Fred cut in upon me by asking that provoking Patlander, that ferocious Fenian, if he had been much cheated by the hackmen in this country.

"Nothing to speak of," said he, "after Dublin. I was seasoned there. You *can't* satisfy a Dublin car-driver. We tried it once when I was in Her Majesty's service,— Twenty-Sixth, line regiment. A bet was made at mess on the subject, and Arthur Ponsonby took it in ponies. If the man asked for more, he was to lose. Pon called a car to take a couple of us to the theatre,—the maker of the bet, and myself as umpire. The theatre was only a square off. When we alighted he pulled out a sovereign and tossed it to the driver, saying, 'Here, Mickey, that will do you for our bit of a drive, won't it?' Pon meant to make it a sure thing; but he had overdone it. Mickey looked at the coin a moment to see if it was good, then at the faces of us

watching, and he seemed to have an instinct of what was
up, for he pulled a regular blarney face and began: 'Ah,
yer 'onor, captain, sure it's a purty piece, and 'ouldn't it
be a shame in me to break it drinkin' yer 'onor's health?
Couldn't ye spare me the small sixpence to the back of it?'
Pon paid the bet, but he never could stand the chaffing he
got in consequence."

They all laughed at this trumpery anecdote, which I
would soon have capped with a far better one, but just
then the fish came on and I had to give my mind to the
salmon: so I lost my chance.

After fish I was thinking of a very striking fact which
happened to me in Iceland, and just running over the
heads in my mind before telling the story, when my *vis-à-
vis*, an Englishman, struck in ahead of me. I do not say
an English *gentleman*, for I do not consider that there is
such a thing in existence: the English are a nation of
snobs, always domineering and pushing out of the way
better men. And no Englishman, in my experience, ever
tells a story without embroidery. If you want to know
what an Englishman is, just read Sir John Mandeville's
travels.

"Ponsonby of the Twenty-Sixth! Wasn't he cousin to
Merivale of the Sixteenth Light Dragoons!"

"Oh, yes, but quite a different style of man, I assure
you."

"I dessay he is; only the name somehow reminded me
of Merivale. (I never taste salmon: capital salmon this,
Mr. Simmons. I suppose it is as easy to bring it from
Norway here as it is to us. Only a little more ice; and,
by Jove! you seem to have ice in loads.) Well, as I was
saying, I never see salmon without thinking of Merivale.
The Sixteenth, you know, were famous for being the
greatest puppies in the service, and Merivale was leading

the pack: at least between him and Charley Ffrench it was neck and neck. I met them once at the Marquis of Downshire's." (Why must an Englishman always lug in a lord?) "One night, in the smoking-room, Ffrench lisped out, 'I thay, Motheth' (he always called Merivale Moses, and Merivale always took it from him, though he would have had out any other man),—'I thay, Motheth, I thaw your fawin fwiend, Pwinth Thalm-Thalm, dining at the Wag and Famish; and, I thay, what do you think he wath doin'?' "'Pon me wawd, I don't know. What did he do?' drawled Merivale. 'He took *cold buttah* with hith thalmon.' 'Did he daye?'"

I had a beautiful thing on the end of my tongue about gravy; only I could not get it into shape before a leg of Southdown mutton was brought in, which changed the subject somewhat. It *was* Southdown, and, as my mutton is not always tender, I confess I was eager to pay my respects to it; and when it went out I was in such a happy frame of mind that I could not think of the point of a good anecdote which the late Louis Philippe always used to tell when I dined with him at the Tuileries. No such good stories are told there *now*.

However, I do think Fred might have asked for it, and that would have given me time to think, as well as have recalled the anecdote. Instead of that, he turned to my neighbor (a Boston man) and asked if he was as fond of billiards as ever.

I say a Boston man, because he wore a coat and pantaloons and those absurd English side-whiskers, "Piccadilly weepers;" but I never feel sure that these Boston men are not strong-mindeds in disguise. I have a small place in the custom-house, and if ever this infamous woman's-rights business comes uppermost, why, voting implies holding office, and then where on earth shall I be?

"I am glad you asked me that?" was the reply of the hateful Boston creature, "for it reminds me of a good thing I have for you. I *do* play billiards as much as ever, and I was at the T—— Club the other night playing with Bill Perkins, and I needed only one point to go out. It was a rather brilliant shot before me, and H—— and some others were looking on, which made me a bit nervous, especially as Bill was only ten behind me. I was so nervous that I made a miss-cue, but after all got the point. H—— clapped his hands as soon as he saw it, and exclaimed, 'How classical!—*Omne tulit punctum, qui miscuit.*' "

"How very good!" said the Englishman. "Really, I did not suppose you did that sort of thing in America."

I had a great mind to put him down with a smashing retort, only I would not help out the Bostonian; but the appearance of canvas-back ducks closed my mouth, or rather opened it to a better purpose.

"Next time!" thought I. Three fellows had had their innings, and the fourth man, Curtis, was as silent as I was. So I let Fred have his own way and get off his stupid stories about the English judges, at which everybody laughed, as in duty bound: when Sosia tells stories, poor Amphitryon has to grin. I am not sure that I have the names quite correct, but everybody will understand what I mean,— that the man who goes out to dine has to applaud the jokes of the fellow who gives the dinner.

At last the fruits and ices came on, and then Fred said to me, "Monkhouse, shall I send you some of the ice?"

"No, thank you," said I. "I once saw ice enough to last me a whole lifetime."

I saw Curtis give a sort of waking-up start, and then fix his eyes on me as if he was going to begin a regular yarn. I hate that sort of thing, and I was bound to get before him, if only for the sake of the rest: so I gave up my chance for the fruit (with a pang, I confess, for I do not get fruit, especially *out* of season, every day), and began at once: "When I was in the South Pacific, gentlemen——"

Here Fred looked queerly and shrugged his shoulders, which was *not* polite at his own table. I should like to know why I have not as good a right to have been in the South Pacific as he, if he *is* a rich man?

I went straight on: "When I was in the South Pacific, on board the razee Independence,—her captain, Commodore Conner, was a friend of mine, and offered me a passage home from Valparaiso,—no, I mean from Quito—" (by the way, *is* Quito a seaport? one's geography slips away from one so; but I could not stop to ask, for they were all watching to cut in)—"we were becalmed off the island of Juan Fernandez. It was in S. lat. 63° 30′, W. long. 104° 22′ (nothing like being accurate in these details), and we saw a huge iceberg approaching us. It was a dead calm, but the ice came on very rapidly. It must have been at least five miles in circumference, and quite a mile high out of water.

"Conner was in a dreadful fright, and I confess I was not quite easy as I watched the enormous mass slowly heaving and settling, and every minute fragments the size of Trinity Church tumbling down its sides. Its color was——"

"Never mind that," said Fred: "we have all seen Church's and Bradford's pictures, and read Dana's 'Two Years before the Mast.' Skip to the catastrophe: did it run over you?"

"No, sir," I retorted: "it did not. On it came, and on, till the boldest held his breath for a time. Every man in the ship was on deck, the nimble topmen swarming far out upon the yards, and the gold bands of the officers' caps gleaming along the quarter-deck. On it came, and the ship was beginning to rock helplessly upon the swell which drove before the mighty mass.

"Conner was just ordering out the boats to try and tow the ship off, when I called his attention to something I had just discovered. (My eyes were very good in those days.) I said, 'Conner, see that black speck coming down the side of the berg?' He turned his glass upon it,—a capital Dollond I had given him,—and exclaimed, 'It is a bear.' 'Conner,' said I, 'who ever saw a *black* bear on ice? It is a man and a brother.' Conner turned red as a beet, but presently, after another look, replied, 'By George! I believe you are right, and he is making signals to us; but we can't help him: no boat would live in that sea which is breaking at the base of the berg, and we've enough to do to save ourselves.'

"The berg, however, must have gone aground,—they are very deep, you know, under water,—for it remained stationary; only the attraction was sucking us in imperceptibly. We saw him reach the water's edge; and how he did it I can't tell,—I was not near enough to see,—but presently he was coming off to us.

"You might have heard a pin drop on the deck, gentlemen, such was the breathless silence of all, which the stern discipline of a man-of-war permitted no one to break. We made out that it was a man in a canoe,—a Marquesas Island canoe; and the strangest thing of all was that he had nothing to propel it with but an umbrella. He neared the side, and Conner and I went to the gangway to hail him. He was dressed in superb sealskins, which would have been a fortune in New York, and he managed his umbrella wonderfully, shooting his light bark along like a racing-wherry. The first words he said were, 'I thought you were in a bad way when I first sighted you, but my craft has come to anchor: so you are all right now. There is a breeze creeping up on the other side of the berg, and you will have it in twenty minutes strong enough to take you clear. To tell you the truth, I was in a great funk when I saw you, for, allowing the half of you to be drowned, I should have hardly more than enough to dine the rest; and if there is anything I hate it is to give my friends short commons.' 'Then you won't come aboard?' said Conner. 'That's a good one! No, I rather think not. Man-o'-war accommodations are a little too close' (he said 'clust,' and then I knew he was a Yankee, and remarked so to Conner) 'quarters for a man who for a month has had a whole iceberg to himself. However, I won't brag, for the berg is shrinking as we get up into the warm latitudes. I *shall* have to leave pretty soon; but as you are bound round the Horn and I am for the Sandwich Islands, I guess I won't trouble you. There is one thing you can do for me, Captain Conner. (B'lieve I've the honor of addressing Captain Conner, of the U. S. razee Independence?) Would you oblige me with your reckoning?' Conner called the First Luff to the side, and they gave him the figures, just as I told you a moment ago. That is why I remembered them so distinctly. 'Pretty well, pretty well!' said he. 'I make you three seconds out of your true latitude, and perhaps a trifle more to the east'ard than you think; but that is near enough for navy men. I have to be a little more particular, *my* craft makes so much leeway. I'll report you, commodore, wherever I conclude to put in. Good-by.' And with that he made off for his berg again.

"Conner ordered the first cutter and gig both to pull after him, but I give you my word, gentlemen, he just walked away from them hand over hand; and before they were half-way to the berg, he was climbing up it with his canoe on his back."

Here I stopped to take breath and a sip of sherry, when that wretched Curtis, whom I thought I had silenced, burst out:

"Thank heaven! I can break the long silence I have kept for fifteen years upon the most remarkable adventure of my life, because nobody would, I thought, believe me. You are my witness, sir: I WAS THAT MAN!"

If ever I dine at Fred's table again, he'll know it,—that's all.

HOW JUBE WAKED THE ELEPHANT.

MRS. M. SHEFFEY PETERS.

[We have given several negro dialect sketches, but the following "story of a dreadfully naughty little black boy" is amusing enough to add to them. Waking elephants is not an altogether safe performance, as Jube found to his cost. The authoress is the wife of Prof. William T. Peters, of the University of Virginia.]

JUBE'S life, ever since he could remember, had been spent in "Ole Isrul's" cabin, underneath a spur of the Alleghanies; and a very happy-go-lucky life it was.

After "freedom come," Israel and Hannah, Jube's nearest of kin, had drifted from the cotton-fields of the Mississippi back to "ole Virginny" and to their old life of tobacco-raising on the Alleghany slopes. They had brought Jube with them, the motherless boy having from babyhood, as Hannah expressed it, "been fotch up by her hand in the way he or'ter go." If ever "fotch up" in the way he should go, the boy, at twelve years of age, had widely departed therefrom, for no more mischievous spirit than naughty little Jube infested the turnpike leading from the cabin to the village beyond.

The day came, however, when Jube was made to pay off at least a part of the score being continually added up against him. Yet the boy himself did not imagine that such a day of reckoning had arrived on that sunshiny morning, when he arose early to deck himself for a holiday which was to be given entirely to the enjoyment of Forepaugh's Great Circus and Menagerie. Twice before, during that week, he had made a pilgrimage to the village, and had spent hours, each time, inspecting the wonderful display of show-papers glaring everywhere. Such riders, such vaulters, such gymnasts, surely never had been known before, even to Jube's vivid imagination. Such animals, too! the sacred bull, the ibex, the llama, the rhinoceros, fiercer than the lion, and the royal Bengal tiger, fiercer than the fiercest of all besides.

"Ki yi, Juba!" saluted Aunt Hannah, as the boy rushed into her cabin that morning, his white eyeballs rolling and his red lips parted in grins of delight. "Isrul, what you s'pose is up wid this nigger, now?"

"Humph!" grunted the cabin's patriarch, puffing, in the breaks of his sentences, volumes of smoke from his short corn-cob pipe. "I 'specs dat boy, Hannah"—puff—"have jes' done"—puff, puff, puff—"gone crazy ober"—puff— "Foreper's surcuss."

"What dat you say? Foreper's surcuss? Juba, whar dat money you fetch me fur de garden-sass an' dem eggs? Ef you jes' done broke one ob dem dozen eggs wid yer capers, I'll Foreper's surcuss you: see ef I don't."

Jube dodged a blow from the hand that had "fotch him up," and proceeded without delay to give up every farthing of his evening's sales.

Aunt Hannah deigned to give a grunt of satisfaction as

the last penny was counted into her hand. Then Jube sidled into the corner of the hearth where "ole Isrul" sat enjoying his pipe. He stood for a moment digging his toes into the cracks of the hearth.

"Daddy!" he drawled, by and by. "Daddy!"

No answer. "Ole Isrul" never so much as winked an eyelash, but sat smoking his pipe as unresponsive as a Camanche Indian.

"Daddy, say! mayn't I go to Foreper's 'nagerie? My! it's a show what is a show! There's beasts an' beasts,— but it's the elerphant what beats all holler! Whew! daddy, dat elephant's a whale, I tell yer!"

"Juba," said Aunt Hannah, severely, "what you sayin', eh? De elerphant am not a whale. How kin it be? It's ag'in' natur'."

Jube subsided.

"Daddy," he whispered, after a few more desperate digs into the seams of the hearth, and under cover of the clatter of Hannah's supper-dishes,—"Daddy, mayn't I go?"

"Whar to?—whar to, Jube?"

"To Foreper's 'nagerie. You is gwine fur ter le' me go? Ain't yer, daddy?"

"Sartain, boy; sartain,—ef yer kin find a silver-mine 'twixt now and show-day."

Jube looked disheartened for a moment. Then his face brightened. He was not lacking in expedients, and it was a great matter to have "Daddy's" consent. He began to do a double shuffle, but brought up in short order as he caught Aunt Hannah's eyes turned upon him.

"You Jube! you jis' shuffle out er dis, an' hang dat las' load ob tobaccy-cuttin's on de scaffold, down by de tree."

[Jube obeyed. The tobacco was duly spread on the scaffold, which was supported on one side by posts and on the other by grape-vines which hung from the limbs of an aged oak-tree. This done, he sat swinging on the scaffold, while he set his wits to work to solve the mystery of that silver-mine. He finally concluded that a silver dollar would serve for the exigencies of the occasion.]

Next morning two of Aunt Hannah's biggest melons were missing from the patch, and a brace of her fattest capons from the roost; but suspicion was diverted from the real culprit by the tracks of huge shoes freely displayed throughout the path.

"'Pears to me, Isrul," said the woe-begone Hannah, " dat thief mus' have wore shoes made upon his own las' : I nebber saw sich a foot on any ob my acquaintance."

" Dat's so, Hanner; dat's gospel trufe. Der ain't no sich build of foot sca'cely sence de days of Goli-er."

Yet, as Hannah turned off in perplexed thought, the old sinner slyly thrust forward his own huge shoes, giving a significant poke with the bowl of his pipe at the sand and clay filling the coarse seams.

" Ki," he inwardly chuckled, " dat boy Jube better not let de old 'ooman know how close under her nose he done 'skiver his silver-mine. She'll have her sheer of interes' off o' him, shore as yer born."

But Jube was as sly as he was naughty. Aunt Hannah was unsuspecting.

"Juba," said she, tenderly, " ef I had the money you should go ter Foreper's 'nagerie to-morrow."

Jube was prompt to seize his golden opportunity.

" Ef I arned the money, mammy, mought I go ?"

" Ye-es," drawled " mammy," cooling a little : " ef Isrul s'poses he kin spar' yer from the 'baccy-gathering, yer mought."

" Ef yer fines the silver-mine, Jube, ef yer fines the silver-mine, yer kin go," said Israel, pressing in the feathery ashes of his pipe with the horny tip of his finger.

[Jube having found his mine in the manner just indicated, he brought home a ticket of admission, which he claimed had been given him for watering some of the circus-horses. But that same afternoon the daring youngster got himself into trouble. In his anxiety to see the elephant during its progress through the town, he sought a narrow street-corner, where he would have been squeezed to death by the huge monster had not the elephant picked him up with his trunk and landed him on the roof of a neighboring shed. This well-meant kindness excited Jube's wrath, and he vowed to get even with the "ole stump-footed critter." That evening he saw the wonderful performance, but failed to revenge himself upon the elephant. Reaching home, he crept into bed with visions of circus splendor swimming in his brain.]

From the over-eating or over-excitement of the day, his sleep was not of long duration. He was aroused, an hour or two before dawn, by the sound of wheels passing along the turnpike. In an instant he was wide awake and on the alert.

"Goodness!" he exclaimed, in a quiver of excitement. "Ef 'tain't Foreper's surcuss and 'nagerie on its travels! Wish-er-may-die if I don't git one more blink at the elerphant!"

[He slipped from his bed, and through the window to the ground. From the gate he watched the passing wagons, and finally saw a ponderous mass loom up in the distance.]

It was Forepaugh's elephant, moving drowsily along. His keeper, riding alongside, seemed half asleep too, as also did the pony he rode. It was evidently a somnambulistic trio, jogging leisurely along in the wake of Forepaugh's show. But Jube was wide awake, and there was a spirit of mischief awake within him, besides.

"I sed I'd be even wi' the tough-hided, stump-footed ole thing," he chuckled, squaring himself for action. "He skeered me to-day; but I'll gin him sich a skeer, now, as never was."

On came the somnolent three. Directly they were abreast of the gate behind which crouched the waiting Jube. Suddenly the gate was flung wide on its hinges, and the boy leaped into the road with a screech and a yell, flinging his arms about, and flapping his very scanty drapery almost in the face of the beast. You may believe his Indian majesty napped no longer! In an instant his proboscis was waved frantically in the air, sounding his trump of alarm, the prolonged, screaming whistle fairly deafening its hearers.

Poor Jube had by no means calculated upon this dire result of his attempt at revenge. His eyeballs rolled, wild and big with terror, as he watched for a second the cloud of dust veiling the wrestling of the fettered beast and his angry guardian. But the struggle was a brief one, as might have been expected from the odds in favor of the elephant. Freed from his keeper, he rushed in pursuit of Jube, pressing him so hotly that he had no time to mount his ladder to the cabin loft. At almost every step, too, the infuriated beat sounded his trump. A roaring blast he gave, as, in his mad haste, he struck against a corner of the cabin, jostling Hannah and Israel from their deep sleep. Terrified out of their wits, the old couple tumbled out upon the floor, and fell upon their knees, thinking it was the horn of Gabriel summoning them from death to judgment. What but destruction and judgment could mean those yells and shouts and bellowings, turning the calm, moonlit night into pandemonium? Clinging together, and quaking, they managed to reach the door, and to open a crack wide enough to peep through.

"Laws, Isrul!" cried Hannah, falling upon her knees again, all in a tremble. "Isrul, it am the judgment-day, as I is a sinner! An' there goes de debbil now arter Jube! Didn't I alluz say he'd git dat boy, shore! He wouldn't say his pra'rs, ner so much ez min' me, what fotch him up by han'. Come in, Isrul, an' latch the do', fer he'll be arter you nex'. Oh, laws, if he'll only be satisfied wi' you an' Juba, Isrul! You is wickeder 'an me,—wickeder sinners; you know yer is, ole man,—you know yer is."

Her "ole man" attempted no self-defence. With a dexterity quite unusual with him, he had managed to latch and chain the door, but now he was leaning up against the lintel, speechless and knock-kneed with terror.

All at once there was a quick, heavy rap upon the door.

Hannah howled, and sunk lower on her knees. "It's de debbil!" she whispered, in a sepulchral tone. "He's done come fer yer, Isrul! Speak up, ole man,—speak perlite, sorter, an' maybe he'll be easy on yer. Answer him, Isrul."

"Who-o—who dar?" chattered Israel, with a dismal whine.

"Open the door!" shouted an angry voice without. "I thought everybody was dead inside there. It's nobody but me,—the keeper of Forepaugh's elephant, that's broke loose and will tramp down all your things here, to say nothing of your rascally boy, who ought to be well whipped. The beast will kill him if I can't get a pitchfork or something. Haven't you a pitchfork somewhere? Hurry!—your boy's in a lot of danger! Stir about, will you? Let's have a pitchfork!"

"Ki yi, Hannah!" exulted Israel, beginning to straighten his bent knees, "yer debbil's nothin' but Foreper's elerphant, arter all. Hi! jes' yer run an' fetch de pitchfork fer de gemman."

"Yer go an' git it yerself, Isrul: I is engaged," was his wife's prompt response.

"Hurry up there!" shouted the voice outside. "Fetch me the fork, or the beast will kill your boy, for certain."

"I say," answered "ole Isrul," with his mouth at the latch-hole,—"I say, massa, I's clean crippled, an' bedrid with the rheumatiz, an' the ole 'ooman here, she's skeered clar inter spasims. You'll find the fork in the shed, so jes' help yerself, as we're onable ter, massa."

With loud mutterings of anger, the keeper departed in search of the pitchfork. While he was gone, the elephant had regularly treed Jube. Too closely pressed to secure the shelter of his room in the cabin loft, Jube instinctively had made for the only other accessible place of refuge. Into the big oak-tree he had scrambled, by the aid of the drying-scaffold suspended from its boughs. Nor, thoroughly scared as he was, did he stop in the lower branches. Not knowing what might be the stretching capacity of that awful proboscis which had once enfolded him, he clambered, hand over hand, until at a considerable elevation he reached the second forking of the tree. Perched therein, he took time to draw his breath and look down at his enemy. Evidently this enemy was determined not to consider himself baffled. He was charging Jube's stronghold with the intrepidity of Napoleon's " Old Guard" and the concentrated strength of a battering-ram. But the oak, although its days of kingly glory were past, was stronger than Forepaugh's elephant. Its bare limbs trembled under the shock, yet the mighty roots held firm. The blow, however, dislodged the drying-scaffold, so that, broken from its fatal clinging, it fell with a great crash to the ground. In default of other prey, the elephant at once charged upon this framework of poles, with its burden of half-dried tobacco-cuttings. He stamped and tore at and pulled to pieces the structure, tossing the cuttings until his eyes and mouth and proboscis were well filled with the dust of the dried tobacco. Frenzied by the fumes and the taste of the weed he hated with a deadly hatred, as well as maddened by the agony of its smarting and burning, the animal's rage seemed to know no bounds. Overjoyed at his reprieve from destruction, Jube began a faint, hysterical laugh as the infuriated beast plunged and charged, snorting and sneezing, about the tree. At last the elephant sounded his trump again frantically, setting off at the top of his speed for the river flowing at the base of the hill.

So, for a time, the coast was left clear; but Jube was too thoroughly scared to think of deserting his present place of security; and, in a little while, his majesty, relieved of the tobacco, again advanced to the attack. This time he was better armed, having filled his trunk at the river with a copious supply of water. Taking fair aim at poor Jube, he let him have the benefit of the whole stream, blowing it into his face with a directness and force for which the boy was utterly unprepared. Of course his balance was destroyed, and, tumbled from his perch, he doubtless would have fallen headlong to the ground, but that he had the good fortune to land in the fork below, where he was just beyond the reach of the dreaded proboscis. Encouraged by this success, the beast charged again, but the ground was now well strewn with the tobacco, and, as he rushed forward, he was again blinded and strangled by the pungent powder. Once more he made a frenzied rush for the river. This time, however, his hind legs became entangled among the grape-vines linking the poles together, so that after some vigorous but vain kicking and shaking, he was compelled to proceed on his way, dragging the scaffold, and much of the tobacco, with him.

At this juncture, the keeper, armed with Israel's long fork, appeared on the scene of action. Taking advantage of the elephant's blinded condition, he attacked him vehe-

mently, goading him right and left. Yet the beast, infuriated, would not cry for mercy. But finally, in one of his
blinded plunges, he rushed upon Hannah's empty root-pit,
and, the slight covering giving way under the enormous
weight, his majesty was pitched headlong in shame and
terror to the bottom of the pit. Then his proud spirit
was conquered by a vigorous assault, and he trumpeted
for mercy.

It was not until he was thus subdued that Jube, noti-
fied by Aunt Hannah, deemed it safe to descend once more
to the ground; even then he did not think it necessary to
show himself to the twinkling eye of his late adversary.
Nor, perhaps, did he feel safe at all until, with the assistance of returned showmen and some of the neighbors, the
elephant had been helped from the pit, and had quietly
continued its journey towards the neighboring town.

"Now, you Juba, jes' you mark my words," was Israel's
closing piece of advice when the tumult had finally subsided, and Jube, clothed and in his right mind, was sitting
on the stool of repentance in the cabin, "If I ever does
hear of you a-findin' ob a silver-mine *anywheres* when Foreper's surcuss am around, shore's I is a livin' man, I'll w'ar
out on yer back some ob dat extry shoe-leather what made
tracks through the ole 'ooman's water-millium-patch. You
hear dat, Juba? Now, you jes' clar outer dis, an' gather
up ebery spear ob dat tobaccy what you an' Foreper's elerphant hab done scattered from Dan to Beershebeh. An'
min' what I say, dat dis ain't Hanner what's foolin' long
wid yer, now."

And since that time Jube has never pined for the circus
on his holidays.

PETER FUNK.

ASA GREENE.

[The author of the following sketch was a New England physician, who came to New York about 1830 and entered into the bookselling business. He wrote several works of humorous tales and sketches, including "The Perils of Pearl Street," "A Glance at New York," etc. He died in 1837. We subjoin a biographical notice of a well-known and ubiquitous city character, who has long outlived his biographer.]

THE firm of Smirk, Quirk, & Co. affected a great parade and bustle in the way of business. They employed a large number of clerks, whom they boarded at the different hotels, for the convenience of drumming, besides each member of the firm boarding in like manner and for a similar purpose. They had an immense pile of large boxes, such as are used for packing dry-goods, constantly before their door, blocking up the sidewalk so that it was nearly impossible to pass. They advertised largely in several of the daily papers, and made many persons believe, what they boasted themselves, that they sold more dry-goods than any house in the city.

But those who were behind the curtain knew better. They knew there was a great deal of vain boast and empty show. They knew that Peter Funk was much employed about the premises and putting the best possible face upon everything.

By the by, speaking of PETER FUNK, I must give a short history of that distinguished personage. When, or where, he was born, I cannot pretend to say. Neither do I know who were his parents, or what was his bringing up. He might have been the child of thirty-six fathers, for aught

I know, and instead of being brought up, have, as the vulgar saying is, come up himself.

One thing is certain, he has been known among merchants time out of mind; and, though he is despised and hated by some, he is much employed and cherished by others. He is a little, bustling, active, smiling, bowing, scraping, quizzical fellow, in a powdered wig, London-brown coat, drab kerseymere breeches, and black silk stockings.

This is the standing portrait of Peter Funk,—if a being who changes his figure every day, every hour, and perhaps every minute may be said to have any sort of fixed or regular form. The truth is, Peter Funk is a very Proteus; and those who behold him in one shape to-day may, if they will watch his transformations, behold him in a hundred different forms on the morrow. Indeed, there is no calculating, from his present appearance, in what shape he will be likely to figure next. He changes at will, to suit the wishes of his employers.

His mind is as flexible as his person. He has no scruples of conscience. He is ready to be employed in all manner of deceit and deviltry; and he cares not who his employers are, if they only give him plenty of business. In short, he is the most active, industrious, accommodating, dishonest, unprincipled, convenient little varlet that ever lived.

Besides all the various qualities I have mentioned, Peter. Funk seems to be endowed with ubiquity,—or at least with the faculty of being present in more places than one at the same time. If it were not so, how could he serve so many masters at once? How could he be seen in one part of Pearl Street buying goods at auction, in another part standing at the door with a quill behind each ear, and in a third figuring in the shape of a box of goods, or cooped up on the shelf, making a show of merchandise where all is emptiness behind?

With this account of Peter Funk, my readers have perhaps by this time gathered some idea of his character. If not, I must inform them that he is the very imp of deception, that his sole occupation is to deceive, and that he is only employed for that purpose. Indeed, such being his known character in the mercantile community, his name is sometimes used figuratively to signify anything which is employed for the purpose of deception,—or, as the sharp ones say, to gull the flats.

Such being the various and accommodating character of Peter Funk, it is not at all surprising that his services should be in great demand. Accordingly, he is very much employed in Pearl Street, sometimes under one name and sometimes under another; for I should have mentioned, as a part of his character, that he is exceedingly apt to change names, and has as many *aliases* as the most expert rogue in Bridewell or the Court of Sessions. Sometimes he takes the name of John Smith, sometimes James Smith, and sometimes simply Mr. Smith. At other times he is called Roger Brown, Simon White, Bob Johnson, or Tommy Thompson. In short, he has an endless variety of names, under which he passes before the world for so many different persons. The initiated only know, and everybody else is gulled.

Peter Funk is a great hand at auctions. He is constantly present, bidding up the goods as though he was determined to buy everything before him. He is well known for bidding higher than anybody else, or, at all events, running up an article to the very highest notch, though he finally lets the opposing bidder take it, merely, as he says, to accommodate him; or, not particularly wanting the article himself, he professes to have bid upon it solely

II.—*l*   14*

because he thought it a great pity so fine a piece of goods should go so very far beneath its value.

It is no uncommon thing to see the little fellow attending an auction in his powdered wig, his brown coat, his drab kerseys, as fat as a pig, as sleek as a mole, and smiling with the most happy countenance, as if he were about to make his fortune. It is no uncommon thing to see him standing near the auctioneer, and exclaiming, as he keeps bobbing his head in token of bidding, "A superb piece of goods! a fine piece of goods! great pity it should go so cheap. I don't want it, but I'll give another twenty-five cents, rather than it should go for nothing." The opposite bidder is probably some novice from the country,—some honest Johnny Raw, who is shrewd enough in what he understands, but has never in his life heard of Peter Funk. Seeing so very knowing and respectable a looking man bidding upon the piece of goods and praising it up at every nod, he naturally thinks it must be a great bargain, and he is determined to have it, let it cost what it will. The result is that he gives fifty per cent. more for the article than it is worth; and the auctioneer and Peter Funk are ready to burst with laughter at the prodigious gull they have made of the poor countryman.

By thus running up goods Peter is of great service to the auctioneers, though he never pays them a cent of money. Indeed, it is not his intention to purchase, nor is it that of the auctioneer that he should. Goods nevertheless are frequently struck off to him; and then the salesman calls out the name of Mr. Smith, Mr. Johnson, or some other among the hundred aliases of Peter Funk, as the purchaser. But the goods, on such occasions, are always taken back by the auctioneer, agreeably to a secret understanding between him and Peter.

In a word, Peter Funk is the great *underbidder* at all the

auctions, and might with no little propriety be styled the underbidder-general. But this sort of characters are both unlawful and unpopular,—not to say odious,—and hence it becomes necessary for Peter Funk, *alias* the underbidder, to have so many aliases to his name, in order that he may not be detected in the underhanded practice of under-bidding.

To avoid detection, however, he sometimes resorts to other tricks, among which one is to act the part of a ventriloquist, and appear to be several different persons, bidding in different places. He has the knack of changing his voice at will and counterfeiting that of sundry well-known persons: so that goods are sometimes knocked off to gentlemen who have never opened their mouths.

But a very common trick of Peter's is to conceal himself in the cellar, from whence, through a convenient hole near the auctioneer, his voice is heard bidding for goods; and nobody but those in the secret knows from whence the sound proceeds. This is acting the part of Peter Funk in the cellar.

But Peter, for the most part, is fond of being seen in some shape or other; and it matters little what, so that he can aid his employers in carrying on a system of deception. He will figure in the shape of a box, bale, or package of goods; he will appear in twenty different places at the same time on the shelf of a jobber,—sometimes representing a specimen of English, French, or other goods, but being a mere shadow, and nothing else,—a phantasma,—a show without the substance. In this manner it was that he often figured in the service of Smirk, Quirk & Co.; and, while people were astonished at the prodigious quantity of goods they had in their store, two-thirds at least of the show was owing to Peter Funk.

THE NEW CHURCH ORGAN.

WILL CARLETON.

[One of the best bits of Carleton's humorous poetry is that here given, from the "Farm Ballads." The spectacle of the ancient sing-ing "sister" struggling with the new-fangled musical invention, and finally giving up the unequal contest in despair, must be familiar to the personal experience of many of our readers. The author was born at Hudson, Michigan, in 1845. He has published several volumes of the poetry of rural life, full of mingled pathos and humor.]

THEY'VE got a brand-new organ, Sue,
    For all their fuss an' search;
They've done just as they said they'd do,
    And fetched it into church.
They're bound the critter shall be seen,
    And on the preacher's right
They've hoisted up their new machine,
    In everybody's sight.
They've got a chorister and choir,
    Ag'in' *my* voice an' vote;
For it was never *my* desire
    To praise the Lord by note!

I've been a sister good an' true
    For five-an'-thirty year;
I've done what seemed my part to do,
    An' prayed my duty clear;
I've sung the hymns both slow and quick,
    Just as the preacher read;
And twice, when Deacon Tubbs was sick,
    I took the fork an' led!

And now their bold, new-fangled ways
    Is comin' all about,
And I, right in my latter days,
    Am fairly crowded out!

To-day, the preacher, good old dear,
    With tears all in his eyes,
Read, " I can read my title clear
    To mansions in the skies;"
I al'ays liked that blessed hymn,—
    I s'pose I al'ays will;
It somehow gratifies my whim,
    In good old Ortonville;
But when that choir got up to sing,
    I couldn't catch a word;
They sung the most dog-gonedest thing
    A body ever heard!

Some worldly chaps was standin' near;
    An' when I seed them grin,
I bid farewell to every fear,
    And boldly waded in.
I thought I'd chase their tune along,
    An' tried with all my might;
But, though my voice is good and strong,
    I couldn't steer it right;
When they was high, then I was low,
    An' also contra'-wise,
And I too fast, or they too slow,
    To " mansions in the skies."

An' after every verse, you know,
    They played a little tune:
I didn't understand, an' so
    I started in too soon.

I pitched it pretty middlin' high,
   I fetched a lusty tone,
But oh! alas! I found that I
   Was singing there alone!
They laughed a little, I am told;
   But I had done my best,
And not a wave of trouble rolled
   Across my peaceful breast.

And Sister Brown,—I could but look,—
   She sits right front of me;
She never was no singin'-book,
   An' never meant to be;
But then she al'ays tried to do
   The best she could, she said;
She understood the time, right through,
   An' kep' it with her head;
But when she tried this mornin', oh,
   I had to laugh, or cough!
It kep' her head a-bobbin' so,
   It e'en-a'most came off!

An' Deacon Tubbs,—he all broke down,
   As one might well suppose:
He took one look at Sister Brown,
   And meekly scratched his nose.
He looked his hymn-book through and through,
   And laid it on the seat,
And then a pensive sigh he drew,
   And looked completely beat.
An' when they took another bout,
   He didn't even rise,
But drawed his red bandanner out
   An' wiped his weepin' eyes.

I've been a sister good an' true
  For five-an'-thirty year;
I've done what seemed my part to do,
  An' prayed my duty clear;
But death will stop my voice, I know,
  For he is on my track,
And some day I to church will go
  And nevermore come back;
And when the folks get up to sing,—
  · Whene'er that time shall be,—
I do not want no patent thing
  A-squealin' over me!

JIM WILKINS'S TACTICS.

FRANCES COURTNEY BAYLOR.

[No work of recent years has been fuller of sprightly humor than "On Both Sides," an amusing contrast of English and American manners which at once established the reputation of the author of our present selection. From a later novel, "Behind the Blue Ridge," we select the following story told by one ex-Confederate soldier to another. It has the advantage of coming out whole,—which is seldom the case with selections from novels.]

"AFTER I got the mill I made money, John. Befo' that it was slow work. I prospered steady, but I never was one to blow 'bout my business. I kep' a still tongue, and done well, and salted down what I made, and done better and better. And I was gettin' ready to fix to build a new house,—sorter settlin' down in my tracks, and takin' things easy, and fixin' to enjoy myself, when, all of a sudden, the ole woman took a notion,—the blamedest notion! —and spiled everything. 'Twas to pull up stakes and

move out to Californy! You see, she had two brothers
out there, and they kep' on writin' to her and put it in
her head. I thought she'd gone plum crazy when she fust
talked 'bout it. It did 'pear like it. 'Break up here,' I
sez to her, 'whur I've got a home, and a good business,
and go balloonin' out yonder, the other side er nowhere?'
But Californy was the greatest place that ever was.
Everybody made big fortunes there befo' they could turn
'round. The grapes there wuz as big as peaches, and the
peaches wuz as big as potatoes, and the potatoes bigger'n
pumkins, and the pumkins as big as all out-doors. The
very chickens hadn't no feathers to pick off, and was
already cooked when you was hungry. You couldn't be
poor out there if you got burnt out twicet a week and lost
all you had. Every boy got to be governor of the State,
and every girl married a rich man. Californy was *heaven.*
Everything was better there than nowhere else. You've
heered that kind er talk, John?"

John Shore nodded, and said, "And I've been fool enough
to believe some of it, too."

"Well, my wife she was full of it. At fust I argyed the
thing with her, like a jack; and, of course, the more I
argyed the more she sot her mind on goin'. She said it
would be the makin' of me and the children, and she
wanted to see them dear brothers of hern. And then I
got mad, and I ain't swore sence Appomattox like I did.
I was ashamed uv myself *good* afterwards, talkin' that
way to a woman. And she was that much more sot, and
bent, and determinated. And then I sulked like a bear
with a sore head for a while. And that done no good; she
got *sotter* every day. You've been a married man, John.
You know how it is. I couldn't bend and I couldn't
break her, and I wouldn't beat her. I was willin' to do
this, and I was willin' to do that,—anything, 'most, to

satisfy her; but she wouldn't be satisfied no way I fixed it,
without we broke up and moved to Californy. I begged
and prayed of her, even, and her a good woman, too,—
says her prayers every night, and reads her Bible on Sundays, and never took off her clothes, but nursed me faithful night and day, when I had the small-pox, and there
ain't never been a better mother made,—but she never
budged. She said she had the children to consider. You
remember how it used to was, John, maybe."

"No, I don't, Jim. I hadn't never no disagreements with
my wife," said John Shore, his voice softening as he spoke.

"Hum, hum! She died *young*. I reklect 'bout that;
she died *mighty young*," said Mr. Wilkins, reflectively.
"Well, John, I seed how 'twould be. I've rode a gover-
ment mule befo' now. So I knowed it warn't no manner
nor sort of use, whatsomedever, to try to turn her head
'round, and I'd already tried her with blinkers and 'thout
blinkers, tight girth and loose girth, barebacked and sad-
dled, coaxed and driv and spurred, and it wouldn't work,
seein' she'd got the bit between her teeth, and *wouldn't* go
my way ef she died fur it. And I know'd, too,—well,
you've been married, John! hum!—I know'd I'd be
throwed 'gin the wall and hurt *bad* ef I didn't stop tryin'.
So I set and studied and *studied* over that thing till at last
I sez to myself, 'You nateral-born pulin' igit! Don't yer
see! This here thing calls fur *tactics*.' So I studied more'n
ever. And then I goes to Blake,—one-eyed Blake, Fifth
Virginia Cavalry, little nubbin of a man with a red head.
You must shorely disremember him? Limped a little;
warn't nothin' uv a soldier,—wouldn't skeer a rabbit,—but
a square, correct fellow. Yer don't say, now, that you've
forgot *Blake*,—the man that give us a cup of hot coffee the
mornin' we started to fall back from Ashby's Gap?"

"Oh, yes! I know *now* who you're talkin' 'bout. It

was mighty cur'ous. That fellow had coffee right straight
through the war, from fust to last! And him only a
private. How he got it the Lord only knows. And it
warn't chicory nor nothin'. It was *coffee*. That there
cup of coffee was 'bout the best thing ever I put in my
mouth befo' or sence. We'd been on the jump, you remember, fur ten days, and I hadn't had no sleep, skasely,
fur three nights, and it was 'bout all I could do to keep
from fallin' off my horse. And when I seed that coffee-
pot I thought I seed the New Jerusalem. And Blake he
poured me out a big tincupful, and I couldn't stop to drink
it, but I warn't goin' to lose nor leave it, not ef I knowed
it. So I called to Blake to charge the cup to Uncle Sam,
and rode off. And my horse would stumble a bit, and it
was as hot as fire, and between 'em I got scalded right
smart, and spilt some, which was worse, but what I got
was just heaven! Oh, yes, I remember Blake!"

"I thought you couldn't er forgot him. Well, as I was
a-tellin' you, I went to him and give him the wink, and we
soon fixed it up between us fust-rate. He was to have the
house, and the mill, and the farm, fur a year free, and was
to make out to ev'rybody like he'd bought it. See? Me
a-keepin' of it all the time, of co'se. See? And then I
sez to the old woman, I sez, 'I don't want to leave my
home, and my friends, and all I've worked so hard fur
ever since the war, and go trapesin' off yonder so fur from
Virginny, but I see you can't be, and ain't a-goin' to be,
happy here no more: so I give in, and you kin pack up,
and we'll strike camp next week and go to Californy.'

"She hadn't never 'lowed fur me to give in, John, and
she looked mighty solemn-like when she heered me say
that,—sorter like she did the day we got married. And
then she hugged and kissed me good, and I told her I'd
sold off everything, and was doin' that thing teetotally

and intirely to pleasure her, and I didn't care a red cent
fur the resks as long as she was pleased. And she
hugged and kissed me ag'in, and said I was the bes'
husband any woman ever had on the face of the yearth;
and I felt about as low as they're made,—as mean as a
skunk. I couldn't skasely keep from tellin' her the truth.
But I know'd I was actin' right, leastways *meanin'* right,
so I never said nothin', and it was settled that er way.
Have a chaw, John? This is the 'Farmer's Friend.'
I like it better'n any of 'em. Well, sir, she went 'round
the house mighty quiet, packin' and sortin', and didn't
talk none hardly. She felt bad, and I seed it, but I
never said nothin'. And I went 'round lookin' like 'twas
all I could do not to bust out cryin'. *Tactics, John; all
tactics!* And when she'd kissed, and cried, and tole good-
by all around to the folks, and we'd got on the train, I sez
to her, 'Look here. I want to tell you one thing: this
here is *your* excursion, Mrs. Wilkins. It ain't *my* excursion. Ef you ain't satisfied in Californy, don't you never
say nothin' to me 'bout comin' back,—that's all,—'cause I
ain't never comin' back.' She promised she wouldn't,
and I seed then she was skeered *bad;* but I never said
nothin'. *Tactics*, John. See?" Mr. Wilkins clapped his
friend's knee, and, throwing back his head, laughed loud
and long, his merry eyes almost disappearing from view.
He was obliged to get out a red cotton handkerchief and
give vent to a couple of trombone-like snorts before he
could resume his story, so great was his own enjoyment
of it, and then he wiped his wet eyes and cheeks.

"I can't help it, John; I'm jes' obleeged to laugh whenever I think uv that thing. It jes' spurts out. I've done
it in church befo' now,—sniggered right out, and caught
Hail Columbia fur it afterwards from the ole woman, and
laughed wuss'n ever, tell I wuz as weak as a new-born

babe, and she said I wuz gittin' ready fur the 'sylum at Stanton. But as I started to tell you. We travelled, and travelled, and travelled, tell I thought we'd passed all creation. And the country kep' on gittin' flatter and flatter. There warn't a mounting to be seen for hundreds uv miles, ef you'll believe me, and an uglier, and a browner, and a more burnt-up country I never seed, and it jest did 'pear to me like we wuz gittin' to the mouth of the bad place. Howsomever, we did git to that heaven of a Californy at last, and met up with her brothers, and I bought a little place from the only smart man that had ever been out there, I reckon, fur he was leavin' it fust chance he got, and we started in.

"Well! sech a country as that was! You wouldn't believe it! It was so dry, John, fur months and months that everything turned to powder, and then it turned loose and drownded ev'ything and ev'ybody out, and I don't know which was wust. You couldn't raise a leaf uv tobacco to save your life! And I never eat a beat-biscuit nor had a mint-julip while I wuz there! It was the most God-forsaken place,—the jumpin'-off place, and no mistake. And there warn't no spring-house, nor no ice-house, nor no smoke-house, and nobody to help with the work. And the climate warn't anything to call a climate, and the ole woman got *mighty* sick uv it in a month, but she was 'shamed to say so. I pertended *I* liked it, and we went on. In 'bout three months she couldn't hold in no longer, and she began sayin' she didn't like this thing and that thing. And I didn't take no notice, no more'n ef I was deef. And when the rainy season come she got droopy and miserable as a wet chicken, and I pertended still I liked it. And she said she never seed nothin' uv her brothers, 'cause they lived a good piece off, and wuz always too busy to come to see nobody, and she werrited

powerful, and talked 'bout livin' and dyin' 'mong strangers
all the time. And I said, 'Oh,'this is Californy! We ain't
goin' to die; nobody don't die out here; we are goin' to
live here for the next fifty years. I'm 'bout as well contented as I ever 'spect to be,' and she was so furious she
wouldn't speak to me fur a week. *Tactics*, John. See?
And we went on fur a while, and the harvest was so poor
we didn't make nothin', skasely. But I lived po', and was
cheerful all the time, and sez to her, ''Pears to me we ain't
comin' out the big end of the horn fur *Californy*, the land
of plenty, but we're here now, and we've got to stay.'
'Why don't you urrigate, Jim?' says she to me, mad-like,
and I tole her I hadn't got the money to fool away on
'bout fifty miles er ditches. I'd heered rain had been
plenty in Virginny, but nothin' couldn't be helped. And,
John, what did that woman do? She got as sweet as
molasses-candy that minnit, and says, 'Ef *you* ain't content here, Jim, I'll go back to Virginny. I won't stay no-
whars whur my dear husband ain't contented.' She *did*.
Women are *'bout* the smartest things the Lord ever made,
John. But I seed things was workin', and I knowed I had
the reins, and was set on drivin' her into a corner; so I sez,
'Thank yer kindly, mother, but I'm all right. I don't
want to go back. I'm suited out here. I *come* to pleasure
you, but I'm goin' to *stay* to pleasure myself. The crop
ain't been good, but in ten years or so maybe I'll be able
to urrigate, and we'll do better.' That beat her. She got
as red as fire, and wouldn't eat a mite that day. Well,
we went on that way for a while ag'in, and then all to
onst she broke plum, teetotally down, and caved in, and
give up, and went to bed, and stayed there, and cried herself into fits, 'most. And when I sez to her, 'What in the
name of goodness has got into you? What's the matter
with you, anyways, mother?' What do you think she sez

to me, after werritin' and devillin' me constant, and never
lettin' me rest tell I give my consent to goin' out there?
She sez, ' What did you ever bring me and my children
out here to starve and die fur? I'll *die* ef you keep me
here.' *She did!* And she meant it, too! Well, I didn't
argy that time, 'n I didn't make no fuss. I seed she was
plum beat out, sho' 'nough, and had surrendered, and I
didn't want to push things. I jes' said, ' You warn't satisfied in your Virginny home, and you ain't satisfied in your
Californy heaven, it 'pears. But I'm still willin' to pleasure
you, and do all I can fur to make you happy : so stop
cryin', and I'll *borrer* the money and take you back home
ag'in'. And she set up in bed straight, and sez, ' Oh, Jim,
Jim, take me home! take me home!' sez she, ' and I'll
break rock on the pike fer a livin'. I'll do anything! I'll
thank and bless yer as long as I've got breath in my body!
I hate Californy wuss'n *pison!'* *I* hadn't to borrer no
money, and I knowed Blake's time was 'most out, and
when it came 'round we lef'. You oughter seed the old
woman! She could have danced a jig for joy, settled
woman that she is. She didn't care no more than nothin'
'bout partin' with them dear brothers of hern. She wuz
crazy-happy, ef ever a creature wuz."

"You must have been mighty happy, both of you,
comin' back together," said John Shore, who had listened
with the greatest interest.

"Well, that's as you may call it, John," replied Mr.
Wilkins, dubiously. " I 'lowed it would be. But, ef you
believe me, the old woman set up as stiff as a ramrod all
the way back, and wouldn't have nothin' more to do with
me than ef I'd treated her the wust in the world all through.
She did! And she's been that way ever sence; you've
noticed her to-day. I darsn't run her. *Not fur my life!*
But when I look at her, I——" Mr. Wilkins here roared

afresh, and was obliged to have recourse again to his handkerchief, his friend joining heartily in his outburst, and
the pair rocking themselves backward and forward in an
ecstasy of amusement for some moments. "Excuse me,
John, but I'd *bust* ef I didn't. Ha! ha! ha! ha! ha! I
made a big trouble and business 'bout tradin' with Blake
to git back my house ag'in (I let on, now, the mill's his'n),
and I tell you she was glad to git back to it! *She'll* never
want to do no more movin'. She'll think twicet befo' she
has any differments with me. She snaps at me like a turtle
jes' now. But, Lor! I don't kyer. I've got the bit in her
mouth, and I ain't goin' to do no sawin' while it's sore.
And it's turned out all right. And she's got all she wants.
But, John Shore, I sez now what I've always said, and
there ain't no man that knows anything 'bout 'em that can
say it ain't true, ' Women's like war. Sometimes they're
a scourge, and then ag'in they're a blessing'; but with
both uv 'em *you've jes' got to have tactics.*' "

ECCENTRIC CHARACTERS.

VARIOUS.

[Our present "Half-Hour" selection is made up of a series of
sketches, each of which has won its way by innate merit to public
appreciation. The first is from Longstreet's once highly-popular
"Georgia Tales;" the second satirizes a form of housewifely self-
depreciation formerly more prevalent than at present. As for the
"spoons" story, it has gone the rounds of the press in more forms
than one. We give the Yankee version of it.]

GEORGIA THEATRICS.

IF my memory fail me not, the 10th of June, 1809,
found me, at about eleven o'clock in the forenoon, ascend-

ing a long and gentle slope in what was called "The Dark Corner" of Lincoln. I believe it took its name from the moral darkness which reigned over that portion of the county at the time of which I am speaking. If in this point of view it was but a shade darker than the rest of the county, it was inconceivably dark. If any man can name a trick or sin which had not been committed at the time of which I am speaking, in the very focus of the county's illumination (Lincolnton), he must himself be the most inventive of the tricky and the very Judas of sinners. Since that time, however (all humor aside), Lincoln has become a living proof "that light shineth in darkness." Could I venture to mingle the solemn with the ludicrous, even for the purposes of honorable contrast, I could adduce from this county instances of the most numerous and wonderful transitions from vice and folly to virtue and holiness which have ever, perhaps, been witnessed since the days of the apostolic ministry. So much, lest it should be thought by some that what I am about to relate is characteristic of the county in which it occurred.

Whatever may be said of the moral condition of the Dark Corner at the time just mentioned, its natural condition was anything but dark. It smiled in all the charms of spring; and spring borrowed a new charm from its undulating grounds, its luxuriant woodlands, its sportive streams, its vocal birds, and its blushing flowers.

Rapt with the enchantment of the season and the scenery around me, I was slowly rising the slope, when I was startled by loud, profane, and boisterous voices which seemed to proceed from a thick covert of undergrowth about two hundred yards in the advance of me, and about one hundred to the right of my road.

"You kin, kin you?"

"Yes, I kin, and am able to do it! Boo-oo-oo! Oh wake snakes, and walk your chalks! Brimstone and —— fire! Don't hold me, Nick Stoval! The fight's made up, and let's go at it. —— my soul if I don't jump down his throat, and gallop every chitterling out of him before you can say 'quit!'"

"Now, Nick, don't hold him! Jist let the wild-cat come, and I'll tame him. Ned 'll see me a fair fight: won't you, Ned?"

"Oh, yes; I'll see you a fair fight, blast my old shoes if I don't."

"That's sufficient, as Tom Haines said when he saw the elephant. Now let him come."

Thus they went on, with countless oaths interspersed, which I dare not even hint at, and with much that I could not distinctly hear.

In mercy's name, thought I, what band of ruffians has selected this holy season and this heavenly retreat for such Pandemonian riots! I quickened my gait, and had come nearly opposite to the thick grove whence the noise proceeded, when my eye caught indistinctly and at intervals, through the foliage of the dwarf-oaks and hickories which intervened, glimpses of a man or men who seemed to be in a violent struggle; and I could occasionally catch those deep-drawn emphatic oaths which men in conflict utter when they deal blows. I dismounted, and hurried to the spot with all speed. I had overcome about half the space which separated it from me, when I saw the combatants come to the ground, and, after a short struggle, I saw the uppermost one (for I could not see the other) make a heavy plunge with both his thumbs, and at the same instant I heard a cry in the accent of keenest torture, "Enough! my eye's out!"

I was so completely horror-struck that I stood trans-

II.—*m*

fixed for a moment to the spot where the cry met me. The accomplices in the hellish deed which had been perpetrated had all fled at my approach ; at least I supposed so, for they were not to be seen.

"Now, blast your corn-shucking soul," said the victor (a youth about eighteen years old) as he rose from the ground, "come cuttin' your shines 'bout me ag'in, next time I come to the Court-house, will you! Git your owl-eye in ag'in if you kin!"

At this moment he saw me for the first time. He looked excessively embarrassed, and was moving off, when I called to him, in a tone emboldened by the sacredness of my office and the iniquity of his crime, "Come back, you brute, and assist me in relieving your fellow-mortal, whom you have ruined forever!"

My rudeness subdued his embarrassment in an instant ; and with a taunting curl of the nose, he replied, "You need't kick before you're spurred. There ain't nobody there, nor hain't been, nother. I was jist seein' how I could 'a' fout." So saying, he bounded to his plough, which stood in the corner of the fence about fifty yards beyond the battle-ground.

And—would you believe it, gentle reader?—his report was true. All that I had heard and seen was nothing more nor less than a Lincoln rehearsal, in which the youth who had just left me had played all the parts of all the characters in a court-house fight.

I went to the ground from which he had risen, and there were the prints of his two thumbs, plunged up to the balls in the mellow earth, about the distance of a man's eyes apart ; and the ground around was broken up as if two stags had been engaged upon it.

AUGUSTUS B. LONGSTREET.

ELDER BLUNT AND SISTER SCRUB.

In one of the Eastern States there is a settlement which has long been celebrated as a stronghold of Methodism. It is an out-of-the-way neighborhood, yet no place in the whole country is better known or more highly esteemed. In the centre of the settlement, just where two roads cut each other at right angles, making a "four corners," is the school-house, painted red, and long familiar as the only place of public worship in the settlement. The people are well off now and have built a nice and commodious church on the opposite corner. A few rods up the road from the school-house lived Squire Scrub. You could tell at first sight that the "Squire" was "well-to-do" in this world, for everything about him denoted it. There was his picket fence all around his garden, painted red and the top tipped with white; there was his house, a modest one story and a half, with a leaning to it in the rear, painted white all over; there was the barn,—a large, well-filled barn it was; there was a farm, a choice lot of one hundred acres, well cultivated; and, besides all this, there were the honors and emoluments of the important office of justice of the peace. The "Squire" was, of course, a man of note in his town. He had been a justice several terms in succession. He was a trustee of the school district, and he was both class-leader and steward in the Methodist church. I have no doubt he would have received other honors at the hands of his fellow-townsmen and brethren, had he been eligible. Still, he was a quiet, unassuming man, and I verily believe he thought more of his religion than of all his ecclesiastical and civil honors. His house was the itinerant's home; and a right sweet, pleasant home it would have been but for a certain unfortunate weakness of the every other way

excellent Sister Scrub. The weakness I allude to was, or
at least it was suspected to be, *the love of praise.* Now, the
good sister was really worthy of high praise, and she often
received it; but she had a way of disparaging herself and
her performances which some people thought was intended
to invite praise. No housewife kept her floors looking so
clean and her walls so well whitewashed as she. Every
board was scrubbed and scoured till further scrubbing and
scouring would have been labor wasted. No one could
look on her white ash floor and not admire the polish her
industry gave it. The "Squire" was a good provider, and
Sister Scrub was an excellent cook; and so their table
groaned under a burden of good things on all occasions
when good cheer was demanded. And yet you could
never enter the house and sit half an hour without being
reminded that "Husband held court yesterday, and she
couldn't keep the house decent." If you sat down to eat
with them she was sorry "she hadn't anything fit to eat:"
she had been scrubbing, or washing, or ironing, or she had
been half sick, and she hadn't got such and such things,
that she ought to have. Nor did it matter how bountiful
or how well prepared the repast really was, there was
always *something* deficient, the want of which furnished a
text for a disparaging discourse on the occasion. I remember once that we sat down to a table that a king
might have been happy to enjoy. There was the light,
snow-white bread, there were the potatoes reeking in
butter, there were the chickens swimming in gravy, there
were the onions and the turnips, and I was sure Sister
Scrub had gratified her ambition once. We sat down and
a blessing was asked. Instantly the good sister began:
she was afraid her coffee was too much burned, or that
the water had been smoked, or that she hadn't roasted
the chicken enough. There ought to have been some

salad : and it was too bad that there was nothing nice to offer us.

We, of course, endured these unjustifiable apologies as well as we could, simply remarking that everything was really nice, and proving by our acts that the repast was tempting to our appetites.

I will now introduce another actor to the reader. It is Elder Blunt, the circuit preacher. Elder Blunt was a good man. His religion was of the most genuine experimental kind. He was a very plain man. He, like Mr. Wesley, would no more dare preach a fine sermon than wear a fine coat. He was celebrated for his common-sense way of exhibiting the principles of religion. He *would* speak just what he thought, and as he felt. He somehow got the name of being an eccentric preacher, as every man, I believe, does who never prevaricates and always acts and speaks as he thinks. Somehow or other, Elder Blunt had heard of Sister Scrub, and of that infirmity of hers, and he resolved to cure her. On his first round, he stopped at "Squire Scrub's," as all other itinerants had done before him. John, the young man, took the elder's horse and put him in the stable, and the preacher entered the house. He was shown into the best room, and soon felt very much at home. He expected to hear something in due time disparaging the domestic arrangements, but he heard it sooner than he expected. This time, if Sister Scrub could be credited, her house was all upside down ; it wasn't fit to stay in, and she was sadly mortified to be caught in such a plight. The elder looked all around the room, as if to observe the terrible disorder, but he said not a word. By and by the dinner was ready, and the elder sat down with the family to a well-spread table. Here, again, Sister Scrub found everything faulty ; the coffee wasn't fit to drink, and she hadn't anything fit to eat. The elder lifted his dark eye to her face; for a moment he seemed to penetrate her very soul with his austere gaze; then, slowly rising from the table, he said, "Brother Scrub, I want my horse immediately: I must leave."

"Why, Brother Blunt, what is the matter?"

"Matter? Why, sir, your house isn't fit to stay in, and you haven't anything fit to eat or drink, and I won't stay."

Both the "Squire" and his lady were confounded. This was a piece of eccentricity entirely unlooked for. They were stupefied. But the elder was gone. He wouldn't stay in a house not fit to stay in, and where there wasn't anything fit to eat and drink.

Poor Sister Scrub! She wept like a child at her folly. She "knew it would be all over town," she said, "and everybody would be laughing at her." And, then, how should she meet the blunt, honest elder again? "She hadn't meant anything by what she had said." Ah! she never thought how wicked it was to say *so much* that didn't mean anything.

The upshot of the whole matter was that Sister Scrub "saw herself as others saw her." She ceased making apologies, and became a wiser and better Christian. Elder Blunt always puts up there, always finds everything as it should be, and, with all his eccentricities, is thought by the family the most agreeable, as he is acknowledged by everybody to be the most consistent, of men.

REV. J. V. WATSON.

THE LANDLORD'S SPOONS.

In a quiet little Ohio village, many years ago, was a tavern where the stages always changed and the passengers expected to get breakfast. The landlord of the said hotel was noted for his tricks upon travellers, who were allowed to get fairly seated at the table, when the driver would blow his horn (after taking his "horn") and sing out, "Stage ready, gentlemen!"—whereupon the passengers were obliged to hurry out to take their seats, leaving a scarcely-tasted breakfast behind them, for which, however, they had to fork over fifty cents. One day, when the stage was approaching the house of this obliging landlord, a passenger said that he had often heard of the landlord's trick, and he was afraid they would not be able to eat any breakfast.

"What!—how? No breakfast!" exclaimed the rest.

"Exactly so, gents; and you may as well keep your seats and tin."

"Don't they expect passengers to breakfast?"

"Oh, yes! they expect you to it, but not to *eat* it. I am under the impression that there is an understanding between the landlord and the driver, that for sundry and various drinks, etc., the latter starts before you can scarcely commence eating."

"What on earth air you all talkin' about? Ef you calkelate I'm goin' to pay four-and-ninepence for my breakfast, and not get the valee on't, yo're mistaken," said a voice from a back seat, the owner of which was one Hezekiah Spaulding,—though "tew hum" they call him "Hez" for short. "I'm goin' to get my breakfast here, and not pay nary red cent till I do."

"Then you'll be left."

"Not as you knows on, I won't."

"Well, we'll see," said the other, as the stage drove up to the door, and the landlord, ready "to do the hospitable," says,—

"Breakfast just ready, gents! Take a wash, gents? Here's water, basins, towels, and soap."

After performing the ablutions, they all proceeded to the

dining-room, and commenced a fierce onslaught upon the edibles, though Hez took his time. Scarcely had they tasted their coffee, when they heard the unwelcome sound of the horn, and the driver exclaim, "Stage ready!" Up rise eight grumbling passengers, pay their fifty cents, and take their seats.

"All on board, gents?" inquires the host.

"One missing," said they.

Proceeding to the dining-room, the host finds Hez very coolly helping himself to an immense piece of steak, the size of a horse's hip.

"You'll be left, sir! Stage going to start!"

"Well, I hain't nothing to say ag'in' it," drawled out Hez.

"Can't wait, sir: better take your seat."

"I'll be gall-darned ef I dew, nother, till I've got my breakfast! I paid for it, and I'm goin' to get the valee on't; and ef you calkelate I hain't, you are mistaken."

So the stage did start, and left Hez, who continued his attack upon the edibles. Biscuits, coffee, etc., disappeared before the eyes of the astonished landlord.

"Say, squire, them there cakes is 'bout eat: fetch on another grist on 'em. You" (to the waiter), "'nother cup of that 'ere coffee. Pass them eggs. Raise your own pork, squire? This is 'mazin' nice ham. Land 'bout here tolerable cheap, squire? Hain't much maple timber in these parts, hev ye? Dew right smart trade, squire, I calkelate?" And thus Hez kept quizzing the landlord until he had made a hearty meal.

"Say, squire, now I'm 'bout to conclude payin' my *devowers* to this 'ere table, but jest give us a bowl of bread-and-milk to top off with, and I'd be much obleeged tew ye."

So out go the landlord and waiter for the bowl, milk, and bread, and set them before him.

"Spoon, tew, ef you please."

But no spoon could be found. Landlord was sure he had plenty of silver ones lying on the table when the stage stopped.

"Say, dew ye—dew ye think them passengers is goin' to pay ye for breakfuss and not get no *compensashun?*"

"Ah, what? Do you think any of the passengers took them?"

"Dew I *think?* No, I don't think, but I'm sartin. Ef they air all as green as yew 'bout here, I'm goin' to locate immediately, and tew wonst."

The landlord rushes out to the stable, and starts a man off after the stage, which had gone about three miles. The man overtakes the stage, and says something to the driver in a low tone. He immediately turns back, and on arriving at the hotel Hez comes out, takes his seat, and says,—

"How air yew, gents? I'm rotted glad to see yew."

"Can you point out the man you think has the spoons?" asked the landlord.

"P'int him out? Sartinly I ken. Say, squire, I paid yew four-and-ninepence for a breakfuss, and I calkelate *I got the valee on't!* You'll find them spoons in the coffee-pot."

"*Go ahead! All aboard, driver.*"

The landlord stared.

ANONYMOUS.

MRS. POTIPHAR'S NEW LIVERY.

GEORGE W. CURTIS.

[Among the multifarious writings of the genial and popular " Easy Chair" may be found a fair share of the element of humor. This is particularly displayed in the " Potiphar Papers," from which record

of the life of a would-be fashionable woman our selection is taken.
Mrs. Potiphar describes in a letter to her dear friend her conversation
with Mr. P. after the grand Potiphar ball, and relates her little livery-
difficulties. The author, George William Curtis, was born at Providence, Rhode Island, in 1824, has acquired a high reputation as a
fluent and cultured lecturer and writer, and has been for many years
past editorially connected with the Harper periodicals.]

MR. P. made a great growling about the ball. But it
was very foolish; for he got safely to bed by six o'clock,
and he need have no trouble about replacing the curtains
and glass, etc. I shall do all that, and the sum-total will
be sent to him in a lump, so that he can pay it.

Men are so unreasonable. Fancy us at seven o'clock
that morning, when I retired. He wasn't asleep. But
whose fault was that?

"Polly," said he, "that's the last."

"Last what?" said I.

"Last ball at my house," said he.

"Fiddle-dee-dee!" said I.

"I tell you, Mrs. Potiphar, I am not going to open my
house for a crowd of people who don't go away till day-
light; who spoil my books and furniture; who involve me
in a foolish expense; for a gang of rowdy boys, who drink
my Margaux, and Lafitte, and Marcobrunner (what kind
of drinks are those, dear Caroline?), and who don't know
Chambertin from liquorice-water; for a swarm of persons,
few of whom know me, fewer still care for me, and to
whom I am only 'Old Potiphar,' the husband of you, a
fashionable woman. I am simply resolved to have no
more such tomfoolery in my house."

"Dear Mr. P.," said I, "you'll feel much better when
you have slept. Besides, why do you say such things?
Mustn't we see our friends, I should like to know, and, if
we do, are you going to let your wife receive them in

a manner inferior to old Mrs. Podge or Mrs. Crœsus?
People will accuse you of meanness, and of treating me
ill; and if some persons hear that you have reduced your
style of living they will begin to suspect the state of your
affairs. Don't make any rash vows, Mr. P.," said I, " but
go to sleep."

(Do you know that speech was just what Mrs. Crœsus
told me she had said to her husband under similar circumstances?)

Mr. P. fairly groaned, and I heard that short, strong
little word that sometimes inadvertently drops out of the
best-regulated mouths, as young Gooseberry Downe says
when he swears before his mother. Do you know Mrs.
Settum Downe? Charming woman, but satirical.

Mr. P. groaned, and said some more ill-natured things,
until the clock struck nine, and he was obliged to get up.
I should be sorry to say to anybody but you, dearest, that
I was rather glad of it; for I could then fall asleep at my
ease; and these little connubial felicities (I think they call
them) are so tiresome. But everybody agreed it was a
beautiful ball; and I had the great gratification of hearing
young Lord Mount Ague (you know you danced with him,
love) say that it was quite the same thing as a ball at
Buckingham Palace, except, of course, in size, and the
number of persons, and dresses, and jewels, and the plate,
and glass, and supper, and wines, and furnishing of the
rooms, and lights, and some of those things, which are
naturally upon a larger scale at a palace than in a private
house. But he said, excepting such things, it was quite as
fine. I am afraid Lord Mount Ague flatters; just a little
bit, you know.

Yes; and there was young Major Staggers, who said
that " Decidedly it was *the* party of the season."

"How odd," said Mrs. Crœsus, to whom I told it, and, I

confess, with a little pride.   "What a sympathetic man!
Would you believe, dear Mrs. Potiphar, that he said precisely the same thing to me, two days after my ball?"

Now, Caroline, dearest, *perhaps* he did.

With all these pleasant things said about one's party, I
cannot see that it is such a dismal thing as Mr. P. tries to
make out.   After one of his solemn talks, I asked Mr.
Cheese what he thought of balls, whether it was so very
wicked to dance, and go to parties, if one only went to
church twice a day on Sundays?   He patted his lips a
moment with his handkerchief, and then he said,—and,
Caroline, you can always quote the Rev. Cream Cheese as
authority,—

"Dear Mrs. Potiphar, it is recorded in Holy Scripture
that the king danced before the Lord."

Darling, *if anything should happen*, I don't believe he'd
object much to your dancing.

What gossips we women are, to be sure!   I meant to
write you about our new livery, and I am afraid I have
tired you out already.   You remember when you were
here I said that I meant to have a livery, for my sister
Margaret told me that when they used to drive in Hyde
Park, with the old Marquis of Mammon, it was always so
delightful to hear him say,—

"Ah!   There is Lady Lobster's livery."

It was so aristocratic.   And in countries where certain
colors distinguish certain families, and are hereditary, so
to say, it is convenient and pleasant to recognize a coat of
arms, or a livery, and to know that the representative of
a great and famous family is passing by.

"That's a Howard, that's a Russell, that's a Dorset, that's
De Colique, that's Mount Ague," old Lord Mammon used
to say as the carriages whirled by.   He knew none of
them personally, I believe, except De Colique and Mount

Ague, but then it was so agreeable to be able to know their liveries.

Now, why shouldn't we have the same arrangement? Why not have the Smith colors, and the Brown colors, and the Black colors, and the Potiphar colors, etc., so that the people might say, "Ah! there goes the Potiphar arms."

There is one difficulty, Mr. P. says, and that is, that he found five hundred and sixty-seven Smiths in the Directory, which might lead to some confusion. But that was absurd, as I told him, because everybody would know which of the Smiths was able to keep a carriage, so that the livery would be recognized directly the moment that any of the family were seen in the carriage. Upon which he said, in his provoking way, "Why have any livery at all, then!" and he persisted in saying that no Smith was ever *the* Smith for three generations, and that he knew at least twenty, each of whom was able to set up his carriage and stand by his colors.

"But then a livery is so elegant and aristocratic," said I, "and it shows that a servant is a servant."

That last was a strong argument, and I thought Mr. P. would have nothing to say against it; but he rattled on for some time, asking me what right I had to be aristocratic, or, in fact, anybody else,—went over his eternal old talk about aping foreign habits, as if we hadn't a right to adopt the good usages of all nations, and finally said that the use of liveries among us was not only a "pure peacock absurdity," as he called it, but that no genuine American would ever ask another to assume a menial badge.

"Why," said I, "is not an American servant a servant still?"

"Most undoubtedly," he said; "and when a man is a servant, let him serve faithfully; and in this country especially, where to-morrow he may be the served, and not the servant, let him not be ashamed of serving. But, Mrs. Potiphar, I beg you to observe that a servant's livery is not, like a general's uniform, the badge of honorable service, but of menial service. Of course a servant may be as honorable as a general, and his work quite as necessary and well done. But, for all that, it is not so respected nor coveted a situation, I believe; and, in social estimation, a man suffers by wearing a livery as he never would if he wore none. And while in countries in which a man is proud of being a servant (as every man may well be of being a good one), and never looks to anything else nor desires any change, a livery may be very proper to the state of society, and very agreeable to his own feelings, it is quite another thing in a society constituted upon altogether different principles, where the servant of to-day is the senator of to-morrow. Besides that, which I suppose is too fine-spun for you, livery is a remnant of a feudal state, of which we abolish every trace as fast as we can. That which is represented by livery is not consonant with our principles."

My dear old Pot is getting rather prosy, Carrie. So when he had finished that long speech, during which I was looking at the lovely fashion-plates in *Harper*, I said,—

"What colors do you think I'd better have?"

He looked at me with that singular expression, and went out suddenly, as if he were afraid he might say something.

He had scarcely gone before I heard,—

"My dear Mrs. Potiphar, the sight of you is refreshing as Hermon's dew."

I colored a little: Mr. Cheese says such things so softly. But I said good-morning, and then asked him about liveries, etc.

He raised his hand to his cravat (it was the most snowy lawn, Carrie, and tied in a splendid bow).

"Is not this a livery, dear Mrs. Potiphar?"

And then he went off into one of those pretty talks, in what Mr. P. calls "the language of artificial flowers," and wound up by quoting Scripture,—"Servants, obey your masters."

That was enough for me. So I told Mr. Cheese that, as he had already assisted me in colors once, I should be most glad to have him do so again. What a time we had, to be sure, talking of colors, and cloths, and gaiters, and buttons, and knee-breeches, and waistcoats, and plush, and coats, and lace, and hat-bands, and gloves, and cravats, and cords, and tassels, and hats! Oh, it was delightful! You can't fancy how heartily the Rev. Cream entered into the matter. He was quite enthusiastic, and at last he said, with so much expression, "Dear Mrs. Potiphar, why not have a *chasseur?*"

I thought it was some kind of French dish for lunch, so I said,—

"I am so sorry, but we haven't any in the house."

"Oh," said he, "but you could hire one, you know."

Then I thought it must be a musical instrument,—a pan-harmonicon, or something of that kind; so I said, in a general way,—

"I'm not very, very fond of it."

"But it would be so fine to have him standing on the back of the carriage, his plumes waving in the wind, and his lace and polished belts flashing in the sun, as you whirled down Broadway."

Of course I knew then that he was speaking of those military gentlemen who ride behind carriages, especially upon the Continent, as Margaret tells me, and who in Paris are very useful to keep the savages and wild beasts at bay in the Champs Elysées, for you know they are intended as a guard.

But I knew Mr. P. would be firm about that: so I asked Mr. Cheese not to kindle my imagination with the *chasseur*.

We concluded finally to have only one full-sized footman, and a fat driver.

"The corpulence is essential, dear Mrs. Potiphar," said Mr. Cheese. "I have been much abroad; I have mingled, I trust, in good—which is to say, Christian—society; and I must say that few things struck me more upon my return than that the ladies who drive very handsome carriages, with footmen, etc., in livery, should permit such thin coachmen upon the box. I really believe that Mrs. Settum Downe's coachman doesn't weigh more than a hundred and thirty pounds; which is ridiculous. A lady might as well hire a footman with insufficient calves, as a coachman who weighs less than two hundred and ten. That is the minimum. Besides, I don't observe any wigs upon the coachmen. Now, if a lady sets up her carriage with the family crest and fine liveries, why, I should like to know, is the wig of the coachman omitted, and his cocked hat also? It is a kind of shabby, half-ashamed way of doing things,—a garbled glory. The cocked-hatted, knee-breeched, paste-buckled, horsehair-wigged coachman is one of the institutions of the aristocracy. If we don't have him complete, we somehow make ourselves ridiculous. If we do have him complete, why, then——"

Here Mr. Cheese coughed a little, and patted his mouth with his cambric. But what he said was very true. I *should* like to come out with the wig,—I mean upon the coachman,—it would so put down the Settum Downes. But I'm sure old Pot wouldn't have it. He lets me do a great deal; but there is a line which I feel he won't let me pass. I mentioned my fears to Mr. Cheese.

"Well," he said, "Mr. Potiphar may be right. I remember an expression of my carnal days about 'coming

it too strong,' which seems to me to be applicable just
here."

After a little more talk, I determined to have red plush
breeches with a black cord at the side, white stockings,
low shoes with large buckles, a yellow waistcoat with
large buttons, lapels to the pockets, and a purple coat, very
full and fine, bound with gold lace, and the hat banded
with a full gold rosette. Don't you think that would look
well in Hyde Park? And, darling Carrie, why shouldn't
we have in Broadway what they have in Hyde Park?

When Mr. P. came in, I told him all about it. He
laughed a good deal, and said, "What next?" So I am
not sure he would be so very hard upon the wig. The
next morning I had appointed to see the new footman,
and as Mr. P. went out he turned and said to me, "Is your
footman coming to-day?"

"Yes," I answered.

"Well," said he, "don't forget the calves. You know
that everything in the matter of livery depends upon the
calves."

And he went out laughing silently to himself, with—
actually, Carrie!—a tear in his eye.

But it was true, wasn't it? I remember in all the books
and pictures how much is said about the calves. In ad-
vertisements, etc., it is stated that none but well-developed
calves need apply; at least it is so in England, and if I
have a livery I am not going to stop half-way. My duty
was very clear. When Mr. Cheese came in, I said I felt
awkward in asking a servant about his calves,—it sounded
so queerly. But I confessed that it was necessary.

"Yes, the path of duty is not always smooth, dear Mrs.
Potiphar. It is often thickly strewn with thorns," said
he, as he sank back in the *fauteuil* and put down his *petit
verre* of Marasquin.

Just after he had gone, the new footman was announced. I assure you, although it is ridiculous, I felt quite nervous. But when he came in, I said calmly,—

".Well, James, I am glad you have come."

"Please, ma'am, my name is Henry," said he.

I was astonished at his taking me up so, and said, decidedly,—

"James, the name of my footman is always James. You may call yourself what you please, I shall always call you James."

The idea of the man's undertaking to arrange my servants' names for me!

Well, he showed me his references, which were very good, and I was quite satisfied. But there was the terrible calf-business that must be attended to. I put it off a great while, but I had to begin.

"Well, James!"—and there I stopped.

"Yes, ma'am," said he.

"I wish—yes—ah!"—and I stopped again.

"Yes, ma'am," said he.

"James, I wish you had come in knee-breeches."

"Ma'am?" said he, in great surprise.

"In knee-breeches, James," repeated I.

"What be they, ma'am? what for, ma'am?" said he, a little frightened, as I thought.

"Oh, nothing, nothing; but—but——"

"Yes, ma'am," said James.

"But—but, I want to see—to see——"

"What, ma'am?" said James.

"Your legs," gasped I; and the path *was* thorny enough, Carrie, I can tell you. I had a terrible time explaining to him what I meant, and all about the liveries, etc. Dear me! what a pity these things are not understood! and then we should never have this trouble about explanations.

However, I couldn't make him agree to wear the livery. He said,—

"I'll try to be a good servant, ma'am, but I cannot put on those things and make a fool of myself. I hope you won't insist, for I am very anxious to get a place."

Think of his dictating to me! I told him that I did not permit my servants to impose conditions upon me (that's one of Mrs. Crœsus's sayings), that I was willing to pay him good wages and treat him well, but that my James must wear my livery. He looked very sorry, said that he should like the place very much, that he was satisfied with the wages, and was sure he should please me, but he could not put on those things. We were both determined, and so parted. I think we were both sorry; for I should have to go all through the calf-business again, and he lost a good place.

However, Caroline dear, I have my livery and my footman, and am as good as anybody. It's very splendid when I go to Stewart's to have the red plush, and the purple, and the white calves springing down to open the door, and to see people look, and say, "I wonder who that is?" And everybody bows so nicely, and the clerks are so polite, and Mrs. Gnu is melting with envy on the other side, and Mrs. Crœsus goes about, saying, "Dear little woman, that Mrs. Potiphar, but so weak! Pity, pity!" And Mrs. Settum Downe says, "Is that the Potiphar livery? Ah! yes. Mr. Potiphar's grandfather used to shoe my grandfather's horses!" (as if to be useful in the world were a disgrace,—as Mr. P. says), and young Downe, and Boosey, and Timon Crœsus come up and stand about so gentlemanly, and say, "Well, Mrs. Potiphar, are we to have no more charming parties this season?" and Boosey says, in his droll way, "Let's keep the ball a-rolling!" That young man is always ready with a witticism.

Then I step out, and James throws open the door, and the young men raise their hats, and the new crowd says, " I wonder who that is?" and the plush, and purple, and calves spring up behind, and I drive home to dinner.

Now, Carrie dear, isn't that nice ?

THE GRAND IMPOSITION HOTEL.

MARIETTA HOLLEY.

[Among our humorists whose laughter-making method consists in an affected rusticity, constant surprise and misapprehension, and an undercurrent of shrewd comment, there is none more popular and widely read than Marietta Holley, the " Josiah Allen's Wife" of our literature of amusement. She has written numerous works, all detailing the opinions and mishaps of Samantha Allen, a retailer of badly-spelled wisdom, our selection being from " Samantha at the Centennial." The writer is said to have not visited the Centennial Exhibition ; yet, if so, few who did visit it could have described it in more accurate detail than is done in the book above named.]

FROM the first minute I had give a thought to goin' to see the Sentinal, my idee had been to git boarded up in a private house. And I had my eye (my mind's eye) upon who was willin' and glad to board us. The Editor of the Auger'ses wife's sister's husband's cousin boarded folks for a livin': she was a Dickey and married to a Lampheare. The Editor of the Auger'ses wife told me early in the spring that if she went she should go through the Sentinal to her sister's, and she happened to mention Miss Lampheare and the fact that she boarded up folks for a livin'. So when we decided to go, I told her when she wrote to her sister to ask her to ask Miss Lampheare if she was willin' to board Josiah and me, and how much she would ask for the boards. She wrote back; her terms was moderate and inside of our means, and my mind was at rest. I almost knew that Josiah would want to throw himself onto his relatives through the Sentinal, but the underpinnin' was no firmer and rockier under our horse-barn than the determination of her that was Samantha Smith, not to encamp upon a 2nd cousin. We had quite a lot of relations a-livin' out to Filadelfy,—though we never seen 'em,—sort o' distant, such as 2nd cousins, and so 4th, till they dwindled out o' bein' any relations at all; descendants of the Daggets and Kidds,—Grandmother Allen was a Kidd,—no relation of old Captain Kidd. No! if any of his blood had been in my Josiah's veins, I would have bled him myself, if I had took a darnin'-needle to it. No! the Kidd'ses are likely folks, as I have heered, and Josiah was rampant to go to cousin Sam Kidd's (a captain in the late war) through the Sentinal. But again I says to him, calmly and firmly,—

"No! Josiah Allen, no! anything but bringin' grief and trouble onto perfect strangers jest because they happened to be born second cousin to you, unbeknown to 'em;" and I repeated with icy firmness,—for I see he was a-hankerin' awfully,—"Josiah Allen, I will not encamp upon Captain Kidd through the Sentinal."

No! Miss Lampheare was my theme and my gole, and all boyed up with hope we arrove at her dwellin'-place. Miss Lampheare met us at the door herself. She was a tall spindlin'-lookin' woman, one that had seen trouble,—for she had always kep' boarders, and had had four husbands, and buried 'em in a row, her present one bein' now in a decline. When I told her who I was, she met me with warmth and said that any friend of she that was Alminy Dickey was dear to her. But friendship, let it be ever so ardent, cannot obtain cream from well-water, or cause iron

II.   17*

bedsteads to stretch out like Injy Rubber. She had expected us sooner, if we come at all, and her house was overflowin', every bed, lounge, corner, and cupboard being occupied, and the buro and stand drawers made up nightly for children.

What *was* we to do? Night would soon let down her cloudy mantilly upon Josiah and me, and what was to become of us? Miss Lampheare seemed to pity us, and she directed us to a friend of hers; that friend was full; he directed us to another friend; that friend was overflowin'. And so it went on till we was almost completely tired out.

At last Josiah come out of a house, where he had been seekin' rest and findin' it not; says he,—

"They said mebbe we could git a room at the 'Grand Imposition Hotel.'" So we started off there, Josiah a-scoldin' every step of the way, and a-sayin',—

"I told you jest how it would be. We ort to have gone to Captain Kidd's."

I didn't say nothin' back on the outside, for I see by his face that it was no time for parley. But my mind was firm on the inside, to board in grocery-stores, and room under my umberell, before I threw myself onto a perfect stranger through the Sentinal.

But a recital of our agony of mind will be of little interest to the gay, and only sadden the tender-hearted; and suffice it to say in an hour's time we was a-follerin' the hired man to a room in the "Grand Imposition Hotel."

Our room was good enough, and big enough for Josiah and me to turn round in one at a time. It had a bed considerable narrer, but good and healthy,—hard beds are considered healthy by the best of doctors,—a chair, a lookin'-glass, and a washstand. Josiah made a sight of fun of that, because it didn't have but three legs.

But says I, firmly, "That is one more than *you* have got, Josiah Allen." I wouldn't stand none of his foolin'. . . .

When we eat supper we had a considerable journey to the dinin'-room, which looked a good deal on the plan of Miss Astor'ses, with lots of colored folks a-goin' round, a-waitin' on the hungry crowd. I didn't see the woman of the house,—mebby she was laid up with a headache, or had gone out for an afternoon's visit,—but the colored waiters seemed to be real careful of her property; they'd catch a teaspoon right out of their pocket and put it in your tea; she couldn't have kep' a closer grip on her teaspoons herself.

I can truly say, without stretching the truth the width of a horsehair, that the chambermaid was as cross as a bear, for every identical thing I asked her for was a extra, —she couldn't do it without extra pay; but she did git me some ice-water once, without askin' me a cent extra for it. After we got to bed Josiah would lay and talk. He would speak out all of a sudden:

"Grand Imposition Hotel!"

And I'd say, "What of it? What if it is?"

And then he'd say, "They have got a crackin' good name, Samanthy. I love to see names that mean sunthin'." And then he'd ask me if I remembered the song about Barbara Allen, and if it would hurt my feelin's if he should lay and sing a verse of it to me, the bed put him in mind of it so.

I asked him what verse; but there was that in my tone that made him say no more about singin': he said it was the verse where Barbara wanted her mother to have her coffin made "long and narrer." And then he'd begin again about the pillars, and say how he wished he'd brought a couple of feathers from home, to lay on, so he could have got some rest.

He had pulled out a little wad of cotton-battin' before we went to bed, to convince me of their ingredients.

But I says to him, "Josiah Allen, a easy conscience can rest even on cotton-battin' pillars," and I added, in awful meanin' tones, "*I* am sleepy, Josiah Allen, and want to go to sleep. It is time," says I, with dignity, "that we was both reposin' in the arms of Morphine."

Nothin' quells him down quicker than to have me talk in a classical high-learnt way, and in a few minutes he was fast asleep.

[Mosquitoes and general misery kept Samantha awake till morning, when they sallied forth to do the Centennial.]

At last we reached the piazza, and emerged into the street. I see that every man, woman, and child was there in that identical street, and I thought to myself, there ain't no Sentinal to-day, and everybody has come out into this street for a walk. I knew it stood to reason that if there had been a Sentinal there would have been one or two men or wimmen attendin' to it, and I knew that every man, woman, and child on the hull face of the globe was right there before me, and behind me, and by the side of me, and fillin' the street full, walkin' afoot, and up in big covered wagons, all over 'em, on the inside, and hangin' on to the outside, as thick as bees a-swarmin'. Some of the horses was hitched ahead of each other, I s'pose so they could slip through the crowd easier. I couldn't see the village hardly any, owin' to the crowd a-crushin' of me ; but, from what little I *did* see, it was perfectly beautiful. I see they had fixed up for us : they had whitewashed all their door-steps, and winder-blinds, white as snow, and trimmed the latter all off with black ribbon-strings.

Everything looked lovely and gay, and I thought, as I walked along, Jonesville couldn't compare with it for size and grandeur. I was a-walkin' along, crowded in body but happy in mind, when all of a sudden a thought come to me that goared me worse than any elbo or umberell that had pierced my ribs sense we sot out from the tavern. Thinks'es I all of a sudden, mebbe they have put off the Sentinal till I come; mebbe I have disappointed the Nation, and belated 'em, and put 'em to trouble.

This was a sad thought, and wore on my mind considerable, and made me almost forget for the time-bein' my bodily sufferin's as they pushed me this way and that, and goared me in the side with parasols and umberells, and carried off the tabs of my mantilly as far as they would go in every direction, and shoved, and stamped, and crowded. I declare, I was tore to pieces in mind and body, when I arrove at last at the entrance to the grounds. The crowd was fearful here, and the yells of different kinds was distractive: one conceited little creeter catched right holt of the tabs of my mantilly, and yelled right up in my face, "Won't you have a guide? Buy a guide, mom, to the Sentinal." And seven or eight others was a-yellin' the same thing to me, the impudent creeters: I jest turned round and faced the one that had got holt of my cape, and says I,—

"Leggo of my tabs!"

He wouldn't leggo; he stood and yelled out right up in my face, "Buy a guide: you hain't got no guide!"

Says I, with dignity, "Yes, I have; duty is my guide, and also, Josiah; and now," says I, firmly, "if you don't leggo of my tabs, I'll *make* you leggo." My mean skairt him; he leggo, and I follered on after my Josiah; but where *was* Josiah? I couldn't see him; in tusslin' with that impudent creeter over my cape, my companion had

got carried by the crowd out of my sight. Oh, the agony
of that half a moment! I turned and says to a policeman
in almost agonizin' tones,—

"Where is my Josiah?"

He looked very polite at me, and says he,—

"I don't know."

Says I, "Find him for me instantly! Have you the
heart to stand still and see husbands and wives parted
away from each other? Have you any principle about
you? Have you got entirely out of pity?"

Says he, with the same polite look, "I don't know."

"Have you a wife?" says I, in thrilling axents. "Have
you any children?"

Says he, "I don't know."

I had heard that there wasn't no information to be extracted from them as a class, and I give up; and I don't
know what my next move would have been if I hadn't
catched sight of that beloved face and that old familiar hat
in front of me; I hastened forred and kep' considerable
calm in mind, while my body was being crowded and
pushed round, for I thought if my conjectures was true
they would have reason enough to goar me.

[Samantha and Josiah have no small trouble in learning the art of
paying their way into the Centennial, and the feelings of the latter
are outraged at being called an "adult" by the gate-keeper. He
doesn't relish being "called names" by a ticket-seller. At length they
get over the difficulty.]

We handed our fifty cents to a man, and he dropped it
down through a little slit in a counter; and a gate that
looked some like my new-fashioned clothes-bars sort o'
turned round with us and let us in one at a time; and
the minute I was inside I see that my gloomy fore-
bodin's had been in vain: they hadn't put off the Sentinal

for me! That was my first glad thought; but my very next thought was, Good land! and Good land! and Good land! Them was my very first words, and they didn't express my feelin's a half or even a quarter. Why, comin' right out of that contracted and crushin' crowd, it seemed as if the place we found ourselves in was as roomy and spacious as the desert of Sarah, s'posin' she, the desert, was fixed off into a perfect garden of beauty, free for anybody to wander round and git lost in.

And the majestic Main Building that nearly loomed up in front of us! Why! if old Ocian herself had turned into glass, and wood-work, and cast iron, and shinin' ruffs, and towers, and flags, and statues, and everything, and made a glitterin' palace of herself, it couldn't (as it were) have looked any more grand and imposin' and roomy; and if every sand by the sea-shore had jumped up and put on a bunnet or hat, as the case may be, there couldn't have been a bigger crowd (seemingly) than there was passin' into it, and a-passin' by, and a-paradin' round Josiah and me.

Under these strange and almost apaulin' circumstances, is it any wonder that I stood stun still, and said, out of the very depths of my heart, the only words I could think of that would anywhere nigh express my feelin's, and they was "Good land!"

But as my senses began to come back to me, my next thought was, as I looked round on every side of me, "Truly did my Josiah say that I would see enough with one eye;" and jest then a band commenced playin' the "Star-Spangled Banner." And hearing that soul-stirrin' music, and seein' that very banner a-wavin' and floatin' out, as if all the blue sky and rainbows sense Noah's rainbow was cut up into its glorious stripes, with the hull stars of heaven a-shinin' on 'em,—why, as my faculties come back to me, a-seein' what I see, and heerin' what I heered, I thought of my 4 fathers, them 4 old fathers, whose weak hands had first unfurled that banner to the angry breeze, and thinks'es I, I would be willin' to change places with them 4 old men right here on the spot, to let them see in the bright sunshine of 1876 what they done in the cloudy darkness of 1776.

LITTLE JOE.

JENNIE WOODVILLE.

[As comedy and tragedy often go together in life, it is meet that they should, occasionally at least, go together in fiction. This conjunction has been skilfully effected in the present selection, which begins with the ludicrous and ends with the pathetic, but is amusing enough in grain to be allotted a place among our Half-hour readings. The sketch is extracted from *Lippincott's Magazine.*]

TOM WISE, a great big, handsome fellow, with a heart of the same order, was standing at the corner talking to a friend. He held a cigar to his mouth with his left hand, and with his right had just struck a match against the lamp-post, when at—or rather under—his elbow a voice exclaimed, cheerily, "Busted ag'in, Mas' Tom!"

Tom threw a glance over his shoulder, and there stood "Little Joe," a small misshapen negro about fifteen years old, with crutches under his arms and feet all twisted out of shape, his toes barely touching the ground as he hopped along. He had on an old straw hat with only a hint of brim. There must be some law of cohesive attraction between straw and wool, for Little Joe's cranium was large, while the hat was small and set back much nearer

the nape of his neck than the crown of his head, yet held
its place like a natural excrescence or a horrible bore. Joe
had met with very few people mean enough to laugh at
him ; for, though he possessed all the brightness and cheer-
fulness and pluck of deformed people generally, there was
a wistful look about his eyes which his want of height
and his position on crutches intensified (indeed, perhaps
created), by keeping them upturned while talking with any
one taller than himself; and this was generally the case, for
there were no grown people so small as Little Joe. His
shirt was torn and his pantaloons ragged, but to gild these
faded glories he wore a swallow-tailed coat with brass
buttons which some one had given him, whether from
a sense of humor or a sentiment of charity let the gods
decide.

"Busted ag'in, Mas' Tom!"

"What 'busted' you this time, Joe?" asked Mr. Wise.

"Lumber, Mas' Tom. I was in de lumber bizness las'
week, buyin' ole shingles an' sellin em' for kindlin'; but
my pardner he maked a run on de bank,—leas'ways on my
breeches-pocket,—an' den runned away hisse'f. Ain't you
gwine to sot me up ag'in, Mas' Tom?"

"What business are you going into this week?"

"'Feckshunerry," replied Joe, taking the quarter Mr.
Wise handed him. "Dis 'll do to buy de goods, but 'twon't
rent de sto', Mas' Tom."

"What store?" asked Mr. Wise.

"Dat big sto' Hunt an' Manson is jes' moved outen.
Mr. Manson say I may hab it for sebben hunderd dollars
ef you'll go my skoorty."

Tom laughed: "Well, Joe, I was thinking I wouldn't
go security for anybody this week. Don't you think you
can do business on a smaller scale?"

Joe's countenance fell, and he suffered visibly, but a

cheering thought presently struck him, and he exclaimed, disdainfully, "Anyhow, I ain't a-keerin' 'bout Hunt an' Manson's ole sto',—der ole sebben-hunderd-dollar sto'! I can git a goods-box, an' turn it upside down, an' stan' it up by de Cap'tol groun's, an' more folks 'll pass 'long an' buy goobers dan would come in dat ole sto' all de year. Dey ain't spitin' *me!*"

As Joe limped off to invest his money, his poor little legs swinging and his swallow-tails flapping, Tom's friend asked who he was.

"Belonged to us before the war," said Tom. "Poor little devil! the good Lord and the birds of the air seem to take care of him. I set him up in business with twenty-five cents every week, and look after him a little in other ways. Sometimes he buys matches and newspapers and sells them again, sometimes he buys ginger-cakes and eats them all; but he is invariably 'busted,' as he calls it, by Saturday night.—Joe! o-oh, Joe!"

Joe looked back, and, with perfect indifference to the fact that he was detaining Mr. Wise, answered that he would "be dar torectly," continuing his negotiations for an empty goods-box lying at the door of a neighboring dry-goods store. "What you want, Mas' Tom?" he asked, on his return.

"Miss Mollie is going to be married week after next, Joe, and you may come up to the house if you like. I was afraid I might forget it."

"'Whoop *you*, sir! Thanky, Mas' Tom. I boun' to see Miss Mollie step off de carpit. But, Lord-a-mussy! dem new niggers you all got ain't gwine to lemme in."

"Come to the front door and ask for me. Cut out, now, and don't get busted this week, because I shall need all my money to buy a breastpin to wait on my sister in.—Come, John, let's register."

Joe's glance followed Mr. Wise and his friend till they were out of sight; then he turned, and paused no more till he reached an out-of-the-way grocery-store, in the window of which were displayed samples of fish and soap and calico and kerosene lamps and dreadful brass jewelry, among which was a frightful breastpin in the shape of a crescent set with red and green glass, and further ornamented by a chain of the most atrocious description conceivable. Before this thing of beauty, which to him had been a joy for weeks, Joe paused and lingered, and smote his little black breast and sighed the sigh of poverty. Then he went in. "What mout be de price o' dat gent's pin in de corner ob de winder?" he inquired.

"I don't see any gent in the corner of the window," said the proprietor of the store.

Joe took the mild pleasantry, and, inquiring, "What mout be de price o' de pin?" was told that it might be anything,—from nothing up,—but it could go for seventy-five cents.

He stood again outside the window, looking sadly and reflecting at the attractive bijou, then seated himself on the curbstone, his crutches resting in the gutter, and thoughtfully smoothed between his finger and thumb the twenty-five-cent note Mr. Wise had given him: "Ef I takes dis, an' de one Mas' Tom gwine to gimme nex' week, dat'll be fifty cents, but it won't be seventy-five: so I got to make a quarter on de two. Ef Miss Mollie knowed, I 'spec' she would wait anoder week to git married, an' den I wouldn't run no resk o' dese; but I ain't gwine to tell her, cos I know she couldn't help tellin' Mas' Tom, an' I want to s'prise him. Mas' Tom is made me feel good a many a time: I want to make him feel good wunst. He don't nuvvur come dis way, an' ain't seed dat pin, or he would ha' had it 'fore now."

Then Little Joe bestirred himself, and, obtaining the assistance of a friend, took his dry-goods box up to Capitol Square. There he turned it upside down, spread a newspaper over the top, and proceeded to display his wares.

A pyramid of three apples stood in one corner; a small stack of peppermint candy was its *vis-à-vis;* a tiny glass of peanuts graced the third, and was confronted by a lemon that had seen life and was now more sere than yellow. But the crowning glory was the centre-piece,— an unhappy-looking pie, of visage pale and thin physique, yet how beautiful to Joe! He stepped back on his crutches, turning his head from side to side as he surveyed the effect, took up a locust branch he had brought with him to brush away the flies, and, leaning against the iron railing, with calm dignity awaited coming events.

His glance presently fell on the figure of a negro boy, who stood gazing with longing eyes on the delicacies of his table, and it was with a strange feeling of kinship that Little Joe continued to regard the new-comer, for he too had been branded by misfortune. He appeared about Joe's age, and should have been taller, but his legs had been amputated nearly up to the knee, and as he stood on the pitiful stumps, supported by a short cane in one hand, his head was hardly as high as the iron railing. He had none of Joe's brightness, but looked ragged and dirty and hungry, and evidently had no Mas' Tom to help the good Lord and the birds of the air to take care of him. His skin was of a dull ashen hue, and the short wool which clung close to his scalp was sunburnt till it was red and crisp and formed a curious contrast to his black face. One arm was bare, only the ragged remains of a sleeve hanging over the shoulder, and it seemed no great misfortune that his legs had been shortened, for he had hardly pantaloons enough to cover what he had left.

He looked at the pie, and Joe looked at him. Presently the latter inquired, seriously, " Whar yo' legs ?'

" Cut off," was the answer.

" How come dey cut off ?"

" Feet was fros'-bit. Like ter kill me."

" What yo' name ?" asked Joe.

" Kiah."

" What were yo' old mas' name ?"

" Didn't have no ole mas'."

" Was you a natchul free nigger ?"

" Dunno what you mean," said Kiah.

" 'Fore we was all *sot* free," explained little Joe. " Was you born wid a ole mas' an' a ole mis', or was you born free ?—jes' natchully free."

" Free," said Kiah, thus placing himself, as every Southerner knows, under the ban of Joe's contempt. " Umph ! my Lor' ! Dat pie sholy do smell good !"

" You look hongry," said Joe, gravely.

" I is," said Kiah,—" hongry as a dog !"

Negroes are generous creatures, and Joe's mind was fully made up to give Kiah a piece of pie ; but before he signified this benevolent intention he rested his crutches under his shoulders and swung his misshapen feet almost in Kiah's face. He leered at him ; he grinned at him ; he stuck his chin in his face, and made a dart at him with the crown of his head, finally snapping his eyes and slapping his sides and swinging his heels to the following edition of " Juba," repeated with incredible rapidity and indescribable emphasis :

> Ruby-eyed 'simmon-seed
> See Billy hoppin' jes' in time :
> Juba dis an' Juba dat,
> Juba killed de yaller cat.
> Roun' de kittle o' 'possum-fat,
> Whoop a-hoy ! whoop a-hoy !

Double step o' Juba !
Forty pound o' candle-grease
Settin' on de mantel-piece.
Don't you see ole Granny Grace !
She look so homely in de face.
Up de wall an' down de 'tition,
Gimme axe sharp as sickle,
Cut de nigger's woozen pipe
What eat up all de snassengers !
Git up dar, you little nigger !
Can't you pat Juba?

He stopped suddenly and grinned ferociously at Kiah. Kiah gazed stolidly back at Joe. Then Joe stepped to the table, took up a rusty old pocket-knife, and cutting out a piece of the pie handed it to Kiah. Kiah bit off a point of the triangle with his eyes fixed on Joe as if in doubt whether he would be allowed to proceed, but, finding that the liberty was not resented, he eagerly devoured the remainder, drew his coat-sleeve across his mouth, and said, " Thanky." And thus their friendship commenced.

[Joe and Kiah soon became the warmest of friends, and on the evening of the wedding the grateful little fellow surprised and touched his benefactor by the present of the breastpin. This Mr. Wise wore through the ceremony, in spite of all remonstrance to the contrary.]

When, however, as the bridal cortége passed through the hall, he saw Joe nudge a fellow-servant with his elbow and point out the pin, he felt repaid, though Miss Annan was holding her head very high indeed.

The next morning little Joe came by the office : " What did de folks say 'bout yo' bres'pin, Mas' Tom ?"

" Say ? Why, they did not know what to say, Joe. They could not take their eyes off me. That pin knocked the black out of everything there. The bridegroom couldn't hold a candle to me," said Mr. Wise; and Joe laughed aloud with delight. "Did they give you your supper?"

"Did dat, Mas' Tom; an' I tuk home a snowball an' a orange to Kiah," said little Joe.

Late on the evening of the same day Mr. Wise was about leaving his office, when Little Joe's crutches sounded in the door-way, and Little Joe himself appeared, sobbing bitterly, tears streaming down his face: "Oh, Lordy, Mas' Tom! oh, Lordy!"

"What is the matter, Joe?"

"Oh, Lordy, Mas' Tom! Kiah's done dead!"

"Kiah! Is it possible? What was the matter?" asked Mr. Wise.

"Oh, Lordy! oh, Lordy!" sobbed Little Joe. "Me an' him went down to de creek, an' was playin' babtizin', an' I'd done babtized Kiah, an'—oh, Lordy! Lordy!—an' Kiah was jes' gwine to babtize me, an' he stepped out too fur, an' his legs was so short he lost his holt on me an' drownded; an' I couldn't ketch him, 'cos I couldn't stan' up widout nothin' to hold on to. Oh, Lordy! I wish I nuvvur had ha' heerd o' babtizin'! I couldn't git him out, an' I jes' kep' on a-hollerin', but nobody didn't come till Kiah was done drownded."

"I am sorry for you, Joe: I wish I had been there. But, as far as Kiah is concerned, he is better off than he was before," said Mr. Wise.

"No, he ain't, Mas' Tom," said Joe, stoutly: "leas'ways, Kiah didn't think so hisse'f, 'cos ef he had a-wanted to die he could ha' done it long an' merry ago. I don't b'leeve in no sech fool-talk as dead folks bein' better off dan dey was befo'."

Tom was silent, and little Joe went on with renewed tears: "I come up to ax you to gimme a clean shirt an' a par o' draw's to put on Kiah. You needn't gimme no socks,

'cos he ain't got no feet. Oh, Lordy! oh, Lord!" sobbed
Little Joe: "ef me an' Kiah had jes' had feet like some
folks, Kiah wouldn't ha' been drownded!"

"Take this up to the house," said Mr. Wise, handing
him a note, "and Miss Mollie will give you whatever you
want."

"Thanky, sir," said Joe. "I know you ain't got no
coffin handy, but you can gimme de money an' I can git
one. I don't reckon it will take much, 'cos Kiah warn't
big."

Then Mr. Wise wrote a note for the undertaker, and
directed Joe what to do with it.

The next day was cold and dark and misty, and the
pauper's hearse that conveyed Kiah to the graveyard was
driven so fast that poor Little Joe, the only mourner, could
hardly keep up as he hopped along behind it on his
crutches.

The blast grew keener and the mist heavier, and before
Kiah was buried out of sight the rain was falling in torrents that drenched the poor little cripple sobbing beside
the grave, and the driver of the hearse, a good-hearted
Irishman, said to him, "In wid ye, or get up here by me,
an' ye're a mind to. I'll take ye back."

But Joe shook his head, and prepared to hop back as he
had hopped out. "Thanky, sir," said he, "but I'd ruther
walk. I feels like I would be gittin' a ride out o' Kiah's
funeral."

The wind blew open his buttonless shirt, and the rain
beat heavily on his loyal little breast, but he struggled
against the storm, and paused only once on his way home.
That was beside the goods-box that he and Kiah had
had for a stall. Now it was drenched with rain and the
sides bespattered with mud, and the newspaper that had
served for a cloth had blown over one corner and was

soaked and torn, but clung to its old companion, though
the wind tried to tear it away and the rain to beat it
down. Little Joe stood a minute beside it, and cried
harder than ever.

For several days Little Joe drooped and shivered and
refused to eat, and at length he grew ill and sent for Mr.
Wise; but Mr. Wise was out of town, and did not return
for a week; and though, when he got home, the first thing
he did was to visit Little Joe, he came too late, for Joe
would never again rise from the straw pallet on which he
lay, nor use the crutches that now stood idle in the corner.

His eyes brightened and he smiled faintly as Tom entered like a breath of fresh air,—so strong and fresh and
vigorous that it made one feel better only to be near him.

"Why, Joe! how is this?"

The little cripple paused to gather up his strength; then
he said, "Busted ag'in, Mas' Tom, and you can't nuvvur
sot me up no mo'."

"Oh, stuff! Dr. North can if I can't. Why didn't you
send for him when you found I was away?"

"I dunno, sir: I nuvvur thought 'bout it."

Turning to the woman with whom Joe lived, "And why
the d——l didn't *you* do it?" said Tom, angrily.

"I didn't know Joe was so sick," said she. "'Tain't no
use sen'in' for no doctor now. I jes' been tellin' Joe he
better not put off makin' peace wid de Lord."

"I don't reckon de Lord is mad wid me, Nancy. What
is I done to Him? I didn't use to cuss, an' I didn't play
marbles on Sunday, 'cos I couldn't play 'em *no* time, like
de boys dat had feet."

"Ef you don't take keer you'll be too late, like Kiah. I
ain't a-sayin' whar Kiah is now,—'tain't for me to jedge,"
said Nancy,—"but you better be a-tryin' to open de gate
o' Paradise."

Piping the words out slowly and painfully, Little Joe replied, "I don't b'leeve I keer 'bout goin' 'less Kiah can git in too; but I spec' he's dar, 'cos I don't see what de good Lord could ha' had ag'in' him. He oughtn't to thought hard o' nothin' Kiah done, 'cos he warn't nuvvur nothin' but a free nigger, an' didn't hav no ole mas' to pattern by. Maybe He'll let us bofe in. I know Kiah's waitin' for me somewhar, but I dunno what to say to Him. You ax him, Mas' Tom."

He spoke more feebly, and his eyes were getting dull, but the old instinct of servitude remained, and he added, "Ain't you got nothin' to spread on de flo', Nancy, so Mas' Tom won't git his knees dirty?"

Immediately and reverently Tom knelt on the clay floor, and, as nearly as he remembered it, repeated the Lord's Prayer.

"Thanky, Mas' Tom," said Little Joe, feebly. "What was dat—ole mis'—used to—sing? 'Oh, Lamb o'—God —I come—I—'" The words ceased, and the eyes remained half closed, the pupils fixed.

Little Joe was dead.

SOME ODD FANCIES.

VARIOUS.

[We give, in the present Half-hour selection, a series of sketches, the first by one of the most popular humorists of the present day, and the second from "Helen's Babies,"* a story which set the whole land laughing ten years ago. The sketch of "How 'Ruby' Played" may be familiar to many of our readers, but is worth reproducing. As for

---

*Now published by T. B. Peterson & Bros.

"Aunt Doleful," most of us would rather meet with this multitudinous character in print than in person.]

THE BRAKEMAN AT CHURCH.

ON the road once more, with Lebanon fading away in the distance, the fat passenger drumming idly on the window-pane, the cross passenger sound asleep, and the tall, thin passenger reading "General Grant's Tour around the World," and wondering why "Green's August Flower" should be printed above the doors of " A Buddhist Temple at Benares." To me comes the brakeman, and, seating himself on the arm of the seat, says,—

"I went to church yesterday."

"Yes?" I said, with that interested inflection that asks for more. "And what church did you attend?"

"Which do you guess?" he asked.

"Some union mission church?" I hazarded.

"No," he said : "I don't like to run on these branch roads very much. I don't often go to church, and when I do I want to run on the main line, where your run is regular and you go on schedule time and don't have to wait on connections. I don't like to run on a branch. Good enough, but I don't like it."

"Episcopal?" I guessed.

"Limited express," he said,—"all palace-cars, and two dollars extra for a seat, fast time, and only stop at the big stations. Nice line, but too exhaustive for a brakeman. All train-men in uniform, conductor's punch and lantern silver-plated, and no train-boys allowed. Then the passengers are allowed to talk back to the conductor, and it makes them too free-and-easy. No, I couldn't stand the palace-cars. Rich road, though. Don't often hear of a receiver being appointed for that line. Some mighty nice people travel on it, too."

"Universalist?" I suggested.

"Broad gauge," said the brakeman; "does too much complimentary business. Everybody travels on a pass. Conductor doesn't get a fare once in fifty miles. Stops at all flag-stations, and won't run into anything but a union dépôt. No smoking-car on the train. Train-orders are rather vague, though, and the train-men don't get along well with the passengers. No, I don't go to the Universalist; though I know some awfully good men who run on that road."

"Presbyterian?" I asked.

"Narrow gauge, eh?" said the brakeman; "pretty track, straight as a rule; tunnel right through a mountain rather than go around it; spirit-level grade; passengers have to show their tickets before they get on the train. Mighty strict road, but the cars are a little narrow; have to sit one in a seat, and no room in the aisle to dance. Then there is no stop-over tickets allowed; got to go straight through to the station you're ticketed for, or you can't get on at all. When the car is full, no extra coaches; cars are built at the shops to hold just so many, and nobody else allowed on. But you don't often hear of an accident on that road. It's run right up to the rules."

"Maybe you joined the Free-Thinkers?" I said.

"Scrub road," said the brakeman; "dirt road-bed and no ballast, no time-card, and no train-despatcher. All trains run wild, and every engineer makes his own time, just as he pleases. Smoke if you want to; kind of a go-as-you-please road. Too many side-tracks, and every switch wide open all the time, with the switchman sound asleep and the target-lamp dead out. Get on as you please and off when you want to. Don't have to show your tickets, and the conductor isn't expected to do anything but amuse the passengers. No, sir, I was offered a pass, but

I don't like the line. I don't like to travel on a road that has no terminus. Do you know, sir, I asked a division superintendent where that road run to, and he said he hoped to die if he knew. I asked him if the general superintendent could tell me, and he said he didn't believe they had a general superintendent, and, if they had, he didn't know anything more about the road than the passengers. I asked him who he reported to, and he said, 'Nobody.' I asked a conductor who he got his orders from, and he said he 'didn't take orders from any living man or dead ghost.' And when I asked the engineer who he got his orders from, he said 'he'd like to see anybody give him orders; he'd run that train to suit himself, or he'd run her in the ditch.' Now, you see, sir, I'm a railroad-man, and I don't care to run on a road that has no time, or makes no connections, runs nowhere, and has no superintendent. It may be all right, but I've railroaded too long to understand it."

"Maybe you went to the Congregational church?" I said.

"Popular road," said the brakeman; "an old road, too, —one of the very oldest in the country. Good road-bed and comfortable cars. Well-managed road, too; directors don't interfere with division superintendents and train-orders. Road's mighty popular, but it's pretty independent, too. Yes, didn't one of the division superintendents down East discontinue one of the oldest stations on this line two or three years ago? But it's a mighty pleasant road to travel on. Always has such a splendid class of passengers."

"Did you try the Methodist?" I said.

"Now you're shouting," he said, with some enthusiasm. "Nice road, eh? Fast time, and plenty of passengers. Engines carry a power of steam, and don't you forget it; steam-gauge shows a hundred and enough all the time.

Lively road; when the conductor shouts, 'All aboard,' you can hear him at the next station. Every train-light shines like a headlight. Stop-over checks are given on all through-tickets; passenger can drop off the train as often as he likes, do the station two or three days, and hop on the next revival train that comes thundering along. Good, whole-souled, companionable conductors; ain't a road in the country where the passengers feel more at home. No passes; every passenger pays full traffic-rates for his ticket. Wesleyan air-brakes on all trains, too. Pretty safe road; but I didn't ride over it yesterday."

"Perhaps you tried the Baptist?" I guessed once more.

"Ah ha!" said the brakeman, "she's a daisy, isn't she? River road, beautiful curves; sweeps around anything to keep close to the river, but it's all steel rail and rock ballast, single track all the way, and not a side-track from the round-house to the terminus. It takes a heap of water to run it, though; double tanks at every station, and there isn't an engine in the shops that can pull a pound or run a mile with less than two gauges. But it runs through a lovely country; these river roads always do; river on one side and hills on the other, and it's a steady climb up the grade all the way till the run ends where the fountain-head of the river begins. Yes, sir, I'll take the river road every time for a lovely trip, sure connections and good time, and no prairie-dust blowing in at the windows. And yesterday, when the conductor came around for the tickets with a little basket punch, I didn't ask him to pass me, but I paid my fare like a little man; twenty-five cents for an hour's run and a little concert by the passengers thrown in. I tell you, Pilgrim, you take the river road when you want——"

But just here the loud whistle from the engine announced a station, and the brakeman hurried to the door, shouting,—

"Zionsville! This train makes no stops between here and Indianapolis!"

Robert J. Burdette.

BUDGE'S STORY OF THE FLOOD.

That afternoon I devoted to making a bouquet for Miss Mayton, and a most delightful occupation I found it. It was no florist's bouquet, composed of only a few kinds of flowers, wired upon sticks, and arranged according to geometric pattern. I used many a rare flower, too shy of bloom to recommend itself to florists; I combined tints almost as numerous as the flowers were, and perfumes to which city bouquets are utter strangers.

At length it was finished, but my delight suddenly became clouded by the dreadful thought, "What will people say?" Ah! I had it. I had seen in one of the library-drawers a small pasteboard box, shaped like a bandbox; doubtless *that* would hold it. I found the box: it was of just the size I needed. I dropped my card into the bottom, —no danger of a lady not finding the card accompanying a gift of flowers,—neatly fitted the bouquet in the centre of the box, and went in search of Mike. He winked cheeringly as I explained the nature of his errand, and he whispered,—

"I'll do it as clane as a whistle, your honor. Mistress Clarkson's cook an' mesilf understhand each other, an' I'm used to goin' up the back way. Niver a man can see but the angels, an' they won't tell."

"Very well, Mike; here's a dollar for you: you'll find the box on the hat-rack, in the hall."

Toddie disappeared somewhere after supper, and came back very disconsolate.

"Can't find my dolly's ka'dle," he whined.

"Never mind, old pet," said I, soothingly. "Uncle will ride you on his foot."

"But I *want* my dolly's k'adle," said he, piteously rolling out his lower lip.

"Don't you want me to tell you a story?"

For a moment Toddie's face indicated a terrible internal conflict between old Adam and Mother Eve; but curiosity finally overpowered natural depravity, and Toddie murmured,—

"Yesh."

"What shall I tell you about?"

"'Bout Nawndeark."

"About *what?*"

"He means Noah an' the ark," exclaimed Budge.

"Datsh what *I* shay,—Nawndeark," declared Toddie.

"Well," said I, hastily refreshing my memory by picking up the Bible,—for Helen, like most people, is pretty sure to forget to pack her Bible when she runs away from home for a few days,—"well, once it rained forty days and nights, and everybody was drowned from the face of the earth excepting Noah, a righteous man, who was saved, with all his family, in an ark which the Lord commanded him to build."

"Uncle Harry," said Budge, after contemplating me with open eyes and mouth for at least two minutes after I had finished, "do you think that's Noah?"

"Certainly, Budge: here's the whole story in the Bible."

"Well, *I* don't think it's Noah one single bit," said he, with increasing emphasis.

"I'm beginning to think we read different Bibles, Budge; but let's hear *your* version."

"Huh?"

"Tell *me* about Noah, if you know so much about him."

"I will, if you want me to. Once the Lord felt so un-

comfortable 'cos folks was bad that he was sorry he ever
made anybody, or any world, or anything. But Noah
wasn't bad; the Lord liked him first-rate; so he told Noah
to build a big ark, and then the Lord would make it rain
so everybody should be drownded but Noah an' his little
boys an' girls an' doggies an' pussies an' mamma-cows an'
little-boy-cows an' little-girl-cows an' hosses an' everything; they'd go in the ark an' wouldn't get wetted a bit
when it rained. An' Noah took lots of things to eat in the
ark,—cookies an' milk an' oatmeal an' strawberries an'
porgies an'—oh, yes, plum-puddings an' pumpkin-pies.
But Noah didn't want everybody to get drownded, so he
talked to folks, an' said, 'It's goin' to rain *awful* pretty
soon; you'd better be good, an' then the Lord'll let you
come into my ark.' An' they jus' said, 'Oh, if it rains
we'll go in the house till it stops;' an' other folks said,
' *We* ain't afraid of rain; we've got an umbrella.'   An'
some more said they wasn't goin' to be afraid of just a
rain. But it *did* rain, though, an' folks went in their
houses, an' the water came in, an' they went up-stairs, an'
the water came up there, an' they got on the tops of the
houses, an' up in big trees, an' up in mountains, an' the
water went after 'em everywhere, an' drownded everybody, only just except Noah an' the people in the ark. An'
it rained forty days an' nights, an' then it stopped, an'
Noah got out of the ark, an' he an' his little boys an' girls
went wherever they wanted to, an' everything in the
world was all theirs; there wasn't anybody to tell 'em to
go home, nor no kindergarten schools to go to, nor no bad
boys to fight 'em, nor nothin'. Now tell us 'nother story."

"An' I want my dolly's k'adle. Ocken Hawwy, I wants
my dolly's k'adle, tause my dolly's in it, an' I wan to shee
her," interrupted Toddie.

Just then came a knock. "Come in!" I shouted.

In stepped Mike, with an air of the greatest secrecy, handed me a letter and the identical box in which I had sent the flowers to Miss Mayton. What *could* it mean? I hastily opened the envelope, and at the same time Toddie shrieked, "Oh, darsh my dolly's k'adle! dare tizh!" snatched and opened the box, and displayed—his doll! My heart sickened, and did *not* regain its strength during the perusal of the following note:

"Miss Mayton herewith returns to Mr. Burton the package which just arrived, with his card. She recognizes the contents as a portion of the apparent property of one of Mr. Burton's nephews, but is unable to understand why it should have been sent to her.
"June 20, 1875."

"Toddie," I roared, as my younger nephew caressed his loathsome doll and murmured endearing words to it, "where did you get that box?"

"On the hat-wack," replied the youth, with perfect fearlessness. "I keeps it in ze book-case djawer, an' somebody took it 'way an' put nasty ole flowers in it."

"Where are those flowers?" I demanded.

Toddie looked up with considerable surprise, but promptly replied,—

"I froed 'em away: don't want no ole flowers in my dolly's k'adle. That's ze way she wocks,—see?"

John Habberton.

HOW "RUBY" PLAYED.

[Jud Brownin, when visiting New York, goes to hear Rubinstein, and gives the following description of his playing.]

Well, sir, he had the blamedest, biggest, catty-cornerdest pianner you ever laid eyes on; somethin' like a distracted billiard-table on three legs. The lid was hoisted, and mighty well it was. If it hadn't been, he'd 'a' tore the entire inside clean out and scattered 'em to the four winds of heaven.

Played well? You bet he did; but don't interrupt me. When he first sit down he 'peared to keer mighty little 'bout playin' and wisht he hadn't come. He tweedle-leedled a little on the treble, and twoodle-oodled some on the base,—just foolin' and boxin' the thing's jaws for bein' in his way. And I says to a man sittin' next to me, says I, "What sort of fool playin' is that?" And he says, "Heish!" But presently his hands commenced chasin' one another up and down the keys, like a passel of rats scamperin' through a garret very swift. Parts of it was sweet, though, and reminded me of a sugar squirrel turnin' the wheel of a candy cage.

"Now," I says to my neighbor, "he's showin' off. He thinks he's a-doin' of it, but he ain't got no idee, no plan of nothin'. If he'd play me a tune of some kind or other, I'd——"

But my neighbor says, "Heish!" very impatient.

I was just about to git up and go home, bein' tired of that foolishness, when I heard a little bird waking up away off in the woods and call sleepy-like to his mate, and I looked up and see that Rubin was beginning to take some interest in his business, and I sit down again. It was the peep of day. The light came faint from the east, the breezes blowed gentle and fresh, some more birds waked up in the orchard, then some more in the trees near the house, and all begun singin' together. People began to stir, and the gal opened the shutters. Just then the first beam of the sun fell upon the blossoms a leetle more, and it techt the roses on the bushes, and the next thing it was broad day; the sun fairly blazed, the birds sung like

they'd split their little throats; all the leaves was movin',
and flashin' diamonds of dew, and the whole wide world
was bright and happy as a king. Seemed to me like
there was a good breakfast in every house in the land,
and not a sick child or woman anywhere. It was a fine
mornin'.

And I says to my neighbor, "That's music, that is."

But he glared at me like he'd like to cut my throat.

Presently the wind turned; it begun to thicken up, and
a kind of gray mist came over things; I got low-spirited
directly. Then a silver rain began to fall. I could see
the drops touch the ground; some flashed up like long
pearl ear-rings, and the rest rolled away like round rubies.
It was pretty, but melancholy. Then the pearls gathered
themselves into long strands and necklaces, and then they
melted into thin silver streams, running between golden
gravels, and then the streams joined each other at the
bottom of the hill, and made a brook that flowed silent,
except that you could kinder see the music, especially
when the bushes on the banks moved as the music went
along down the valley. I could smell the flowers in the
meadow. But the sun didn't shine, nor the birds sing: it
was a foggy day, but not cold.

The most curious thing was the little white angel-boy,
like you see in pictures, that run ahead of the music brook
and led it on, and on, away out of the world, where no
man ever was, certain. I could see that boy just as plain
as I see you. Then the moonlight came, without any sunset, and shone on the graveyards, where some few ghosts
lifted their hands and went over the wall, and between the
black, sharp-top trees splendid marble houses rose up, with
fine ladies in the lit-up windows, and men that loved 'em,
but could never get anigh 'em, who played on guitars
under the trees, and made me that miserable I could have

cried, because I wanted to love somebody, I don't know
who, better than the men with the guitars did.

Then the sun went down, it got dark, the wind moaned
and wept like a lost child for its dead mother, and I could
'a' got up then and there and preached a better sermon
than any I ever listened to. There wasn't a thing in the
world left to live for, not a blame thing, and yet I didn't
want the music to stop one bit. It was happier to be
miserable than to be happy without being miserable. I
couldn't understand it. I hung my head and pulled out
my handkerchief, and blowed my nose loud to keep me
from cryin'. My eyes is weak anyway; I didn't want
anybody to be a-gazin' at me a-sniv'lin', and it's nobody's
business what I do with my nose. It's mine. But some
several glared at me mad as blazes. Then, all of a sudden,
old Rubin changed his tune. He ripped out and he rared,
he tipped and he tared, he pranced and he charged like the
grand entry at a circus. 'Peared to me that all the gas in
the house was turned on at once, things got so bright, and
I hilt up my head, ready to look any man in the face, and
not afraid of nothin'. It was a circus and a brass band and
a big ball all goin' on at the same time. He lit into them
keys like a thousand of brick; he give 'em no rest day or
night; he set every livin' joint in me a-goin', and, not bein'
able to stand it no longer, I jumped spang onto my seat,
and jest hollered,—

"*Go it, my Rube!*"

Every blamed man, woman, and child in the house riz
on me, and shouted, "Put him out! put him out!"

"Put your great-grandmother's grizzly gray greenish
cat into the middle of next month!" I says. "Tech me
if you dare! I paid my money, and you jest come anigh
me!"

With that some several policemen run up, and I had to

II.—*p*

simmer down. But I would 'a' fit any fool that laid hands
on me, for I was bound to hear Ruby out or die.

He had changed his tune again. He hop-light ladies
and tip-toed fine from end to end of the key-board. He
played soft and low and solemn. I heard the church bells
over the hills. The candles of heaven was lit, one by one ;
I saw the stars rise. The great organ of eternity began
to play from the world's end to the world's end, and all the
angels went to prayers. . . . Then the music changed to
water, full of feeling that couldn't be thought, and began
to drop,—drip, drop—drip, drop,—clear and sweet, like
tears of joy falling into a lake of glory. It was sweeter
than that. It was as sweet as a sweet-heart sweetened
with white sugar mixed with powdered silver and seed-
diamonds. It was too sweet. I tell you the audience
cheered. Rubin he kinder bowed, like he wanted to say,
"Much obleeged, but I'd rather you wouldn't interrup'
me."

He stopped a moment or two to ketch breath. Then he
got mad. He run his fingers through his hair, he shoved
up his sleeve, he opened his coat-tails a leetle further, he
drug up his stool, he leaned over, and, sir, he just went for
that old pianner. He slapped her face, he boxed her jaws,
he pulled her nose, he pinched her ears, and he scratched
her cheeks, until she fairly yelled. He knocked her down
and he stamped on her shameful. She bellowed like a
bull, she bleated like a calf, she howled like a hound, she
squealed like a pig, she shrieked like a rat, and *then* he
wouldn't let her up. He run a quarter stretch down the
low grounds of the base, till he got clean in the bowels of
the earth, and you heard thunder galloping after thunder
through the hollows and caves of perdition ; and then he
fox-chased his right hand with his left till he got 'way out
of the treble into the clouds, whar the notes was finer than

the p'ints of cambric needles, and you couldn't hear nothin'
but the shadders of 'em. And *then* he wouldn't let the old
pianner go. He for'ard two'd, he crost over first gentleman, he chassade right and left, back to your places, he
all hands'd aroun', ladies to the right, promenade all, in
and out, here and there, back and forth, up and down, perpetual motion, double twisted and turned and tacked and
tangled into forty-eleven thousand double bow-knots.

By jinks! it was a mixtery. And then he wouldn't let
the old pianner go. He fetcht up his right wing, he fetcht
up his left wing, he fetcht up his centre, he fetcht up his
reserves. He fired by file, he fired by platoons, by company, by regiments, and by brigades. He opened his
cannon,—siege-guns down thar, Napoleons here, twelve-
pounders yonder,—big guns, little guns, middle-sized guns,
round shot, shells, shrapnels, grape, canister, mortar, mines
and magazines, every livin' battery and bomb a-goin' at the
same time. The house trembled, the lights danced, the walls
shuk, the floor come up, the ceilin' come down, the sky split,
the ground rocked—heavens and earth, creation, sweet potatoes, Moses, ninepences, glory, tenpenny nails, Samson in
a 'simmon-tree, Tump, Tompson in a tumbler-cart, roodle-
oodle-oodle-oodle —ruddle-uddle-uddle-uddle—raddle-addle-
addle-addle — riddle-iddle-iddle-iddle — reedle-eedle-eedle-
eedle—p-r-r-r-rlank! Bang!!! lang! perlang! p-r-r-r-r-r!!
Bang!!!!

With that bang! he lifted himself bodily into the a'r,
and he come down with his knees, his ten fingers, his ten
toes, his elbows, and his nose, striking every single solitary
key on the pianner at the same time. The thing busted
and went off into seventeen hundred and fifty-seven thousand five hundred and forty-two hemi-demi-semi-quivers,
and I know'd no mo'.

When I come to, I were under ground about twenty

foot, in a place they call Oyster Bay, treatin' a Yankee that I never laid eyes on before and never expect to ag'in. Day was breakin' by the time I got to the St. Nicholas Hotel, and I pledge you my word I did not know my name. The man asked me the number of my room, and I told him, "Hot music on the half-shell for two!"

George W. Bagby.

AUNTY DOLEFUL'S VISIT.

How do you do, Cornelia? I heard you were sick, and I stepped in to cheer you up a little. My friends often say, "It's such a comfort to see you, Aunty Doleful. You have such a flow of conversation, and are *so* lively." Besides, I said to myself, as I came up the stairs, "Perhaps it's the last time I'll ever see Cornelia Jane alive."

You don't mean to die yet, eh? Well, now, how do you know? You can't tell. You think you are getting better: but there was poor Mrs. Jones sitting up, and every one saying how smart she was, and all of a sudden she was taken with spasms in the heart and went off like a flash. But you must be careful, and not get anxious or excited. Keep quite calm, and don't fret about anything. Of course, things can't go on just as if you were down-stairs; and I wondered whether you knew your little Billy was sailing about in a tub on the mill-pond, and that your little Sammy was letting your little Jimmy down from the veranda roof in a clothes-basket.

Gracious goodness! what's the matter? I guess Providence 'll take care of 'em. Don't look so. *You thought Bridget was watching them?* Well, no, she isn't. I saw her talking to a man at the gate. He looked to me like a burglar. No doubt she let him take the impression of the door-key in wax, and then he'll get in and murder you all. There was a family at Kobble Hill all killed last week for fifty dollars. Now, don't fidget so; it will be bad for the baby.

Poor little dear! How singular it is, to be sure, that you can't tell whether a child is blind, or deaf and dumb, or a cripple, at that age. It might be *all*, and you'd never know it.

Most of them that have their senses make bad use of them, though: *that* ought to be your comfort, if it does turn out to have anything dreadful the matter with it. And more don't live a year. I saw a baby's funeral down the street as I came along.

How is Mr. Kobble? *Well, but finds it warm in town, eh?* Well, I should think he would. They are dropping down by hundreds there with sun-stroke. You must prepare your mind to have him brought home any day. Anyhow, a trip on these railroad-trains is just risking your life every time you take one. Back and forth every day as he is, it's just trifling with danger.

Dear! dear! now to think what dreadful things hang over us all the time! Dear! dear!

Scarlet fever has broken out in the village, Cornelia. Little Isaac Potter has it, and I saw your Jimmy playing with him last Saturday.

Well, I must be going now. I've got another sick friend, and I shan't think my duty done unless I cheer her up a little before I sleep. Good-by. How pale you look, Cornelia! I don't believe you have a good doctor. Do send him away and try some one else. You don't look so well as you did when I came in. But if anything happens, send for me at once. If I can't do anything else, I can cheer you up a little.

MARY KYLE DALLAS.

THE WHISKERS.

SAMUEL WOODWORTH.

[The author of the familiar " Old Oaken Bucket" did not disdain
to descend into humor, of which we have evidence in the following
amusing contrast of the heroic and the practical in self-abnegation.
The author formed one of our older circle of poets, as he was born (at
Scituate, Massachusetts) in 1785, and died in 1842.   In conjunction
with George P. Morris, he founded, in 1823, the *New York Mirror*.]

THE kings who ruled mankind with haughty sway,
The prouder pope, whom even kings obey,
Love, at whose shrine both popes and monarchs fall,
And e'en self-interest, that controls them all,
Possess a petty power, when all combined,
Compared with fashion's influence on mankind:
For love itself will oft to fashion bow;
The following story will convince you how:

A *petit-maître* wooed a fair,
Of virtue, wealth, and graces rare,
But vainly had preferred his claim:
The maiden owned no answering flame.
At length, by doubt and anguish torn,
Suspense too painful to be borne,
Low at her feet he humbly kneeled,
And thus his ardent flame revealed:

" Pity my grief, angelic fair,
Behold my anguish and despair;
For you this heart must ever burn,—
Oh, bless me with a kind return!
My love no language can express,
Reward it, then, with happiness;

Nothing on earth but you I prize;
All else is trifling in my eyes,
And cheerfully would I resign
The wealth of worlds to call you mine.
But, if another gain your hand,
Far distant from my native land,
Far hence from you and hope, I'll fly,
And in some foreign region die."

The virgin heard, and thus replied:
" If my consent to be your bride
Will make you happy, then be blest;
But grant me, first, one small request:
A sacrifice I must demand,
And in return will give my hand."

" A sacrifice!   Oh, speak its name!
For you I'd forfeit wealth and fame:
Take my whole fortune,—every cent——"

" 'Twas something more than wealth I meant."

" Must I the realms of Neptune trace?
Oh, speak the word!—where'er the place,
For you, the idol of my soul,
I'd e'en explore the frozen pole,
Arabia's sandy deserts tread,
Or trace the Tigris to its head."

" Oh, no, dear sir; I do not ask
So long a voyage, so hard a task:
You must—but, ah! the boon I want,
I have no hope that you will grant."

"Shall I, like Bonaparte, aspire
To be the world's imperial sire?
Express the wish, and here I vow
To place a crown upon your brow."

"Sir, these are trifles," she replied;
"But, if you wish me for your bride,
You must—but still I fear to speak—
You'll never grant the boon I seek."

"Oh, say," he cried, "dear angel, say,
What must I do, and I obey:
No longer rack me with suspense;
Speak your commands, and send me hence."

"Well, then, dear, generous youth," she cries,
"If thus my heart you really prize,
And wish to link your fate with mine,
On one condition I am thine;
'Twill then become my pleasing duty
To contemplate a husband's beauty,
And, gazing on your manly face,
His feelings and his wishes trace,
To banish thence each mark of care,
And light a smile of pleasure there.
Oh, let me, then, 'tis all I ask,
Commence at once the pleasing task;
Oh, let me, as becomes my place,
Cut those huge whiskers from your face."

She said—but, oh! what strange surprise
Was pictured in her lover's eyes!
Like lightning from the ground he sprung,
While wild amazement tied his tongue;

A statue, motionless, he gazed,
Astonished, horror-struck, amazed.
So looked the gallant Perseus when
Medusa's visage met his ken;
So looked Macbeth, whose guilty eye
Discerned an "air-drawn dagger" nigh;
And so the Prince of Denmark stared
When first his father's ghost appeared.

At length our hero silence broke,
And thus in wildest accents spoke:
"Cut off my whiskers! Oh, ye gods!
I'd sooner lose my ears, by odds:
Madam, I'd not be so disgraced,
So lost to fashion and to taste,
To win an empress to my arms,
Though blest with more than mortal charms.
My whiskers! zounds!" He said no more,
But quick retreated through the door,
And sought a less obdurate fair
To take the beau with all his hair.

FRANKLIN AND THE GOUT: A DIALOGUE.

BENJAMIN FRANKLIN.

[Of Franklin's humorous writings the following is one of the best examples. There was a strong vein of humor in his composition, though it was, like everything else in his writings, a humor that taught a lesson, quaint, practical, and full of the wisdom of experience.]

Franklin. Eh! oh, eh! what have I done to merit these cruel sufferings?

Gout. Many things: you have ate and drank too freely,

and too much indulged those legs of yours in their indolence.

F. Who is it that accuses me?

G. It is I, even I, the Gout.

F. What, my enemy in person?

G. No, not your enemy.

F. I repeat it, my enemy; for you would not only torment my body to death, but ruin my good name. You reproach me as a glutton and a tippler: now, all the world, that knows me, will allow that I am neither the one nor the other.

G. The world may think as it pleases; it is always very complaisant to itself, and sometimes to its friends; but I know very well that the quantity of meat and drink reasonable for a man who takes a reasonable degree of exercise would be too much for another who never takes any.

F. I take—eh! oh!—as much exercise—eh! as I can, Madam Gout. You know my sedentary state, and on that account, it would seem, Madam Gout, as if you might spare me a little, seeing it is not altogether my own fault.

G. Not a jot; your rhetoric and your politeness are thrown away; your apology avails nothing. If your situation in life is a sedentary one, your amusements, your recreations, at least, should be active. You ought to walk or ride, or, if the weather prevents that, play at billiards. . . . You eat an inordinate breakfast, four dishes of tea, with cream, and one or two buttered toasts, with slices of hung beef, which I fancy are not things the most easily digested. Immediately afterwards you sit down to write at your desk, or converse with persons who apply to you on business. Thus the time passes till one, without any kind of bodily exercise. But all this I could pardon, in regard, as you say, to your sedentary condition. But what is your practice after dinner? Walking in the beautiful gardens of those friends with whom you have dined, would be the choice of men of sense; yours is to be fixed down to chess, where you are found engaged for two or three hours. . . . What can be expected from such a course of living but a body replete with stagnant humors, ready to fall a prey to all dangerous maladies, if I, the Gout, did not occasionally bring you relief by agitating those humors, and so purifying and dissipating them? . . . Fie, Mr. Franklin! But, amidst my instructions, I had almost forgot to administer my wholesome corrections; so take that twinge, and that.

F. Oh! eh! oh! ohhh! As much instruction as you please, Madam Gout, and as many reproaches; but pray, madam, a truce with your corrections.

G. No, sir, no; I will not abate a particle of what is so much for your good: therefore——

F. Oh! ehhh! It is not fair to say I take no exercise, when I do very often, going out to dine and returning in my carriage.

G. That, of all imaginable exercises, is the most slight and insignificant, if you allude to the motion of a carriage suspended upon springs. . . . Providence has appointed few to roll in carriages, while he has given to all a pair of legs, which are machines infinitely more commodious and serviceable. Be grateful, then, and make a proper use of yours. . . . Behold your fair friend at Auteuil, a lady who received from bounteous nature more really useful science than half a dozen such pretenders to philosophy as you have been able to extract from all your books. When she honors you with a visit, it is on foot. She walks all hours of the day, and leaves indolence and its concomitant maladies to be endured by her horses. In this see at once the preservative of her health and personal charms. But when you go to Auteuil you must have your carriage, though it is no further from Passy to Auteuil than from Auteuil to Passy.

F. Your reasonings grow very tiresome.

G. I stand corrected. I will be silent and continue my office: take that, and that.

F. Oh! ohh! Talk on, I pray you!

G. No, no; I have a good number of twinges for you to-night, and you may be sure of some more to-morrow.

F. What! with such a fever! I shall go distracted. Oh! eh! Can no one bear it for me?

G. Ask that of your horses: they have served you faithfully.

F. How can you so cruelly sport with my torments?

G. Sport! I am very serious. I have here a list of offences against your own health distinctly written, and can justify every stroke inflicted on you.

F. Read it, then.

G. It is too long a detail; but I will briefly mention some particulars.

F. Proceed. I am all attention.

G. Do you remember how often you have promised yourself, the following morning, a walk in the grove of Boulogne, in the garden de la Muette, or in your own garden, and have violated your promise, alleging at one time it was too cold, at another too warm, too windy, too moist, or what else you pleased, when in truth it was too nothing but your insuperable love of ease?

F. That, I confess, may have happened occasionally, probably ten times in a year.

G. Your confession is very far short of the truth; the gross amount is one hundred and ninety-nine times.

F. Is it possible?

G. So possible that it is fact; you may rely on the accuracy of my statement. You know Mr. Brillon's gar-

dens, and what fine walks they contain; you know the
handsome flight of one hundred steps which lead from the
terrace above to the lawn below. You have been in the
habit of visiting this amiable family twice a week, after
dinner, and it is a maxim of your own that "a man may
take as much exercise in walking a mile, up- and down-
stairs, as in ten on level ground." What an opportunity
was here for you to have had exercise in both these ways!
Did you embrace it? and how often?

F. I cannot immediately answer that question.

G. I will do it for you. Not once.

F. Not once?

G. Even so. During the summer you went there at
six o'clock. You found the charming lady, with her lovely
children and friends, eager to walk with you and entertain
you with their agreeable conversation, and what has been
your choice? Why, to sit on the terrace, satisfying yourself with the fine prospect, and passing your eye over the
beauties of the gardens below, without taking one step to
descend and walk about in them. On the contrary, you
call for tea and the chess-board; and, lo! you are occupied
in your seat till nine o'clock, and that besides two hours'
play after dinner; and then, instead of walking home,
which would have bestirred you a little, you step into
your carriage. How absurd to suppose that all this carelessness can be reconcilable with health, without my inter-
position!

F. I am convinced now of the justice of Poor Richard's
remark, that "our debts and our sins are always greater
than we think for."

G. So it is. You philosophers are sages in your maxims and fools in your conduct.

F. But do you charge among my crimes that I return
in a carriage from Mr. Brillon's?

G. Certainly; for, having been seated all the while, you cannot object the fatigue of the day, and cannot want, therefore, the relief of a carriage.

F. What, then, would you have me do with my carriage?

G. Burn it, if you choose; you would at least get heat out of it once in this way; or, if you dislike that proposal, here's another for you; observe the poor peasants who work in the vineyards and grounds about the villages of Passy, Auteuil, Chaillot, etc.; you may find every day, among these deserving creatures, four or five old men and women, bent and perhaps crippled by weight of years and too long and too great labor. After a most fatiguing day, these people have to trudge a mile or two to their smoky huts. Order your coachman to set them down. This is an act that will be good for your soul, and at the same time, after your visit to the Brillons, if you return on foot, that will be good for your body.

F. Ah! how tiresome you are!

G. Well, then, to my office: it should not be forgotten that I am your physician. There.

F. Ohhh! what a devil of a physician!

G. How ungrateful you are to say so! Is it not I who, in the character of your physician, have saved you from the palsy, dropsy, and apoplexy? one or other of which would have done for you long ago but for me.

F. I submit, and thank you for the past, but entreat the discontinuance of your visits for the future; for, in my mind, one had better die than be cured so dolefully. Permit me just to hint that I have also not been unfriendly to *you.* I never feed physician or quack of any kind to enter the list against you; if then you do not leave me to my repose, it may be said you are ungrateful too.

G. I can scarcely acknowledge that as any objection. As to quacks, I despise them; they may kill you, indeed, but cannot injure me. And as to regular physicians, they are at last convinced that the gout, in such a subject as you are, is no disease, but a remedy; and wherefore cure a remedy? But to our business—there.

F. Oh! oh! For heaven's sake leave me, and I promise faithfully never more to play at chess, but to take exercise daily and live temperately.

G. I know you too well. You promise fair; but after a few months of good health you will return to your old habits; your fine promises will be forgotten like the forms of the last year's clouds. Let us then finish the account, and I will go. But I leave you with an assurance of visiting you again at a proper time and place; for my object is your good, and you are sensible now that I am your *real friend.*

THE FIRE-HUNT.

W. T. THOMPSON.

[The following sketch is by a Southern writer of some note in his day as a humorist, the author of " Major Jones's Courtship," " Major Jones's Sketches of Travel," etc. These depend largely for their fun on bad spelling and situations decidedly lacking in refinement. We select instead a hunting-sketch in which a Georgia "Sam Lawson" figures as the hero and has some awkward " consequences" to endure.]

SAMUEL SIKES was one of the most inveterate hunters I ever knew. He delighted in no other pursuit or pastime, and though he pretended to cultivate a small spot of ground, yet so large a portion of his time was spent in the pursuit of game that his agricultural interests suffered much for the want of proper attention. He lived a few miles from town, and as you passed his house, which stood a short distance from the main road, a few acres of corn and a small patch of potatoes might probably attract your notice, as standing greatly in need of the hoe, but the most prominent objects about Sam's domicile pertained to his favorite pursuit. A huge pair of antlers—a trophy of one of his proudest achievements—occupied a conspicuous place on the gable end; some ten or a dozen tall fishing-poles, though modestly stowed behind the chimney, projected far above the roof of the little cabin; and upon its unchinked walls many a coon- and deer-skin was undergoing the process of drying. If all these did not convince you that the proprietor was a sportsman, the varied and clamorous music of a score of hungry-looking hounds, as they issued forth in full cry at every passer-by, could not fail to force the conviction.

Sam had early found a companion to share with him his good or ill luck; and, though he was yet on the green side of thirty, he was obliged to provide for some five or six little tallow-faced "responsibilities;" so he not only followed the chase from choice, but when his wife—who hated "fisherman's luck" *worse* than Sam did a "miss" or a "nibble"—took him to account for spending so many broken days, Saturday afternoons, rainy days, and odd hours, to say nothing of whole nights, in the woods, without bringing home so much as a cut-squirrel or hornyhead, his ready reply was that he was "'bleeged" to do the best he could to get meat for her and the "childer."

The fire-hunt was Sam's hobby; and though the legislature had recently passed an act prohibiting that mode of hunting, he continued to indulge as freely as ever in his favorite sport, resolutely maintaining that the law was "unconstitootional and ag'in' reason." He had often urged me to accompany him, just to see how "slick" he could shine a buck's eyes; and such were the glowing accounts

he had from time to time given me of his achievements in
that way that he had drawn from me a promise to go with
him "some of these times."

I was sitting one evening, after tea, upon the steps of
the porch, enjoying the cool autumnal breeze, when my
friend Sam Sikes suddenly made his appearance. He had
come for me to go with him on a fire-hunt, and was mounted
on his mule Blaze, with his pan upon one shoulder and his
musket on the other. Determined to have everything in
readiness before calling on me, he had gone to the kitchen
and lit a few light-wood splinters, which were now blazing
in his pan, and which served the double purpose of lighting
him through the enclosure and of demonstrating to me the
manner of hunting by night. As he approached the house,
his light discovered me where I was sitting.

"Good-evenin', major," said he. "I've come out to see
if you've a mind to take a little hunt to-night."

"I believe not, Mr. Sikes," I replied, feeling entirely too
well satisfied with my pleasant seat in the cool breeze to
desire to change it for a night-ramble through the woods.
"Not to-night, I thank you: it looks like rain."

"Oh, pshaw! 'tain't gwine to rain, nohow; and I'm all
fixed. Come, come along, major."

As he spoke, he rode close to the porch, and his mule
made several efforts to crop the shrubbery that grew by
the door, which Sam very promptly opposed.

"How far are you going, Mr. Sikes?" I inquired, en-
deavoring to shake off the lazy fit which inclined me to
keep my seat.

"Only jest up the branch a little bit,—not beyant a mile
from your fence, at the outside. Look at him!" he exclaimed, in a louder tone, as he gave the reins a jerk.
"Thar's deer a plenty up at the forks, and we'll have rale
sport. Come, you better go, and—why, look at him!"

giving the reins another jerk, at the same time that he sent a kick to his mule's ribs that might have been heard a hundred yards—"and I'll show you how to shine the eyes of a buck."

As he sat in his saddle persuading me to go, his mule kept frisking and turning in such a manner as to annoy him exceedingly. Upon his left shoulder he bore his blazing pan, and upon his right he held his musket, holding the reins also in his right hand: so that any efforts on his part to restrain the refractory movements of his animal were attended with much difficulty. I had about made up my mind to go, when the mule evinced a more resolute determination to get at the shrubbery.

"Whoa! whoa, now!—blast your heart—now, look at him!"—then might be heard a few good lusty kicks. "Come, major, git your gun, and let's—will you hold up yer head, you 'bominable fool?—and let's take a little round: it'll do you good."

"As I only go to satisfy my curiosity, I'll not take a gun. You will be able to shoot all the deer we meet."

"Well, any way you mind, major."

We were about to start, when suddenly the mule gave a loud bray, and, when I turned to look, his heels were high in the air, and Sam clinging to his neck, while the fire flew in every direction. The mule wheeled, reared, and kicked, and still Sam hung to his neck, shouting, "Look at him! —whoa!—will you mind!—whoa!—whoa, now!"—but all to no purpose, until at length the infuriated animal backed to the low paling fence which enclosed a small flower-garden, over which he tumbled,—Sam, pan, gun, and all, together!

When Sam had disengaged himself, he discovered that the saddle-blanket was on fire, which had been the cause of the disaster.

"Cuss the luck!" said he; "I thought I smelt somethin' burnin'." Then, addressing himself to the mule in a louder tone, he continued, "That's what comes o' jerkin' yer dratted head about that-a-way. Blast your infernal heart, you've spilt all my fixin's; and here's my pan, jest as crooked as a fish-hook!"—then there was a kick or two, and a blow with the frying-pan: "take that, you bowdacious fool, and hold yer head still next time, will you? And you've skinned my leg all to flinders, dadfetch your everlastin' picter to dingnation!—take that under your short-ribs, now, will you!—Whoa! I've a great mind to blow yer infernal brains out this very night! And you've broke the major's palin's down, you unnatural cuss. Whoa! step over now, if you's satisfied."

By this time Sam had got the mule out of the enclosure and had gathered up most of his "fixin's." The whole scene, after the upsetting of the pan, had transpired in the dark, but from the moment I saw the mule's heels flying and Sam clinging to his neck it was with the utmost difficulty I restrained my laughter. During his solo in the enclosure I was absolutely compelled to stuff my handkerchief in my mouth to prevent his hearing me.

"Did you ever *see* the likes o' that, major?" exclaimed Sam, as I approached the spot where he was engaged in readjusting his saddle and putting other matters to rights that had been deranged by the struggles of the mule to free himself from the burning blanket.

"I am very sorry it happened," I replied, "as it will prevent us from taking our hunt."

"No, I'll be dadfetcht if it does, though: I ain't to be backed out that-a-way, major,—not by no means. You know 'a bad beginnin' makes a good endin',' as the old woman said. He isn't done sich a monstrous sight o' harm, nohow,—only bent the handle of my pan a little, and raked some skin off one o' my shins; but that's neither here nor thar. So, if you'll jest hold Blaze till I go and git a torch, we'll have a shoot at a pair o' eyes yit, to-night."

I took the bridle while Sam procured a torch, and after he had gathered up the fagots which he had brought to burn in his pan, we set off for the branch,—Sam upon his mule, with a torch in one hand, while I walked by his side.

It was only necessary for us to go a short distance, before we were at the designated spot.

"Thar," said Sam, as he dismounted, "here's as good a place as any: so I'll jest hitch Blaze here, and light our pan."

Accordingly, Blaze was made fast to a stout sapling, and Sam proceeded to kindle a fire in his pan, at the same time explaining to me, in a low voice, the *modus operandi* of the fire-hunt, which he accompanied with sundry precautionary hints and directions for my own special observance on the present occasion.

"Now, major," said he, "you must keep close to me, and you mus'n't make no racket in the bushes. You see, the way we does to shine the deer's eyes is this: we holds the pan so, on the left shoulder, and carries the gun at a trail in the right hand. Well, when I wants to look for eyes, I turns round slow, and looks right at the edge of my shadder, what's made by the light behind me in the pan, and if ther's a deer in gun-shot of me his eyes 'll shine 'zactly like two balls of fire."

This explanation was as clear as Sam could make it, short of a demonstration, for which purpose we now moved on through the woods. After proceeding a few hundred yards, Sam took a survey as described, but saw no eyes.

"Never mind, major," said he. "We'll find 'em; you'll see."

We moved on cautiously, and Sam made his observations as before, but with no better success. Thus we travelled on in silence from place to place, until I began to get weary of the sport.

"Well, Mr. Sikes," I remarked, "I don't see that your bad beginning to-night is likely to insure any better ending."

"Oh, don't git out of patience, major: you'll see."

We moved on again. I had become quite weary, and fell some distance behind. Sam stopped, and when I came up he said, in a low voice, "You better keep pretty close up, major, 'case if I should happen to shine your eyes, you see, I moughtn't know 'em from a deer, and old Betsey here totes fifteen buckshot and a ball, and slings 'em to kill."

I fell behind no more.

We had wandered about for several hours, and the sky, which had not been the clearest in the commencement, now began to assume the appearance of rain. I had more than once suggested the propriety of going home; but Sam was eager to show me how to shine the eyes of a buck, and no argument or persuasion could win him from his purpose. We searched on as before for another half-hour, and I was about to express my determination to go home, when Sam suddenly paused.

"Stop, stop," said he; "thar's eyes, and whappers they is, too. Now hold still, major."

I raised on tiptoe with eager anticipation. I heard the click of the lock; there was a moment of portentous silence, then the old musket blazed forth with a thundering report, and in the same instant was heard a loud squeal, and a noise like the snapping of bridle-reins.

"Thunder and lightnin'!" exclaimed Sam, as he dropped gun, pan, and all, and stood fixed to the spot; "I've shot old Blaze!"

So soon as he had recovered from the shock, we hastened to the spot, and, sure enough, there lay the luckless mule, still floundering in the agonies of death. The aim had been but too good, and poor Blaze was hurt " past all surgery." Sam stood over him in silent agony, and, notwithstanding the bitter maledictions he had so recently heaped upon him, now that he saw the poor animal stretched upon the ground in death, and knew that his " infernal picter" would greet him no more forever, a flood of tender recollections of past services poured over his repentant heart. He uttered not a word until after the last signs of life were extinct; then, with a heavy sigh, he muttered,—

"Pore old cretur! Well, well, I reckon I's done the business now, sure enough. That's what I calls a *pretty* night's work, anyhow!"

"A 'bad beginning doesn't always make a good ending,' Mr. Sikes," I remarked.

"Cuss the luck! it will run so, sometimes," said he, in a sullen tone, as he commenced taking the saddle off his deceased donkey. "I'm blamed if I see how I got so turned round."

By this time it had commenced to rain, and we were anxious to get home; but Sam had dropped his gun and pan as the awful truth rushed upon him that he had killed the only mule he possessed in the world, and we now found it difficult to recover them. After searching about for near half an hour in the drizzling rain, Sam chanced to come upon the spot from which he had taken the hapless aim, and, having regained his gun and pan, we endeavored to strike a fire: all our efforts, however, to produce a light proved ineffectual, and we essayed to grope our way amid the darkness.

"Hello, major: whar is you?"

"Here."

" Whar you gwine ?"

" Home."

" Well, that ain't the way."

" Why, we came this way."

" No, I reckon not."

" I'm sure we didn't come that way."

" Whar, in the devil's name, is the branch ?" petulantly inquired Sam. " If I could only see the branch, I could soon find the way."

" It must be down this way," I replied.

" Somehow or other I'm tetotatiously deluded to-night," remarked Sam, as he came tearing through the briers with his stirrup-irons dangling about him, his gun in one hand and frying-pan in the other. " If I hadn't 'a' been completely dumfoozled, I'd never 'a' killed Blaze like I did."

I volunteered to carry his gun, but he was in no humor for the interchange of civilities: " still harping" on his mule, he trudged on, grumbling to himself.

" What," he muttered, " will Polly say now ? I'll never hear the last of that critter, the longest day I live. That's worse than choppin' the coon-tree across the settin' hen's nest ; and I liked never to hearn the eend o' that."

After groping through the brush and briers, which seemed to grow thicker the farther we proceeded, for some time, Sam stopped.

" I swar, major, this ain't the way."

" Well, then, lead the way, and I'll follow you," I replied, beginning, myself, to think I was wrong.

Changing our direction, we plodded on, occasionally tumbling over logs and brush, until Sam concluded that all our efforts to find the way were useless.

" Oh, thunderation !" said he, as he tore away from a thick jungle of briers in which he had been rearing and pitching for more than a minute, " it ain't no manner of use for us to try to find the way, major: so let's look out a big tree and stop under it till morning."

Seeing no alternative, I reluctantly acceded to his proposal.

Accordingly, we nestled down under the shelter of a large oak. For a time neither spoke, and all was still, save the incessant buzz of the countless hosts of mosquitoes that now seemed intent upon devouring us. At length I broke silence, by remarking,—at the same time that I gave myself a box upon the ear, intended for the mosquito that was biting me,—

"I think this will be my last fire-hunt, Mr. Sikes."

"The fact is," replied Sam, "this 'ere ain't very incouragin' to new beginners, major, that's a fact; but you mus'n't give it up so. I hope we'll have a better showin' next time."

"My curiosity is satisfied," I remarked. "I wouldn't pass such another night in the woods for all the deer in Georgia."

"Pshaw, I wouldn't care a tinker's cuss," said Sam, "if I only jest hadn't killed Blaze. That's what sets me back, monstrous."

"That was indeed an unlucky mistake. I should think a few such exploits as that would cure you of your fire-hunting propensity. But I expect you never had such luck before to-night."

"No, not 'zactly; though I've had some monstrous bad luck in my time, too. I reckon you never hearn about the time I got among the panters?"

"No. How was that?"

"Why, it was 'bout this time last fall, I and Dudley went out and camped on Sperit Creek. Well, he took his pan and went out one way, and I went another. I went shinnin' along jest like you seed me to-night, till I got a

good bit from the camp, and bimeby, shore enough, I sees
eyes not more'n forty yards off. I fotched old Betsey up
to my face and cut loose, and the deer drapped right in
his tracks, but somehow in my hurryment I drapt my
pan, jest like I did to-night when I heard old Blaze squeal.
While I was tryin' to kindle up a light, what should I see
but more eyes shinin' way down in the holler! I drapt
the fire and loaded up old Betsey as quick as I could, to
be ready for the varmint, whatever it was. Well, the
eyes kep' comin' closer and closer, and gettin' bigger and
brighter, and the fust thing I knowed ther' was a whole
grist of 'em all follerin' right after the fust ones, and
dodgin' up and down in the dark like they was so many
dancin' devils. Well, I began to feel sort o' jubous of 'em,
so I raised old Betsey and pulled at the nearest eyes; but
she snapped. I primed her ag'in, and she flashed; and
when I flashed, sich another squallin' and yellin' you never
did hear, and up the trees they went all round me.
Thinks I, them must be somethin' unnatural, bein' as my
gun wouldn't shoot at 'em: so I jest drapt old Betsey, and
put out for the camp as hard as I could split. Well, we
went back the next mornin', and what do you think them
infernal critters had done?—eat the deer up slick and
clean, all but the bones and horns, and a little ways off lay
old Betsey, with four fingers of buckshot and bullets, but
not a bit of powder in her. Then I know'd they was
panters."

"Why, they might have eaten you too."

"That's a fact. Dudley said he wondered they didn't
take hold of me."

The drizzling shower which had already nearly wet us
to the skin now turned to a drenching storm, which continued for more than an hour without intermission. When
the storm abated, we discovered the dawn approaching,

and shortly after were enabled to ascertain our where-abouts. We were not more than five hundred yards from the clearing, and probably had not been, during the night, at a greater distance than a mile from the house which we had left in the evening.

As we stepped from the wood into the open road, I con-templated, for a moment, the ludicrous appearance of my unfortunate companion. Poor Sam! daylight, and the prospect of home, brought no joy to him; and as he stood before me, with the saddle and bridle of the deceased Blaze girded about his neck, his musket in one hand and pan in the other, drenched with rain, his clothes torn, and a countenance that told of the painful conflict within, I could not but regard him as an object of sympathy rather than ridicule.

" Well," said he, with a heavy sigh, and without looking me in the face, " good-mornin', major."

" Good-morning," I replied, touched with sympathy for his misfortune, and reproaching myself for the mirth I had enjoyed at his expense,—" good-morning, Mr. Sikes. I am very sorry for your loss, and hope you will have better luck in future."

" Oh, major," said he, " it ain't the vally of the mule that I mind so much ; though old Blaze was a monstrous handy cretur on the place. But thar's my wife : what'll she say when she sees me comin' home in this here fix ? How-somedever, what can't be cured must be endured, as the feller said when the monkey bit him."

" That's the true philosophy," I remarked, seeing that he endeavored to take courage from the train of reasoning into which he had fallen ; " and Mrs. Sikes should bear in mind that accidents *will* happen, and be thankful that it's no worse."

" To be sure she ought," replied Sam ; " but that ain't

the way with her: she don't believe in accidents, nohow;
and then she's so bowdacious unreasonable when she's
raised.   But she better not," he continued, with a stern
look as he spoke,—" she better not come a-cavortin' 'bout
me with any of her rantankerous carryin's-on this mornin',
for I ain't in no humor, nohow!"   And he made a threatening gesture with his head, as much as to say he'd make the
fur fly if she did.

. We parted at the gate, Sam for his home, and I for my
bed,—he sorely convinced that "a bad beginning" does
not *always* "make a good ending," and I fully resolved
that it should be my first and last FIRE-HUNT.

CAPTAIN CUTTLE'S ESCAPE.

JOHN BROUGHAM.

[John Brougham, the popular comedian, was a native of Ireland,
born in Dublin in 1810.   He came to the United States in 1842, where
he remained till his death in 1880.   In addition to his merit as an
actor, he wrote several comedies which achieved considerable success,
and a volume or two of stories of Irish life.   In another of his productions, " The Bunsby Papers," he brings Jack Bunsby and Captain
Cuttle, two of Dickens's characters, to New York, and describes their
adventures in the New World.   We give below the story of their
experience in a daguerrotype-gallery.]

As the Cap'n and me was a dubitatin' what we'd do
with ourselves, this morning, he suddenly started up, and
says,—

"Jack!"

"Ay, ay," says I.

"S'posin' we goes and gets our phisogs took off," says
he.

"How?" says I.

"Why, by the new light system. Them there derogatorytypes," says he.

"Werry well," says I. So off we went, in search of what they calls a hoperator. 'Twarn't long afore we bore down on a sign as give us to hunderstand sich things was a-doin' hup-stairs; hup-stairs we travelled, accordin'ly,—a wonderful high house it was, with stories enough to make a "Friendship's hofferin'." Howsomdever, arter two or three restin'-spells, we found ourselves right smack up at the sky-parlor, and a little beyond.

We had to take our time, in coorse, so down we sot, in a terrible light room for a bashful human, there bein' a whole heap o' people a-settin' as stiff as a lot o' Hegyptian mummies. As for the Cap'n, he'd scarcely look up off the ground, he was so took aback. Soon there came in a hard-lookin' chap, with a countenance like a ship's block, as had the measles bad, and he bowed and scraped, 'specially to the feminines,—the hartful scoundrel,—as consisted of two elderly females, dressed up to the nines, together with a squad of smaller speciments, hall curls and conceit.

When we'd been there about an hour and a half, the last batch of candidates for hexecution havin' bin drafted off, the Cap'n uplifted his voice for the first time, and says he,—

"Jack, old tar, shall we lie to, still, or 'bout ship?"

"I was towld this here description o' pictur'-takin' was done in a jiffy; and see how we've been a-wastin' o' the blessed moments as never kin come back to us. Come along. My name's O. P. H."

Jest at that time comes the lignum-witey-faced hoperator, and—

"Now, gentlemen," says he, "I'm ready."

With that the Cap'n divested himself of the tarpaulin,

and, runnin' o' his hook through his hair, for to give it a becomin' twist hover the bald, purceeded along with me to the hartist's sanctum snorum, both on us wonderin' how a feller could take your face off in a few sekinds o' time, as we'd heard they could.

When we got hinto the place, I looked around, but I couldn't see no paints nor brushes, nor no harticles as you hexpects to see in a hartist's hestablishment; there warn't nothin' but a bit o' a box on three legs, with a sort o' hovergrown gun-barrel a-peepin' out o' the middle, and on a table a whole cargo o' strong-smellin' physicky-lookin' combustickles.

The Cap'n was a-hangin' back, scared a trifle, I should say, by my own feelin's; for there warn't anybody in the hestablishment but us and the not-hover-pleasin'-faced individual as busied hisself about the dangerous-lookin' machine, hover in a dark corner. You see, we'd been readin' some o' them 'ere hawful books about the city and its diabolicals, and warn't altogether sartain that we hadn't got into a tight corner hunawares.

The Cap'n was the first to be hoperated hupon, and then he got a start in right earnest. The smilin' willan of a hoperator sot him down in a cheer, and as soon as he'd fixed his wenerable head by a-screwin' it on to a crooked piece of hiron, as it seemed to me, he goes to the hinfernal machine and p'ints it slap at the Cap'n's heyes. This was too much for him.

"Awast, mesmet!" he cried hout, a-shieldin' of his heyes with the hook. "Jest turn the muzzle o' that 'ere thing a little aside: I ain't a-goin' to stand no sich capers as that. I knows yer city tricks well.".

Would you believe it? the fellow laughed like a good 'un at the Cap'n, for he had pluck enough not to flinch afore the danger, though he did wink a little.

" You're not afraid, sir ?" says the indiwidual.

" Afraid !" says the Cap'n, a-givin' of his nose a contemptible toss; " that there hisland doesn't lie in my geehography ; but it rather *is* cool to be lookin' into the barrel of a new-fangled thingamy and not know what the creeter's loaded with."

" It ain't werry dangerous," says the fellow, who was hevidently henjoyin' the Cap'n's distress o' mind.

" What's in it, anyhow ?" says the Cap'n.

" Some'at as 'ill take your head off without hurting you in the least," says the other, with a nasty sort of a grin.

" That would be capital hexecution and no mistake," says the old tar, a-laughin' woraciously at his own joke, being more at his hease, by reason that the mouth of the hinstrument was covered with a brass plug ; besides which, it's a good way to swindle yourself into the belief that you're not frightened.

I was jest beginnin' to wonder why the chap didn't begin to chalk out the Cap'n, or how he was a-goin' to pictur' him at all, he bein' so busy with that there mysterious box, and not makin' no hapology to ne'ther of us for the delay, when the ruffian politely hinsinuated that I had better walk hout, which I did, but took care to keep my heye and hear at the door-crack.

" Now for it," I heard him say. " Are you prepared ?"

" In coorse I am," says the Cap'n, as patient as a lamb, " a-waitin' on your conwenience."

" Don't you wenture to stir, then," says he.

" Whatsomdever happens, I'm resigned," says the Cap'n, seein' the chap had his hand on the brass coverin', and not knowin' ezactly how to ward hoff the comin' catastrophe.

" Not a word," says he. Off came the plug, away went the hoperator, as bif to avoid the hexplosion, and there sot the courageous old wictim, expectin' of it to fire some'at at his nose hevery sekind.

It must 'a' been a hawful situation, judgin' from my own feelin' houtside. But the wagabone had some natur' left, for, jest as I was makin' up my mind to rush in and keel him hover and his machine together, he thought better of it, hinasmuch as he went hisself and shut up the thing, werry much to the Cap'n's relief, and no more to mine, bein' now conwinced that we'd stumbled upon one of them horrors as was so wiwidly depicted by the city historians as we'd been a-readin'. Arter a few minutes of terrible suspense, what should I see but the Cap'n a-movin' soft and cautious across the floor, like a big cat towards a canary, a-hopenin' the door quiet, and stealin' hout sagacious.

"Hush, Jack, old shipmet," says he, in a whisper; "make no sound;" then he crept silently away down one flight o' stairs, cut like blazes down the rest, and never breathed a comfortable breath until we were three or four streets hoff from the place.

When we felt ourselves safely away from the danger, I asked the Cap'n how he'd guv the rascal the slip, when he squeezed my hand as heloquent as a bushel of halphabets, as much as to say, "Thank heaven, we're here," and—

"Jack," says he, "we've had a huncommon narrow hescape. When I seed the warmint a-divin' into a black cubboard of a consarn, hevidently for the purpose of pro-curin' a fresh load o' combustickles, the first one havin' missed fire, I started quick. What's the use in fellows gas'n and purtendin' to hexpose the mysterious crimes o' this here metropolis, and never to say nothin' about that diabolical inwention?"

"It was a mercy it didn't go hoff," says I, "whatever it was stuffed with."

This I will say, and it's a dreadful thing to contemplate upon, that of all the poor wretches who went into that fearful den, *not one of 'em came out ag'in,*—as I could see. I mention this fact in horder that it may come to the hears of the hauthorities, so that if so be they have any time on hand that they can devote to the hinterests of the public, that they may be hinduced to take the subject into their serious consideration, and hendeavor, as in duty bound, to prewent their fellow-creeters from bein' taken hoff in such a houtrageous manner, in the wery face of the broad day-light.

SPECIMEN BRICKS.

VARIOUS.

[Of the humor "lying loose" around our country, North, South, East, and West, we gather a few specimen bricks, as examples of good building-material.]

THE HOOSIER AND THE SALT PILE.

"I'm sorry," said Dan, as he knocked the ashes from his regalia, as he sat in a small crowd over a glass of sherry, at Florence's, New York, one evening,—"I'm sorry that the stages are disappearing so rapidly. I never enjoyed travelling so well as in the slow coaches. I've made a good many passages over the Alleghanies, and across Ohio, from Cleveland to Columbus and Cincinnati, all over the South, down East, and up North, in stages, and I generally had a good time.

"When I passed over from Cleveland to Cincinnati, the last time, in a stage, I met a queer crowd. Such a *corps,*

such a time, you never did see. I never was better amused
in my life. We had a good team,—spanking horses, fine
coaches, and one of them drivers you read of. Well, there
was nine 'insiders,' and I don't believe there ever was a
stage full of Christians ever started before, so chuck full
of music.

"There was a beautiful young lady going to one of the
Cincinnati academies; next to her sat a Jew peddler,—for
Cowes and a market; wedging him in was a dandy black-
leg, with jewelry and chains around about his breast and
neck enough to hang him. There was myself, and an
old gentleman with large spectacles, gold-headed cane,
and a jolly, soldering-iron-looking nose; by him was a
circus-rider, whose breath was enough to breed yaller
fever and could be felt just as easy as cotton velvet! A
cross old woman came next, whose *look* would have given
any reasonable man the double-breasted blues before breakfast; alongside of her was a rale backwoods preacher, with
the biggest and ugliest mouth ever got up since the flood.
He was flanked by the low comedian of the party, an
Indiana hoosier, 'gwine down to Orleans to get an army
contract' to supply the forces then in Mexico with beef.

"We rolled along for some time. Nobody seemed inclined to 'open.' The old aunty sot bolt upright, looking
crab-apples and persimmons at the hoosier and the preacher;
the young lady dropped the green curtain of her bonnet
over her pretty face, and leaned back in her seat to nod
and dream over japonicas and jumbles, pantalets and
poetry; the old gentleman, proprietor of the Bardolph
nose, looked out at the corduroy and swashes; the gambler fell off into a doze, and the circus covey followed
suit, leaving the preacher and me *vis-à-vis* and saying nothing to nobody. 'Indiany' he stuck his mug out at the
window and criticised the cattle we now and then passed.

I was wishing somebody would give the conversation a start, when 'Indiany' made a break.

"'This ain't no great stock-country,' says he to the old gentleman with the cane.

"'No, sir,' says the old gentleman. 'Ther's very little grazing here, and the range is pretty much wore out.'

"Then there was nothing said again for some time. Bimeby the hoosier opened ag'in:

"'It's the d——dest place for simmon-trees and turkey-buzzards I ever did see!'

"The old gentleman with the cane didn't say nothing, and the preacher gave a long groan. The young lady smiled through her veil, and the old lady snapped her eyes and looked sideways at the speaker.

"'Don't make much beef here, I reckon,' says the hoosier.

"'No,' says the gentleman.

"'Well, I don't see how in h—ll they all manage to get along in a country whar thar ain't no ranges and they don't make no beef. A man ain't considered worth a cuss in Indiany what hasn't got his brand on a hundred head.'

"'Yours is a great beef country, I believe,' says the old gentleman.

"'Well, sir, it ain't anything else. A man that's got sense enuff to foller his own cow-bell with us ain't in no danger of starvin'. I'm gwine down to Orleans to see if I can't git a contract out of Uncle Sam to feed the boys what's been lickin' them infernal Mexicans so bad. I s'pose you've seed them cussed lies what's been in the papers about the Indiany boys at Bony Visty.'

"'I've read some accounts of the battle,' says the old gentleman, 'that didn't give a very flattering account of the conduct of some of our troops.'

"With that, the Indiany man went into a full explanation of the affair, and, gettin' warmed up as he went along, begun to cuss and swear like he'd been through a dozen campaigns himself. The old preacher listened to him with evident signs of displeasure, twistin' and groanin' till he couldn't stand it no longer.

" 'My friend,' says he, 'you must excuse me, but your conversation would be a great deal more interesting to me —and I'm sure would please the company much better— if you wouldn't swear so terribly. It's very wrong to swear, and I hope you'll have respect for our feelin's, if you hain't no respect for your Maker.'

"If the hoosier had been struck with thunder and light-nin', he couldn't have been more completely tuck aback. He shut his mouth right in the middle of what he was sayin', and looked at the preacher, while his face got as red as fire.

" 'Swearin',' says the old preacher, 'is a terrible bad practice, and there ain't no use in it, nohow. The Bible says, Swear not at all, and I s'pose you know the commandments about swearin'?'

"The old lady sort of brightened up,—the preacher was her 'duck of a man;' the old fellow with the nose and cane let off a few 'umph, ah! umphs;' but 'Indiany' kept shady: he appeared to be *cowed* down.

" 'I know,' says the preacher, 'that a great many people swear without thinkin', and some people don't b'lieve the Bible.'

"And then he went on to preach a regular sermon ag'in' swearing, and to quote Scripture like he had the whole Bible by heart. In the course of his argument he under-took to prove the Scriptures to be true, and told us all about the miracles and prophecies and their fulfilment. The old gentleman with the cane took a part in the conversation, and the hoosier listened, without ever opening his head.

" 'I've just heard of a gentleman,' says the preacher, 'that's been to the Holy Land and went over the Bible country. It's astonishin' to hear what wonderful things he has seen. He was at Sodom and Gomorrow, and seen the place whar Lot's wife fell.'

" 'Ah!' says the old gentleman with the cane.

" 'Yes,' says the preacher; 'he went to the very spot; and, what's the remarkablest thing of all, he seen the pillar of salt what she was turned into.'

" 'Is it possible!' says the old gentleman.

" 'Yes, sir: he seen the salt, standin' thar to this day.'

" 'What!' says the hoosier, 'real genewine, good salt?'

" 'Yes, sir, a pillar of salt, jest as it was when that wicked woman was punished for her disobedience.'

" All but the gambler, who was snoozing in the corner of the coach, looked at the preacher,—the hoosier with an expression of countenance that plainly told us that his mind was powerfully convicted of an important fact.

" 'Right out in the open air?' he asked.

" 'Yes; standin' right in the open field, whar she fell.'

" 'Well, sir,' says 'Indiany,' 'all I've got to say is, if she'd dropped in our parts, the cattle would have licked her up afore sundown!'

" The preacher raised both his hands at such an irreverent remark, and the old gentleman laughed himself into a fit of asthmatics, what he didn't get over till we came to the next change of horses. The hoosier had played the mischief with the gravity of the whole party: even the old maid had to put her handkerchief to her face, and the young lady's eyes were filled with tears for half an hour afterwards. The old preacher hadn't another word to say on the subject; but whenever we came to any place, or met anybody on the road, the circus-man nursed the thing along by asking what was the price of salt."

DANFORTH MARBLE.

[To the above Western yarn may be added the following incident from "away down South."]

"DOING" A SHERIFF.

Many persons in the county of Hall, State of Georgia, recollect a queer old customer who used to visit the county site regularly on "general muster" days and court week. His name was Joseph Johnson, but he was universally known as Uncle Josey. The old man, like many others of that and the present day, loved his dram, and was apt, when he got among "the boys" in town, to take more than he could conveniently carry. His inseparable companion on all occasions was a black pony, who rejoiced in the name of "General Jackson," and whose diminutiveness and sagacity were alike remarkable.

One day, while court was in session in the little village of Gainesville, the attention of the judge and bar was attracted by a rather unusual noise at the door. Looking towards that aperture, "his honor" discovered the aforesaid pony and rider deliberately entering the hall of justice. This, owing to the fact that the floor of the court-house was nearly on a level with the ground, was not difficult.

"Mr. Sheriff," said the judge, "see who is creating such a disturbance of this court."

"It's only Uncle Josey and Gin'ral Jackson, judge," said the intruder, looking up with a drunken leer,—"jest me an' the Gin'ral come to see how you an' the boys is gettin' along."

"Well, Mr. Sheriff," said the judge, totally regardless of the interest manifested in his own and the lawyers' behalf by Uncle Josey, "you will please collect a fine of ten dollars from Uncle Josey and the General, for contempt of court."

"Look a-here, judge, old feller," continued Uncle Josey, as he stroked the "Gin'ral's" mane, "you don't mean to say it, now, do yer? This child hain't had that much money in a coon's age; and as for the Gin'ral here, I know he don't deal in no kind of quine, which he hain't done, 'cept fodder and corn, for these many years."

"Very well, then, Mr. Sheriff," continued his honor: "in default of the payment of the fine, you will convey the body of Joseph Johnson to the county jail, there to be retained for the space of twenty-four hours."

"Now, judge, you ain't in right down good yearnest, is you? Uncle Josey hain't never been put into that there boardin'-house yet, which he don't want to be, neither," appealed the old man, who was apparently too drunk to know whether it was a joke or not.

"The sheriff will do his duty immediately," was the judge's stern reply, who began to tire of the old man's drunken insolence. Accordingly, Uncle Josey and the "Gin'ral" were marched off towards the county prison, which stood in a retired part of the village. Arriving at the door, the prisoner was commanded by the sheriff to "light."

"Look a-here, Jess, horse-fly, you ain't a-gwine to put yer old uncle Josey in there, is yer?"

"'Bliged to do it, Uncle Josey," replied the sheriff. "Ef I don't, the old man [the judge] will give me *goss* when I go back. I hate it powerful, but I must do it."

"But, Jess, couldn't you manage to let the old man git away? Thar ain't nobody here to see you. Now, do, Jess. You know how I *fit* for you in that last run you had 'longer Jim Smith, what like to 'a' beat you for sheriff, which he would 'a' done it, if it hadn't been for yer uncle Josey's influence."

"I know that, Uncle Josey, but thar ain't no chance. My oath is very p'inted against allowin' anybody to escape. So you must go in, 'cos thar ain't no other chance."

"I tell you what it is, Jess: I'm afeard to go in thar. Looks too dark and dismal."

"Thar ain't nothing in thar to hurt you, Uncle Josey, which thar hain't been for nigh about six months."

"Yes, thar is, Jess. You can't fool me that a-way. I know thar is somethin' in thar to ketch the old man."

"No, thar ain't; I pledge you my honor thar ain't."

"Well, Jess, if thar ain't, you jest go in and see, and show Uncle Josey that you ain't afeard."

"Certainly. I ain't afeard to go in."

Saying which, the sheriff opened the door, leaving the key in the lock. "Now, Uncle Josey, what did I tell you? I knowed thar wa'n't nothin' in thar."

"Maybe thar ain't whar you are standin'; but jest le's see you go up into that dark place in the corner."

"Well, Uncle Josey," said the unsuspecting sheriff, "I'll satisfy you thar ain't nothin' thar either." And he walked towards the "dark corner." As he did so, the old man dexterously closed the door and locked it.

"Hello, thar!" yelled the frightened officer; "none o' yer tricks, Uncle Josey. This is carryin' the joke a cussed sight too far."

"Joke! I ain't a-jokin', Jess: never was more in yearnest in my life. Thar ain't nothin' in thar to hurt you, though; that's one consolation. Jest hold on a little while, and I'll send some of the boys down to let you out."

And, before the "sucked-in" sheriff had recovered from his astonishment, the pony and his master were out of hearing.

Uncle Josey, who was not as drunk as he appeared, stopped at the grocery, took a drink, again mounted the "Gin'ral," and called the keeper of the grocery to him, at the same time drawing the key of the jail from his pocket. "Here, Jeems, take this 'ere key, and ef the old man or any them boys up thar at the court-house inquires after Jess Runion, the sheriff, jest you give 'em this key and my compliments and tell 'em Jess is safe. Ketch 'em takin' in old Uncle Josey, will yer? Git up, Gin'ral: these boys here won't do to trust: so we'll go into the country, whar people's honest, if they *is* poor."

The sheriff, after an hour's imprisonment, was released, and severely reprimanded by the judge, but the sentence of Uncle Josey was never executed, as he never troubled the court again, and the judge thought it useless to imprison him with any hope of its effecting the slightest reform.

T. A. Burke.

[The doings of a "Down-Easter" abroad come next in order.]

GAPE-SEED.

A Yankee, walking the streets of London, looked through a window upon a group of men writing very rapidly, and one of them said to him, in an insulting manner, "Do you wish to buy some gape-seed?" Passing on a short distance, the Yankee met a man, and asked him what the business of those men was in the office he had just passed. He was told that they wrote letters dictated by others, and transcribed all sorts of documents: in short, they were writers. The Yankee returned to the office, and inquired if one of the men would write a letter for him, and was answered in the affirmative. He asked the price, and was told one dollar. After considerable talk, the bargain was made,—one of the conditions of which was that the scribe should write just what the Yankee told him to, or he should receive no pay. The scribe told the Yankee he was ready to begin; and the latter said,—

"Dear marm," and then asked, "Have you got that deown?"

"Yes," was the reply. "Go on."

"I went to ride t'other day: have you got that deown?"

"Yes; go on, go on."

"And I harnessed up the old mare into the wagon: have you got that deown?"

"Yes, yes, long ago. Go on."

"Why, how fast you write! And I got into the wagon, and sat deown, and drew up the reins, and took the whip in my right hand: have you got that deown?"

"Yes, long ago; go on."

"Dear me! how fast you write! I never saw your equal. And I said to the old mare, 'Go 'long,' and jerked the reins pretty hard: have you got that deown?"

"Yes; and I am impatiently waiting for more. I wish you wouldn't bother me with so many foolish questions. Go on with your letter."

"Well, the old mare wouldn't stir out of her tracks, and I hollered, 'Go 'long, you old jade! go 'long.' Have you got that deown?"

"Yes, indeed, you pestersome fellow; go on."

"And I licked her, and licked her, and licked her"— [*continuing to repeat these words as rapidly as possible*].

"Hold on, there! I have written two pages of 'licked her,' and I want the rest of the letter."

"Well, and she kicked, and she kicked, and she kicked" —[*continuing to repeat these words with great rapidity*].

"Do go on with your letter; I have several pages of 'she kicked.'"

[*The Yankee clucks as in urging horses to move, and continues the clucking noise with rapid repetition for some time.*]

The scribe throws down his pen.

"Write it deown! write it deown!'

" I can't !"

" Well, then, I won't pay you."

[*The scribe, gathering up his papers.*] " What shall I do with all these sheets upon which I have written your nonsense ?"

"Ye may use them in doing up your *gape-seed.*   Good-by !"

ANONYMOUS.

VIXANNA DAW'S PROTÉGÉS.

SALLIE PRATT McLEAN.

[The author of the following selection has produced some of the best humorous work among our recent novelists. Her "Cape Cod Folks" is brimful of amusing situations and characters, and is well worthy a reading by all who enjoy a hearty laugh. The selection here given is from another of her works, "Towhead," the leading character being an orphan child, who is sent, with a servant, governess, and guardian, to the house of a friend in the country. The authoress, now Mrs. S. P. McL. Greene, was born at Simsbury, Connecticut, in 1858. She has written several other novels besides those above-named. "Cape Cod Folks" is partly descriptive of her own experiences while a teacher on the Massachusetts coast.]

THE spring was waking after a gorgeous fashion peculiar to the place when little Miss Bodurtha came to that particular section of Dymsbury, which, from its extensiveness and general air of inutility, had long been known to the country-people thereabouts as *Dymsbury Park.*

Little Miss Bodurtha had never known anything so

delightful as the drive from the railway-station to Dymsbury Park in Deacon Cadmus Pinchon's family wagon.
Change beatific! from the gloomy upholstery of curtained
coaches, and the profound rumble of aristocratic wheels,
to a world grown suddenly so illimitable, with its woods,
and fields, and mountains, and a perch on one of the
craziest, most enchanting old vehicles that ever rent the
pensive country air with its rattlings and groanings and
periodic shrieks.

"She needs ilein'," observed Job French, gravely. Job
French was known as the "chore-boy" at Deacon Cadmus
Pinchon's, and had been sent to fetch the company from
the dépôt. "She needs ilein'. The dekin's fust-rate on a
hoss-trade," he continued, "but I never bet on his wagins."

At this the supercilious look on the face of the German
governess, Miss Schomanhaufer, changed to one more resembling dismay; and Mr. Higgins, who, as little Miss
Bodurtha's guardian, was escorting her to her destination,
inquired somewhat anxiously,—

"But the wagon is puffectly safe, I presume, my good
boy?"

"I tell ye, I don't bet on 'em," the chore-boy replied, a
touch of asperity in his tone. "The dekin might ride
from Dam to Bissheby in this 'ere wagin and not bust a
screw, and then ag'in I've known 'em to fall all ter pieces
jest a-goin' to mill. I tell ye, I don't bet on 'em. But the
dekin never keeps a *hoss* but what *is* a hoss," he added,
reassuringly, after a moment's pause.

Mr. Higgins would have derived a ghastly satisfaction
from pursuing the subject with the boy, but Job French,
having, as he believed, said all that to any fairly sensible
mind could be said in regard to a horse and wagon, relapsed
into that taciturn silence which was habitual with him.

Mr. Higgins and Miss Schomanhaufer poised themselves

in attitudes studiously unconscious and at the same time suggestive of a readiness to leap. But poor old Excelluna, the serving-woman, the "drudge," at little Miss Bodurtha's side, sat perfectly motionless, like one in a happy dream.

Excelluna was gazing through her "fur-offs." This ancient serving-woman, by the way, possessed three pairs of spectacles endowed with such peculiar qualities of vision that she was accustomed to term them, respectively, her "nigh-tos," her "mejums," and her "fur-offs." The first-named, it may be said here, she employed for such occasional diversion as she found in reading; the second, for housework and general duty; the third, dearest and last, for such purely æsthetic delights as she derived from the contemplation of the scenery; and now her quaint eyes gazed afar, with such a rapt expression in them that little Miss Bodurtha was moved to ask, with wondering awe, "Is that where *God* lives, Luny?"

The child had unconsciously solved a growing mystery to Excelluna's mind. The simple creature gazed upon her as though verily she believed the little one inspired. "It are," she answered, almost inaudibly, nodding her head in solemn confirmation of her words. "Yis, ever and a darlin' orphing lamb,—for sech I call you,—it *are*, and I thank you for them words."

[The journey continued till they reached the deacon's house in the dusk of evening, where an ebon-hued woman stood awaiting them on the porch.]

Excelluna made a desperate search in her pocket for her mejums, but, adjusting her nigh-tos by mistake, the full effect of the vision was overpowering. "Somehow, some-wheres," she exclaimed, "I've seen that perdicious emblem of curiosity before! Vixanna Daw!"

At this, a significant gleam passed over the countenance

of the negress in the door-way. In what world and amid
what scenes these two had formerly beheld each other,
was not then divulged, but their wanderings had been
unspeakable, their experiences vast, and, in the present
crisis, their mutual gaze, which betrayed no warmer
emotion, was expressive neither of tolerance nor of animosity. "It's a co-ordinance," said Excelluna, solemnly.
"That's what it is. It's a co-ordinance."

The night was chill, and Vixanna Daw ushered the
travellers into a spacious apartment, where a table was
spread, and a fire burned on the hearth, and a company
of comely and extremely dirty children, reduced to a momentary condition of awe by the advent of the strangers,
stared at them open-mouthed. By this time the countenances of Mr. Higgins and Miss Schomanhaufer had assumed an aspect of considerable bewilderment.

"Ah," said Mr. Higgins, who was short-sighted, and had
not detected the Saxon fairness of the children underneath
their accidental coating of earth and molasses,—"ah," said
he, turning helplessly to Vixanna Daw, "you have a very
—a very—ah—elaborate family, Mrs. Pinchon. Where—
ah—is Deacon Cadmus Pinchon?"

"Massy sakes alive!" screamed Vixanna, dropping into
a chair and holding her sides in an uncontrollable fit of
laughter, "*I* ain't Miss Deacon Cadmus Pinchon,—I ain't.
Oh, Lawd! oh, Lawd!" she gasped, "*dis'll* kill me, sho'.
Hold on to me, somebody, 'fo' I busts myself. Oh, Lawd!
Oh, Lawd! But I *hab* allus been brought up in berry
pious fam'lies, dat's a fac'," she added, assuming with
marvellous quickness a composed and reassuring dignity
of demeanor. "I neber libed wid nuffin *less'n* a deacon,
'fo' de Lawd. Gen'ly it's been ministers; 'casionally a
Mefodist or 'Piscopal,—do, fo' myself, I's mo' inclined to
de Presbyteriums."

As Vixanna uttered these words in a truly mellifluous tone of voice, her face was expressive of sentiments the most exclusively orthodox, and, having set all the young Pinchons giggling by means of a covert wink, she next eyed them with a long gaze of heart-smitten reproach. "Chilluns," said she, "yo' do grieve me so'ly. Can't you 'member to follow yo' master's 'structions, allus to 'have yo'selves 'fo' company? But I was gwine to tell yo'," she continued, to her spell-bound audience, "how de folks all come to be gone.

"Yo' see, dese youngems, dey's allus *some* of 'em up to *somefin'*, and what should Cammus Junyah take into his head, dis berry arternoon, but he must run away to de Watkinses to play wid dem Watkins chilluns, dat's nuffin but a po' low fam'ly anyway; and he took his little sister Ruf wid 'im, dat's jes' the mos' gentle and 'missive little girl dat ebber was, but she allus min's what de las' pusson tells her las'. But Miss Deacon Cammus ag'in and ag'in she's posi'vely fo'bid de chilluns gwine to dem Watkinses to play; and only las' ebenin' I heard her say, 'Whatebber you does, chilluns, don' let me hear o' dat.' So when she 'skivered as dey was gone, she had mejit 'spicions o' wha' dey was, and she sent Vinny Noble—dat's Miss Pinchonses secon' girl," said Vixanna, parenthetically, with an accent of undisguised contempt—"fo' to look 'em up. Fo' dat Vinny Noble she nebber foun' anyfin' yet from mawnin' to sunset: but jist as soon as dey's anyfin' los' she's 'spatched fo' it 'mejit.

"Wall, co'se she went, and co'se she stayed; and bimeby I tol' Miss Deacon Cammus dat *sumfin'* had orter be done, and ef it wa'n't fo' all de 'ponsibility o' 'spectin' company, says I, 'I'd go and hunt dem chilluns up myse'f.'

"So den Miss Cammus say *she* was a-gwine,—and Miss Cammus *ain't* a berry fas' walker. She make a great fuss and stew 'bout gittin' along, Miss Cammus does, but some-how she's one o' dat kin' dat ain't nebber succeeded in gittin' ober much groun'.

" So bimeby, arter she's been gone a while, Deacon Cam-mus he come along, an' I tol' him how 'twas, an' says I, ' It's ra'ly gittin' time de case was 'tended to.' So den he started off; and Deacon Cammus allus has de bes' o' 'ten-tions, but I know dat jes' as like as not, 'fo' he git half a dozen rods, he fo'git w'at he started fo'; or ef he should meet somebody ter talk wid on the road, he'd nebber know how fas' de time flew.

" So bimeby 'Gusto Brown he come along; and *him* I can gen'ly 'pend on; an' says I, ' De 'mergency 's ra'ly gittin' pressin'.' So den he say he start right off, and he asks Miss Deacon Cumminses niece—dat's Miss Mollie Ebbelyn, dat's here visitin'—ef she wouldn't like ter walk along wid him, and she says yis : *so den I gibs 'em all up fo' sho'.*"

[By the favor of fortune the runaways got safely home in advance of the corps of searchers. After some very mild scolding the family prepared to partake of the evening meal, when little Miss Bodurtha was secretly invited by Cadmus Junior to take part in a less stately supper in the kitchen. She gladly consented, and followed him.]

Excelluna turned rather sharply on Cadmus Pinchon, Junior, " What do you mean," she exclaimed, " by bringin' *that* child into the kitching ?"

" Oh laws, now," interposed Vixanna Daw, " nebber min' wha' we eats, ef we's only libely and genteel. We're all 'ware o' de fac' dat dis chile's berry han'some and high-bo'n."

" She's a towhead," persisted Cadmus Junior, in pathetic vindication of his own crown, which glimmered with locks of a hue unmitigably red.

" Yo's a *putty* one to scoff at folks' ha'r, yo' is, Cammus Junyah!" retorted Vixanna, "and yo' own head jist a-bustin' out wid jedgment flame! Dat's w'at it is, cl'ar jedgment flame." . . .

"I's sorry not to hab any doxothology said ober dis yer meal," Vixanna remarked incidentally. "'Gusto Brown asks de most beautiful doxothology yo' ebber heerd, but since Miss Mòllie Ebbelyn come, he took a notion to eat in de odder room, do', 'fo' she come, he was gen'ly 'customed to eat with me and de chillun.—'Fo' Mista and Misses Pinchon,' says he, 'dey's berry good folks,' says he, 'but dey ain't de libeliest company dat ebber was. Dey ain't fo'mal 'zac'ly,' says he, 'nor yit dey ain't joc'lar.'"

"Who is Agusto Brown?" inquired Excelluna.

"Wall," replied Vixanna, suddenly assuming a mysterious air, "he's a 'nigma, dat's what he is. In odder words, Luny, dey's a mystery 'bout 'Gusto Brown. And I don't min' tellin' *yo'*, Luny, w'at 'Gusto Brown 'fided to me and de chilluns in de mos' strickes' privacy, dat he's no mo' nor less dan de eldes' son of a forrum juke. 'But I quarrelled wid de ol' juke, Vixy,' says he, 'w'ich 'counts fo' my bein' in dis kentry in such 'duced succumstances.' And he 'vealed to us his forrum name, dat de name o' dat Jummun gub'ness ain't *nuffin* to it."

"And what is Agusto Brown now?" inquired Excelluna, with implicit confidence.

"Wall," said Vixanna Daw, "jes' at pres'n' he's Deacon Cammus Pinchonses hi'd man. But he w'ars de mos' beautiful clo's, and he nebber wu'ks widout glubs on, and he's 'spectin' an apologum from de ol' juke, callin' ob 'im back, ebbery day of his life, 'Gusto Brown is."

Now, the good Excelluna revelled in mysteries. Her eyes rolled upon Vixanna Daw with a look of solemn exultation. "I knew there was something extraorjaner about that Agusto Brown the minute I set eyes on him," said she.

"I don' min' tellin' *yo'*, Luny," continued Vixanna, "dat de reason w'y 'Gusto Brown lef' de ol' juke was dis: de ol' juke wan'ed 'Gusto Brown to marry one o' dem furrum princesses wid a name dat 'Gusto Brown's hisself wasn't *nuffin* to it. 'But I couldn't,' says he. 'Why?' says I. ''Cos,' says 'Gusto Brown, 'my buzzums wasn't fi'd wid de holy spa'k ob lub.' But, 'tween yo' and 'me, Luny, it's my 'pinion dat 'Gusto Brown's pretty much in lub now wid Miss Mollie Ebbelyn, and she wid him, do' she's a mos' drefful case to flirt, Miss Mollie is; and 'Gusto Brown carries hisse'f so high and ca'm, dey's no tellin' allus wa't his 'motions is. And Miss Mollie's nuffin' but de daughter ob a Presbyterium minister: dat ain't no great ketch, to be sho', fo' sech a figga as 'Gusto Brown, and he eldes' son ob a forrum juke."

"It appeared to me," said Excelluna, investing this splendid romance with a sudden dark suggestion of tragedy,—"it appeared to me jest afore supper that Mr. Higgins was a-makin' up to Mrs. Deking Cadmuses niece and Miss Shoe-mine-off-ear was a-makin' up to Agusto Brown."

"Oh, laws, Luny," exclaimed Vixanna Daw, highly amused. "Yo' ain't had much ob de 'sper'ences ob lub, ef you tinks dey's anyfin' to dat. Dey's only jes' a-playin' off. *Lub*, Luny," said Vixanna, suddenly wearing an air of supreme significance, "'s like dis yer 'lasses dat I'm a-flowin' onto my mush. It's sweet, Luny, but it's 'stremely 'pricious; it's 'stremely 'pricious."

Vixanna Daw sat at the head of the table and dispensed the steaming oatmeal mush with a long iron spoon, like one who wields a royal though blithe prerogative. The little Pinchons had individual molasses-cups. They laughed, they shouted, they dabbled with their fingers in that sweet refection. Little Miss Bodurtha had never been so happy. She suddenly evinced qualities calculated to cope in every instance with those youthful Pinchons. She consumed her food from the palm of her dainty hand. Ripples and peals of laughter fell from her rosy lips. At her delight tears of sympathetic joy rolled down Excelluna's cheeks. . . .

After the banquet, little Miss Bodurtha was abducted from these charming companions and led into the parlor, from which she was again speedily rescued by the dauntless Cadmus Junior, and introduced to the most marvellous, the most unspeakable wanderings with the little Pinchons, in the cellar, in the garret, through the mysteries of a great gloomy old barn, preceded by Vixanna Daw, with her lantern, and followed by the wondering and helpless Excelluna.

Then there was the enchanting period during which Vixanna peeped through an aperture in the floor over the parlor, known as the "dummy-hole," and regaled her hearers with a choice, if not veracious, account of what was going on in the room below. Vixanna had besought the privilege of using Excelluna's fur-offs for this purpose, and such an admission of advanced years on her part, as well as the recognition of the subtle qualities of Excelluna's spectacles, had made the latter a more willing votary of her crime. But Vixanna Daw had no need of spectacles. They became entangled in the meshes of her curly hair, while she stretched herself flat on the floor, save for a slight elevation of the heels at one extreme and an immersion of the head in the dummy-hole at the other, which order was occasionally reversed, as she recounted to her audience, in a muffled whisper, the result of her observations:

"It's jes' as I 'spected, chilluns; we's jes' in de nick o' time. 'Gusto Brown and dat Jummum gub'ness am a-settin' on de sofy by de winder, lookin' at de phogertrapha'bums, and Miss Mollie and Mista Higgins dey's a-settin' on de sofy by de grate, flirtin' fit to make yo' ha'r stan' on end.

"And 'Gusto Brown he's a-'havin' rale p'lite, but he looks kinda wore out, and once in a w'ile his eyes shoots over dreffel to'ds Miss Mollie. But Miss Mollie and Mista Higgins dey keeps on a-flirtin' fit to make yo' ha'r stan' on end."

"*Where is Deking Cadmus Pinchon?*" inquired Excelluna, very gravely.

"He's jes' gone out to hunt de chilluns up, to bring 'em in to pra'rs," responded Vixanna.

"And where is *Miss* Deking Cadmus Pinchon?" inquired Excelluna.

"She's a-settin' by de centa-table, readin' de New York R'ligious 'Bserver," answered Vixanna.

Gradually Vixanna's head sank lower and lower into the dummy-hole. The resurrections became less frequent, and endured for briefer periods of time. "Mista Higgins he's talkin' in dat voice o' his dat soun's jes' like de po'k a-cripsin' in de bottom o' de pot, only mo' sof'. Miss Mollie's a-flirtin' dreff'ul.

"Mista Higgins say he's nuffin but a po' f'lo'n bachelum, gwine back to his lonely home in de great city. Don' she t'ink Miss Mollie gib 'im one kiss to take back wid 'im, when he hab to go back all alone on de midnight owltrain?

"Den would she be mo'tally 'fended ef he steal one?"

Vixanna's head made one brief reappearance, and then sank hopelessly from view.

"He'p me up, chilluns!" she exclaimed, weakly at last. "He'p me up, chilluns!" And, as she rose, she wore an aspect impressively silent and awful.

"Vixanna Daw," slowly ejaculated Excelluna, "did that Mr. Higgins—did he kiss Miss Deking Cadmus Pinchonses niece?"

"Luny," returned Vixanna Daw, with equal solemnity, "I swa' to de immo'tal Moses, an' ef I was on my dyin' bed I couldn't say no different, dat *jes' at dat p'int I shet my eyes.* Come, chilluns, le's all go down to pra'rs."

THE SEXTON AND THE THERMOMETER.

WILLIAM ALLEN BUTLER.

[William Allen Butler, the author of the well-known and at one time highly-popular poem "Nothing to Wear," was born at Albany, New York, in 1825. He is a lawyer by profession, but has written a considerable number of poems, grave and gay, all good in their way. We append an example of his humorous productions, less long-drawn-out than the poetic legend of Flora McFlimsey.]

A BUILDING there is, well known, I conjecture,
To all the admirers of church architecture,
Flaunting and fine, at the head of Broadway,
Cathedral-like, gorgeous, and Gothic, and gay,
Soaring sublimely, just as it should,
With its turrets of marble, and steeple of wood,
And windows so brilliant and polychromatic,
Through which the light wanders with colors erratic,—
Now golden and red on the cushions reposes,
Now yellow and green on parishioners' noses;
While, within and without, the whole edifice glitters
With grandeur in patches, and splendor in fritters,
With its parsonage "fixed" in the style of the Tudors,
And, by way of example to all rash intruders,

Its solid dead wall, built up at great labor
To cut off the windows cut out by its neighbor,—
An apt illustration, and always in sight,
Of the way that the Church sometimes shuts out the Light!

Now, it chanced at the time of the present relation,
Not a century back from this generation,
When, just as in these days, the world was divided,
And some people this way and that way decided,
And like silly questions the public was vexed on,
One DIGGORY PINK of this church was the sexton.
None of your sextons grave, gloomy, and gruff,
Bell-ringers, pew-openers, takers of snuff,
 Dusters of cushions and sweepers of aisles,
But a gentleman sexton, ready enough
 For bows and good manners, sweet speeches and smiles;
A gentleman, too, of such versatility,
In his vocation of so much agility,
Blest with such wit and uncommon facility,
That his sextonship rose, by the means he invented,
To a post of importance quite unprecedented.

 No mere undertaker was he, or, to make
The statement more clear, for veracity's sake,
There was nothing at all he did *not* undertake;
Discharging at once such a complex variety
Of functions pertaining to genteel society,
As gave him with every one great notoriety;
Blending his care of the church and the cloisters
With funerals, fancy balls, suppers and oysters,
Dinners for aldermen, parties for brides,
And a hundred and fifty arrangements besides;
Great as he was at a funeral, greater
As master of feasts, purveyor, *gustator,*

Little less than the host, but far more than the waiter.
Very brisk was his business, because, in advance,
Pink was sure of his patron whatever might chance.
If the turtle he served agreed with him, then
At the next entertainment he fed him again;
If it killed him, Pink grieved at the sudden reversal,
But, shifting his part, with a rapid rehearsal,
With all that was richest in pall and in plumes,
Conveyed him, in state, to the grandest of tombs.
Thus whatever befell him, gout, fever, or cough,
It was Pink, in reality, carried him off,—
The magical Pink, as well skilled in adorning
The houses of feasting as houses of mourning,
For 'twas all the same thing, on his catholic plan,
If he laid out the money or laid out the man.
But most with the ladies his power was supreme;
Of disputing his edicts nobody would dream,
For 'twas generally known that Pink kept the key
Of the very selectest society;
Parvenus bribed him to get on his list;
Woe to the man whom his fiat dismissed!
The best thing he could do was to cease to exist,
And retire from a world where he wouldn't be missed.

Thus, plying all trades, but still keeping their balance
By his quick, ready wit and pre-eminent talents,
His life might present, in its manifold texture,
An emblem quite apt of the church architecture,
Which unites, in its grouping of sculpture and column,
A great deal that is comic with much that is solemn.

One Sunday, Friend Pink, who all night had been kept
At a ball in the Avenue, quite overslept,

And though to the church instanter he rushed,
His breakfast untasted, his beaver unbrushed,
He reached it so late that he barely had time
To kindle the fires, when a neighboring chime
(For 'tis thus that all church-bells must figure in rhyme)
Proclaimed that the hour for the service was near;
And, as ill luck would have it, though sunny and clear,
'Twas the coldest of all the cold days in the year.

Poor Pink, if some artist, with pencil or pen,
Had been on the spot to sketch him just then,
As bewilderment drove him first here and then there,
From chancel and transept to gallery stair,
Now down in the vaults, and now out in the air,
Might have stood as a model of Utter Despair,
Whose crowning expression his countenance wore
As he paused, for a moment, within the grand door,
And glanced at a gentleman, portly and neat,
Advancing quite leisurely up from Tenth Street.
" Mr. Foldrum is coming; oh! what shall I do?
He's got a thermometer hung in his pew!
As sure as it's there, and the mercury in it,
He'll find what the temperature is in a minute;
And, being a vestryman, isn't it clear
That minute will cost me a thousand a year?"

But luck, luck, wonderful luck!
Which never deserts men of genius and pluck,
No matter how deep in the mire they are stuck,
In this very crisis of trouble and pain,
With a brilliant idea illumined his brain;
Down the aisle, like a cannon-ball, Diggory flew,
Snatched the thermometer out of the pew,

And then plunged it, bodily, into the fire
Of the nearest furnace, just by the choir;
Soon to 100 the mercury rose,
And Pink, stealing quietly back on tiptoes,
Hung it up stealthily on the brass nail,
Just as Foldrum was entering, under full sail.

The church was as chilly and cold and cavernous
As the regions of ice round the shores of Avernus;
Like icebergs, pilasters and columns were gleaming,
While pendants and mouldings seemed icicles streaming.
Foldrum shivered all over, and really looked blue,
As he opened the door and went into his pew,
Then, clapping his spectacles firmly his nose on,
Took down the thermometer, surely supposing
The glass would be cracked, and the mercury frozen.
  No such thing at all; but, surprising to view,
  The mercury stood at 72!

It had never deceived him, that great regulator,
Not once to the atmosphere proved itself traitor;
Had it fallen to zero on the equator,
 He had shivered all over and doubted it not;
Or if, upon Greenland's iciest shore,
It had happened to rise to 80, or more,
 Had thrown off his bearskin and swore it was hot.
"Place me," might he cry, with the poet of old,
"In the hottest of heat or the coldest of cold,
On Libyan sands, or Siberian barren height,
You never shall shake my faith in my Fahrenheit!"

'Twas charming to see, then (Pink watched him with care),
What a wonderful change came over his air,—

How he rubbed both his hands, and a genial glow
Came flooding his cheeks like a sunbeam on snow;
How quickly he doffed both his scarf and his coat,
Unbuttoned his waistcoat down from the throat,
And, stifling a sort of shiver spasmodic,
With assumptions of warmth, very clear and methodic,
And with all sorts of genial and satisfied notions,
With fervor engaged in the usual devotions.
   Just then enter Doldrum,
    Who sits behind Foldrum,
And gauges himself, from beginning to end
Of the year, by his old thermometrical friend,
Well knowing that he takes his practical cue
From the mercury hanging up there in his pew,
And can't make the mistakes that some people do.
So off goes *his* pilot-cloth, spite of the cold or
A twinge of rheumatics in his left shoulder;
'Twas freezing, 'twas dreadful, it must be confessed,
But there sat Squire Foldrum, who surely knew best,
With his overcoat off and an unbuttoned vest!
What's mercury made for, except by its ranges
To declare, without fail, atmospherical changes?

At the door the friends met. "Cold in church, was it
  not?"
Says Doldrum. "Oh, no! on the contrary, hot;
Thermometer 70; with these high ceilings
You must go by the mercury,—can't trust your feel-
  ings.
Take a glass, after dinner, of old Bourbon whiskey,
Nothing like it to keep the blood active and frisky,
If you're cold; but the air was quite spring-like and
  mellow;
Why, Doldrum, you're growing old fast, my dear fellow!"

But on Tuesday the joke was all over the town;
Pink enjoyed it so much that he noted it down,
And, thinking it shouldn't be laid on the shelf,
At the risk of his place, he told it himself,
To one of the vestry, to use at discretion,
And in very short time 'twas in public possession.
Foldrum heard of it, too; saw how it was done,
And felt that he owed the sexton one.
Next Sunday he paid him. "Pink," said he,
"I owe you a dollar: here, take your fee."
"A dollar, sir? no, sir; what for, if you please?"
"*For raising the mercury forty degrees!*
Extra service like this deserves extra pay,
Especially done, as this was, on Sunday.
So pocket the cash, without further remark,
But, Pink, for the future, just mind and keep dark."
"Thank you, sir," said the sexton; "I'm not a dull scholar:
So, if you take the joke, why, I'll take the dollar!"

UNDEVELOPED GENIUS.

JOSEPH C. NEAL.

[We have already given a short extract from "Charcoal Sketches,"
and add the following biographical description of genius nipped in the
bud,—or spoiled in the baking. It cannot be said that our author's
humor is very rich in conception or delicate in finish, and the ensuing
selection is presented only in consideration of the former great popularity of Neal's humorous writings.]

P. PILGARLICK PIGWIGGEN, ESQ., as he loves to be styled,
is one of these unfortunate undeveloped gentlemen-about-
town. The arrangement of his name shows him to be no

common man. Peter P. Pigwiggen would be nothing, except a hailing title to call him to dinner, or to insure the safe arrival of dunning letters and tailors' bills. There is as little character about it as about the word *towser*, the individuality of which has been lost by indiscriminate application. To all intents and purposes, he might just as well be addressed as "You Pete Pigwiggen," after the tender maternal fashion in which, in his youthful days, he was required to quit dabbling in the gutter, to come home and be spanked. But

P. Pilgarlick Pigwiggen, Esq.—

the aristocracy of birth and genius is all about it. The very letters seem tasselled and fringed with the cobwebs of antiquity. The flesh creeps with awe at the sound, and the atmosphere undergoes a sensible change, as at the rarefying approach of a supernatural being. It penetrates the hearer at each perspiratory pore. The dropping of the antepenultimate in a man's name, and the substitution of an initial therefor, has an influence which cannot be defined,—an influence peculiarly strong in the case of P. Pilgarlick Pigwiggen,—the influence of undeveloped genius, analogous to that which bent the hazel rod, in the hand of Dousterswivel, in the ruins of St. Ruth, and told of undeveloped water.

But to avoid digression, or rather to return from a ramble in the fields of nomenclature, P. Pilgarlick Pigwiggen is an undeveloped genius,—a wasted man; his talents are like money in a strong box, returning no interest. He is, in truth, a species of Byron in the egg; but, unable to chip the shell, his genius remains unhatched. The chicken moves and faintly chirps within, but no one sees it, no one heeds it. Peter feels the high aspirations and the mysterious imaginings of poesy circling about the interior of his cranium; but there they stay. When he attempts to give them utterance, he finds that nature forgot to bore out the passage which carries thought to the tongue and to the finger-ends; and, as art has not yet found out the method of tunnelling or of driving a drift into the brain, to remedy such defects and act as a general jail-delivery to the prisoners of the mind, his divine conceptions continue pent in their osseous cell. In vain does Pigwiggen sigh for a *splitting* headache,—one that shall ope the sutures and set his fancies free; in vain does he shave his forehead and turn down his shirt-collar, in hope of finding the poetic vomitory and of leaving it clear of impediment; in vain does he drink vast quantities of gin to raise the steam so high that it may burst imagination's boiler and suffer a few drops of it to escape; in vain does he sit up late o' nights, using all the cigars he can lay his hands on, to smoke out the secret. 'Tis useless all. No sooner has he spread the paper, and seized the pen to give bodily shape to airy dreams, than a dull dead blank succeeds. As if the flourish of the quill were the crowing of a " rooster," the dainty Ariels of his imagination vanish. The feather drops from his checked fingers, the paper remains unstained, and P. Pilgarlick Pigwiggen is still an undeveloped genius.

Originally a grocer's boy, Peter early felt that he had a soul above soap and candles, and he so diligently nursed it with his master's sugar, figs, and brandy, that early one morning he was unceremoniously dismissed with something more substantial than a flea in his ear. His subsequent life was passed in various callings; but, call as loudly as they would, our hero paid but little attention to their voice. He had an eagle's longings, and, with an inclination to stare the sun out of countenance, it was not to be expected that he would stoop to be a barn-yard fowl.

Working when he could not help it, at times pursuing
check speculations at the theatre doors, by way of turning an honest penny, and now and then gaining entrance
by crooked means, to feed his faculties with a view of the
performances, he likewise pursued his studies through all
the ballads in the market, until qualified to read the pages
of Moore and Byron. Glowing with ambition, he sometimes pined to see the poet's corner of our weekly periodicals graced with his effusions. But, though murder may
out, his undeveloped genius would not. Execution fell so
far short of conception that his lyrics were invariably
rejected.

Deep, but unsatisfactory, were the reflections which
thence arose in the breast of Pigwiggen.

"How is it," said he,—"how is it I can't level down my
expressions to the comprehension of the vulgar, or level
up the vulgar to a comprehension of my expressions?
How is it I can't get the spigot out, so my verses will run
clear? I know what I mean myself, but nobody else does,
and the impudent editors say it's wasting room to print
what nobody understands. I've plenty of genius,—lots of
it, for I often want to cut my throat, and would have done
it long ago, only it hurts. I'm chock full of genius, and
running over; for I hate all sorts of work myself, and all
people mean enough to do it. I hate going to bed, and I
hate getting up. My conduct is very eccentric and singular. I have the miserable melancholies all the time, and
I'm pretty nearly always as cross as thunder, which is a
sure sign. Genius is as tender as a skinned cat, and flies
into a passion whenever you touch it. When I condescend
to unbuzzum myself, for a little sympathy, to folks of
ornery intellect,—and, caparisoned to me, I know very few
people that aren't ornery as to brains,—and pour forth the
feelings indigginus to a poetic soul, which is always biling,

they ludicrate my sitiation, and say they don't know what
the deuce I'm driving at. Isn't genius always served o'
this fashion in the earth, as Hamlet, the boy after my own
heart, says? And when the slights of the world, and of
the printers, set me in a fine frenzy, and my soul swells
and swells, till it almost tears the shirt off my buzzum,
and even fractures my dickey,—when it expansuates and
elevates me above the common herd,—they laugh again,
and tell me not to be pompious. The poor plebinians and
worse than Russian serfs!—It is the fate of genius; it is
his'n—or rather, I should say, her'n—to go through life
with little sympathization and less cash. Life's a field of
blackberry- and raspberry-bushes. Mean people squat
down and pick the fruit, no matter how they black their
fingers; while genius, proud and perpendicular, strides
fiercely on, and gets nothing but scratches, and holes torn
in its trousers. These things are the fate of genius; and
when you see 'em, there is genius too, although the editors
won't publish its articles. These things are its premoni-
tories, its janissaries, its cohorts, and its consorts.

"But yet, though in flames in my interiors, I can't get
it out. If I catch a subject, while I am looking at it, I
can't find words to put it in. Sometimes I have plenty of
words, but then there is either no ideas, or else there is
such a waterworks and catarack of them that when I catch
one the others knock it out of my fingers. My genius is
good, but my mind is not sufficiently manured by 'ears."

[We shall spare the reader the infliction of following the career of
P. Pilgarlick to its inevitable termination,—arrest for debt at the
suit of his landlady,—with the usual hard-heartedness of the judge
destitute of a soul for poesy and appreciation of genius in the bud.
As he has no money, and can get no bail, he suffers the fate of the
days of imprisonment for debt, and finds his body locked up as firmly
as his poetic soul has been.]

Alas! Pilgarlick knew that his boat was past bailing. Few are the friends of genius in any of its stages; very few are they when it is undeveloped. He therefore consented to sojourn in "Arch west of Broad," until the whitewashing process could be performed, on condition he were taken there by the "alley-way;" for he still looks ahead to the day when a hot-pressed volume shall be published by the leading booksellers, entitled "Poems, by P. Pilgarlick Pigwiggen, Esq."

COLONEL CRICKLEY'S HORSE.

HENRY HOWARD PAUL.

["Out West" is brimful of good stories. Some of these overflow to the East. We have caught one of these on its floating journey, and place it upon record here.]

I HAVE never been able to ascertain the origin of the quarrel between the Crickleys and the Drakes. They had lived within a mile of each other in Illinois for five years, and from the first of their acquaintance there had been a mutual feeling of dislike between the two families. Then some misunderstanding about the boundary of their respective farms revealed the latent flame; and Colonel Crickley, having followed a fat buck all one afternoon and wounded him, came up to him and found old Drake and his sons cutting him up. This incident added fuel to the fire, and from that time there was nothing the two families did not do to annoy each other. They shot each other's ducks in the river, purposely mistaking them for wild ones, and then, by way of retaliation, commenced killing off each other's pigs and calves.

One evening Mr. Drake the elder was returning home with his pocket full of rocks, from Chicago, whither he had been to dispose of a load of grain.

Sam Barston was with him on the wagon, and, as they approached the grove which intervened between them and Mr. Drake's house, he observed to his companion, "What a beautiful mark Colonel Crickley's old roan is over yonder!"

"Hang it!" muttered old Drake, "so it is."

The horse was standing under some trees, about twelve rods from the road.

Involuntarily Drake stopped his team. He glanced furtively around, then with a queer smile the old hunter took up his rifle from the bottom of the wagon, and, raising it to his shoulder, drew a sight on the colonel's horse.

"Beautiful!" muttered Drake, lowering his rifle with the air of a man resisting a powerful temptation. "I could drop old roan so easy."

"Shoot," suggested Sam Barston, who loved fun in any shape.

"No, no; 'twouldn't do," said the old hunter, glancing cautiously round him again.

"I won't tell," said Sam.

"Wal, I won't shoot this time anyway, tell or no tell. If he was fifty rods off instead of twelve, so there'd be a bare possibility of mistaking him for a deer, I'd let fly. As it is, I'd give the colonel five dollars for a shot."

At that moment the colonel himself stepped from behind a big oak not half a dozen paces distant, and stood before Mr. Drake.

"Well, why don't you shoot?"

The old man stammered in some confusion, "That you,

colonel?   I—I was tempted to, I declare.   And, as I said,
I'll give five dollars for one pull."

"Say ten, and it's a bargain!"

Drake felt of his rifle, and looked at old roan.

"How much is the hoss wuth?" he muttered in Sam's
ear.

"About fifty.'"

"Gad, colonel, I'll do it."

The colonel pocketed the ten, muttering, "Hanged if I
thought you'd take me up!"

With high glee the old hunter put a fresh cap on his
rifle, stood up in his wagon, and drew a close sight on old
roan. Sam Barston chuckled. The colonel put his hand
before his face and chuckled too.

Crack! went the rifle. The hunter tore out a horrid
oath, which I will not repeat. Sam was astonished. The
colonel laughed. Old roan never stirred.

Drake stared at his rifle with a face black as Othello's.

"What's the matter with you, hey? First time you
ever sarved me quite such a trick, I swan!" And Drake
loaded the piece with great wrath and indignation.

"People said you'd lost your trick of shooting," observed
the colonel, in a cutting tone of satire.

"Who said so? It's a lie!" thundered Drake. "I can
shoot—a horse at ten rods! Ha! ha!"

Drake was livid.

"Look yere, colonel, I can't stand that," he began.

"Never mind; the horse can," sneered the colonel. "I'll
risk you." Grinding his teeth, Drake produced another
ten-dollar bill.

"Here!" he growled, "I'm bound to have another shot,
anyway."

"Crack away!" cried the colonel, pocketing the note.

Drake did crack away,—with deadly aim, too,—but the

horse did not mind the bullet in the least. To the rage and unutterable astonishment of the hunter, old roan looked him right in the face as if he rather liked the fun.

"Drake," cried Sam, "you're drunk! A horse at a dozen rods!—oh, my eye!"

"Just you shut your mouth, or I'll shoot you!" thundered the excited Drake. "The bullet was hollow, I'll swear. The man lies who says I can't shoot! Last week I cut off a goose's head at fifty rods, and kin dew it again. By the Lord Harry, colonel, you can laugh, but I'll bet now thirty dollars I can bring down old roan at one shot."

The wager was readily accepted. The stakes were placed in Sam's hands. Elated by the idea of his two tens and making another ten into the bargain, Drake carefully selected a perfect ball and even buckskin patch, and beaded his rifle.

It was now nearly dark, but the old hunter boasted of being able to shoot a bat on the wing by starlight, and without hesitation drew a clear sight on old roan's head.

A minute later Drake was driving through the grove, the most enraged and most desperate of men. His rifle, innocent victim of his ire, lay with broken stock on the bottom of the wagon. Sam Barston was too much frightened to laugh. Meanwhile, the gratified colonel was rolling on the ground convulsed with mirth, and old roan was standing undisturbed under the trees.

When Drake reached home, his two sons, discovering his ill humor and the mutilated condition of his rifle-stock, hastened to arouse his spirit with a piece of news which they were sure would make him dance for joy.

"Clear out!" growled the angry old man. "I don't want to hear any news; get away, or I shall knock one of you down."

"But, father, it's such a trick!"

"Confound you and your tricks!"

"Played off on the colonel."

"On the colonel?" beginning to be interested. "Gad! if you've played the colonel a trick, let's hear it."

"Well, father, Jed and I went out this afternoon for deer."

"Hang the deer! Come to the trick."

"Couldn't find any deer, but thought we must shoot something: so Jed banged away at the colonel's old roan, —shot him dead."

"Shot old roan!" thundered the hunter. "By the Lord Harry, Jed, did you shoot the colonel's hoss?"

"True, sir, true."

"Devil!—devil!" groaned the hunter.

"And then," pursued Jed, confident that the joke part of the story must please his father, "Jim and I propped the horse up and tied his head back with a cord, and left him standing under the trees exactly as if he was alive."

"Ha! ha! Fancy the colonel going to catch him! Ho! ho! ho!—wasn't it a joke?"

Old Drake's head fell upon his breast. He felt of his empty pocket-book, and looked at his broken rifle. Then in a rueful tone he whispered to the boys,—

"It is a joke! But if you ever tell of it, or if you do, Sam Barston, I'll skin you alive! By the Lord Harry, boys, I've been shooting at that dead horse half an hour, at ten dollars a shot!"

At that moment Sam fell into the gutter. Jed dragged him out insensible. Sam had laughed himself almost to death

PANAMA AND THE BEAR.

ED. MOTT.

[The following story, from the " Pike County Folks" of Ed. Mott, is not offered as a specimen of refined Americanism. Pike County folks are not refined. But as a genuine " Pike" it will pass muster, and the discomfiture of the "old settler," who could draw the long bow with a strong hand himself, but did not like rivalry, is worthy of reproduction.]

" I DON'T suppose there s any one here who would ever think of doubting the word of old Squire Overfed, is there?" inquired the sheriff.

" Why?" promptly responded the old settler, straightening up in his chair. It was plain that he had a suspicion in his mind, but did not care to act upon it without further information.

" Well," said the sheriff, " the last time I saw the squire he told me a very remarkable story, and——"

" That's it," shouted the old settler. " Thar you be! I knowed it, boys; b'gosh, I knowed it! He's gointer spring a lie ag'in' us ez'll make Annynias and Sapiry turn over, an' he wants to lay it to poor ole Squire Overfed,—poor ole Squire Overfed, ez is ben playin' on a harp fur twenty year, an' never tole a lie in his life. Gosht'lmighty! It makes me wish I'd 'a' ben born a—well, born a temper'nce-lect'rer, boys, an' was here a-sayin' ' Tech not, taste not, handle not,' 'stead o' gittin' up, as I'm gointer, an' sayin', ' Yes, b'gosh, boys, I'll jine ye!' "

" But this story is a ripper," said the sheriff, after they had all sat down again, " and if anybody else had told it but the old squire I'd have been a little shaky of it. As near as I can remember it, there was a family named Mushback lived over back of Ball Hill——"

"Look a yer, shurf," interrupted the old settler, "this ain't the time o' year fur me to go a-raisin' no muss with nobody, with Chris'mas a-comin' on so clus, an' everybody a-feelin' good. Me an' you's lived neighbors a good while, an' my ole woman an' yourn's borried so many things o' one another, off an' on, an' to an' fro, that mine can't tell whuther it's yourn ez owes her a pair o' flatirons, or whuther it's her ez owes yourn a cup o' ginger, the heft o' evidence bein', howsumever, that the flatirons is due. But that ain't neither yer nor thar. I don't wanter raise no muss, but I kin tell you right yer, b'gosh, an' I'm a-layin' it out to you with a straight edge, that they ain't no durn man ez trapeses this county, shurf nor no shurf, neighbor nor no neighbor, ez kin git up when I'm on the taps an' throw up to me what any o' the Mushbacks done. I want ye to un'erstand, b'gosh, that I had an aunt ez married a Mush-back, an' I won't have no one a-lyin' about 'em. What a ye want a come yer fur, anyway, an' rake up them ole Mushback scrapes ez was furgot forty year ago? They was a good many things laid to 'em ez they never done, anyhow, an' I'll bate it's jest one o' them you've got a holt on; likely ez not that consarned lie 'bout Uncle Harp. Mushback bein' ketched one night a-leadin' a hoss ez didn't b'long to him, which the hoss were loaded with a passel o' mutton that had ben in Solly Clute's spring-house when Solly went to bed that night. But I give ye warnin', shurf. Don't ye say nothin' ag'in' the Mushbacks, or I'll make things howl 'round yer to-night, an' the loudest thing'll be you, b'gosht'lmighty!"

"But, major," said the sheriff, "this ain't any story about the Mushbacks. I don't know anything about the Mushbacks. It's about a man that bought a house of a family by that name."

"Don't care!" said the old settler. "The Mushbacks is

mixed up in it, an' it'll be a lie, anyhow, if you tell it, an' I won't have it!"

"See here, sheriff," said the county clerk, "you better put that story off. I've heard you tell it twice, anyway, and the last time you told it you got it quite a little different from the first time. Take a week and think it up, and I'll tell a story to-night myself."

"Thar!" exclaimed the old settler, beaming with satisfaction, "now we'll git suthin' ez'll wash. We'm sure o' straight goods now, boys, an' we won't have to go hum to-night a-feelin' that all men is liars. Go on, ole man. Prewarication is the thief o' time."

And the old settler lay back in his chair with closed eyes and a smile on his face, and waited for the county clerk's straight goods, which were measured off as follows:

"Big Hickory Hollow ain't the place it used to be, even twenty-five years ago. The old stock of people that once lived there is all run out, and the scrub-oak has levied on 'most everything there is there. But take it sixty years ago——"

"I'm durn sorry this is a second-hand yarn," said the old settler, opening his eyes and looking disappointed. 'But then, o' course, you got it from yer fam'ly afore you, an' that's good 'nough recondemnation fur it." And the smile came back to the old settler's face.

"But take it sixty years ago," continued the county clerk, without making any declaration as to his authorities, "and Big Hickory Hollow was about as chipper a settlement as there was between the head of the Bushkill and the Narrows of the Lackawack. There was some curious people scattered through that corner of the county, though, and Curley Ben Teeter was one of the queerest of the lot. They called him Curly Ben because he wore two curls, nearly a foot long, one in front of each ear. Ben was about as tough a fighter as the Hollow could turn out, although it was a tolerable even thing between him and Hipe Sloppensifter, who lived on the clearing next but one to Curly's. Curly never missed a dance, a stone-frolic, a wedding, a funeral, or a lawsuit, that came off anywhere within a day's walk of his cabin. He'd go further, though, to get in on a lawsuit than for anything else. The principal reason for that, they used to say, was because lawsuits were always held at the tavern, and whenever Curly Ben struck a tavern he was just moving in society, and no mistake. They always knew when he was looking for a fight. It came on by degrees. First he'd throw one curl over behind his ear. Then he was beginning to get mad. By and by he'd flop t'other curl over t'other ear. Then he was awful mad, and the boys that wasn't game would begin to drop out of the bar-room. But when he tied the curls in a hard knot behind his head the business was in, and he'd fight as long as there was anybody left, or until the curls came untied. When they got loose the fight was done, for it wasn't etiquette in Big Hickory Hollow to hit Ben after his hair came loose. When the muss was ended, Curly'd get over his mad gradually by bringing first one and then t'other curl back to the front of his ears. Then he'd ask every one in the house to have a drink, and away he'd pike for home.

"When Curly Ben Teeter first struck the Hollow he'd been married fifteen years. His oldest child was a daughter, by the name of Keturah, but they called her Ketu. Curly's clearing was at the foot of a steep, barren ridge, about a hundred feet high, and his cabin was built as near the bottom of the slope as he could get it. When Ketu Teeter got to be sixteen she was a little the slickest chunk there was in the Hollow, and what should young Panama Sloppensifter do but tumble head over heels in love with her. Panama was the son of old Hipe Sloppensifter I mentioned awhile ago. Old Hipe was a queer Dick, too. He had a big family, and he took all their names out of the geography. Some were named after mountains, some after rivers, and so on. There was his daughters Hecla, Andes, Carthagena, and Amazon, and his sons Darien, Nicaragua, Popocatepetl, and Panama. They weren't bad sort of people, as people went in Big Hickory Hollow, but there was great animosity between Curly Ben and Hipe.

"Panama Sloppensifter made a living by splitting shingles. He was about twenty-one years old, and never took to a gun. In fact, he had never killed a deer, let alone a bear or a panther, and he wasn't popular among the young bucks of the Hollow on that account.

"Well, Panama got to hanging around the Teeter cabin quite considerable, and finally Curly Ben said he'd see about it. Ketu she liked the youngster, and when Ben asked her if she did, she owned up. One day he found Panama and her talking together by the front door, and he says to the young man,—

"'Panama,' says he, 'ye got sort of a sneakin' notion for Ketu, ain't ye?'

"'Wall, now, Curly,' said Panama,—everybody called Ben Curly,—'ye've struck the proper tree for shingles this time,' says he.

"'Wanter marry her, don't ye?' said Curly.

"'Wall, now, ruther,' said Panama.

"'Ye ain't much on the shoot, be ye?' said Curly. 'Never plugged a deer yit, did ye? Ain't rasled 'round the swamps with many b'ar yit, hev ye? Don't know how it feels to hev a painter chaw ye, do ye? Ye ain't never even shot a rabbit, hev ye?' And Ben threw one curl behind his ear.

"'I've snared 'em,' said Panama, feeling his knees begin to shake.

"'Ye've snared 'em, hev ye?' yelled Ben, slinging t'other curl behind t'other ear. 'Ye've snared 'em, hev ye? Wall, looky yer; I wanter plant it inter ye that ye can't come a-snarin' nothin' round this yer clearin'! B'ars is what counts whar I rule the roost! *B'ars*, ye shingle-splittin' lummix! *B'ars!* B'ARS!' And Curly danced around poor Panama like an Indian.

"About the time that Panama and Ketu were nearly scared to death, Curly quieted down. He took one curl from behind his ear.

"'Say, kin ye fetch me in a b'ar, d'ye s'pose?' he asked. 'Ef ye kin fetch me in a b'ar, ye kin hev the gal, ez wuthless ez ye be!'

"'Curly,' said Panama, 'ef they's a b'ar ez nigh ez forty mile o' Big Hick'ry, I'll git him for you, ef I foller him a year!'

"Panama felt that it would be about as safe to meet a bear as to have Curly ever tie them curls together. Ben took t'other curl from behind his ear.

"'Fotch me a b'ar,' said he, 'and the gal's yourn. An' don't you come foolin' 'round yer ag'in till you do fotch the b'ar, nuther. Now git!'

"Panama started for home, but he hadn't got out of hearing when Curly called him back.

"'Looky yer,' said he. 'Ye un'erstan', o' course, that it's to be a live b'ar, don't ye?'

"'A live b'ar?' gasped Panama.

"'It's to be a live b'ar. A live, wild b'ar. They ain't goin' to be no buyin' o' some secon'-han' carcass o' b'ar an' a-workin' of it off onter me fur the gal. A live b'ar. Ye un'derstan'?'"

"Bully fur Curly Ben!" said the old settler as the

county clerk paused to light his pipe. "Oh, this yer yarn is suthin' like. Listen to dead fac's, shurf, an' arter this try an' stick to 'em." And the old settler smiled and beamed on everybody, he was so pleased.

"Panama said he understood," continued the county clerk, "and went back to his shingle-splitting with his heart in his boots. He felt that Curly had told him in a delicate way that any connection between the Teeter and Sloppensifter families was not to be thought of.

"There had been an unusual fall of snow that winter, and an awful heavy crust had formed on it. One day Panama was up in the mountain, five miles from the Hollow, hunting shingle-trees. Over on the east edge of Burnt Hill he found some good ones, and while he was marking 'em with his axe a big bear jumped out of a hollow place in a tree just at his side. Mechanically, in his fright, he whacked away at the bear with his axe, and the next minute the axe was flying through the air, and he and the bear were having a little hugging-match. The crust was so slippery that neither of 'em could keep his feet, lucky for Panama, and the first thing that he knew both he and the bear were whizzing down that mountain like a streak of chain-lightning. Burnt Hill is more than a thousand feet high, and on the east side is one straight slope from top to bottom, at an angle of about forty-five degrees. Well, sir, Panama afterwards said that they went so fast that neither him nor the bear could change his position nor do any fighting. The bear was in under, on its back, and Panama was laying in its hug. At the foot of the mountain a road that was cut to snake logs and wood down to the settlement branched off to the east. It was all the way down-hill from the mountain, and terrible steep at that. When the bear and Panama struck this road they kept right on down, with no slackening of speed.

They kept the road for four miles, where it made a sharp turn to the left. Of course they couldn't make the turn, and away they went straight ahead for a quarter of a mile through the brush, and their speed was so high that when they struck the foot of a ridge that runs across the country there, a hundred feet or more high, it never stopped them, but they shot up that ridge as if they were being pulled up by a steam-engine, slid over the top of it in a jiffy, and in less than three seconds were tearing down the other sider faster than ever."

The smile had gradually left the old settler's face. He had raised in his chair. He had ceased to beam, and was clutching his cane nervously.

"Suddenly," continued the county clerk, "when Panama had made up his mind they'd never stop much this side of sunrise, they struck something. The next thing Panama knew, he was crawling out from under the roof of a house that had fallen on him. The bear was crawling out on one side of him, and on the other, from among a lot of logs, shingles, and household furniture of various kinds, came Curly Ben Teeter, the most astonished and worst tore-up looking man that ever trod the footstool. As soon as he could get his breath he exclaimed,—

"'What under the gol-durn canopy hez dropped on us? Be we struck by lightnin', or be we rattled up by an 'arthquake?'

"Panama took it all in at once. The bear had got out by this time, and was ready to begin the fight all over again.

"'It's only me, jest got in with that live b'ar ye were so durn anxious fur to git,' said Panama. 'I wanted to s'prise ye, so I come right in without knockin'. Thar's yer b'ar, and I'm jest a-reckonin' that me an' Ketu is gointer buckle.'

" You see——"

The old settler arose and walked to the door without a
word. Pausing with his hand on the knob, he turned to
the county clerk, shook his cane at him, and said,—

" Yes, b'gosh, we see! We see that it's durn easy to be
mistook. We see that if a man kin lie good he kin make
more Pike County hist'ry in a quarter of an hour than
could 'a' happened sence the flood, an' *you* kin give 'em *all*
p'ints a-makin' it, b'gosht'lmighty!"

And the old settler went out and slammed the door
until the windows jingled. The boys laughed; then they
smiled; then they all went home.

FLOATING FUN.

ANONYMOUS.

[The present Half-hour reading is made up of a series of anecdotes,
which we have found floating on the surface of literature, most of
them old, and perhaps well known to many of our readers, but none
the worse for their age or familiarity. Any good thing is worth a
reperusal.]

THE INDIANS AND THE MUSTARD.

A PARTY of Indians were being *fêted* on the occasion of
their first introduction to the manners and customs of the
" pale-faces." The stoicism of the red man is a well-known
trait. From childhood these children of the forest are
schooled to endure pain without wincing or crying, and to
be equally undemonstrative in their emotions of joy. Any
departure from this standard of manliness they regard as
a contemptible weakness. The Indians of our story were
true " braves," whom no new experience, either of pleasure

or displeasure, could startle into any sign more expressive than a grunt, their countenances being uniformly grave and impassive. Behold them at the festal board. Everything is novel and strange, yet they give no token of surprise, and scorn to betray their sense of awkwardness even by so much as asking questions. They take what is offered them and gulp it down with stern and desperate gravity. To one of them a pot of mustard is handed. He helps himself liberally to the mild-looking mixture, and swallows a good spoonful of it. Spirit of the tornado! Fiend of the burning prairie! What is this molten fire, compared to which the "fire-water" of the trader is as bland as milk? The unhappy warrior struggled to conceal his agony; but, though he succeeded in avoiding any contortion of the features, the tears, to his unspeakable disgust, chased themselves in a stream down his dusky cheeks. What would he not have given for an opportunity of scalping the innocent occasion of his trouble!

Meanwhile, his discomfort had not escaped the keen eyes of an Indian who sat beside him. Nudging his tearful comrade, the latter inquired, in low, guttural accents, the cause of his emotion. Suppressing his rage, the other mildly answered that he was thinking of his honored father who had lately gone to the happy hunting-grounds. Whether this explanation was regarded by the questioner as perfectly satisfactory we have no means of knowing; he did not, however, press his inquiries any further, nor does he appear to have suspected that the contents of the little jar had had anything in particular to do with the doleful memories of his friend. Presently the mustard came to *him.* It was a compound all untried; but the warrior was a stranger to fear. He took the condiment without hesitation, and he swallowed it freely—just once. Ah!!

Death and torments? Is he on fire? Will he die? He
is not quite sure; but it requires all his strength to keep
quiet. The blood mounts to his head, and the tears—
ugh! that he should thus play the squaw before all the
company!—rush from his bulging eyes. Indian No. 1 is
an interested observer of this little incident. His eyes
had been upon the mustard-pot, and he had quietly
awaited developments. His turn had now come; his
revenge was at hand. Nudging his inwardly-writhing
neighbor, he asked, in mildest gutturals, "My brother,
why do you weep?" To which the furious sufferer gently
replied, "I was weeping to think that when your precious
father went to the happy hunting-grounds what a pity it
was he did not take you with him."

STUTTERING WIT.

[The following anecdotes are ascribed to Mr. William M. Travers, of
New York, a gentleman in whom wit and stammer are about equally
mingled. Some of his witticisms are of the first quality, and would
do credit to Charles Lamb.]

"Mr. Travers," says Jay Gould, "once went to a dog-
fancier's in Water Street, to buy a rat-terrier.

"'Is she a g-g-good ratter?' asked Travers, as he poked
a little, shivering pup with his cane.

"'Yes, sir; splendid. I'll show you how he'll go for a
rat,' said the dog-fancier; and he put him in a box with a
big rat."

"How did it turn out?" I asked Mr. Gould.

"Why, the rat made one dive, and laid out the frightened
terrier in a second; but Travers turned around and said,
'I say, Johnny, w-w-what'll you t-t-take for the r-r-rat?'"

Henry Clews, the well-known bald-headed banker, who
always prides himself on being a self-made man, during a

recent talk with Mr. Travers had occasion to remark that he was the architect of his own destiny,—that he was a self-made man.

"W-w-what d-did you s-say, Mr. Clews?" asked Travers.

"I say with pride, Mr. Travers, that I am a self-made man,—that I made myself——"

"Hold, H-henry," interrupted Travers, as he dropped his cigar. "W-while you were m-m-making yourself, why the deuce d-did-didn't you p-put some more hair on the t-top of your h-head?"

[Another choice example of the wit of a stammerer is the following.]

An old fellow who was noted through the town for his stuttering as well as for his shrewdness in making a bargain stopped at a grocery and inquired,—

"How many t-t-turkeys have you g-got?"

"Eight, sir," replied the grocer.

"T-tough or t-t-tender?"

"Some are tough and some tender."

"I k-keep b-b-boarders," said the customer. "P-pick out the four t-toughest t-turkeys, if you p-p-please."

The grocer very willingly complied with this unusual request, and said, in his politest tones,—

"These are the tough ones, sir."

"S-sure of that?"

"Oh, yes. I can judge them well."

Upon which the shrewd customer coolly laid his hand on the remaining four, and said,—

"I'll t-t-take *th-th-these.*"

GRIST TO THE MILL.

In Pennsylvania, not many years ago, dwelt the descendants of an ancient German settler. The farm had descended for generations from father to son, and the original customs had been faithfully adhered to. But a youth was born to the family who had inspired some of the modern radical ideas and was likely to come into conflict with his father's stolid conservatism.

One day Johannes was told to saddle the horse and take the grist to the mill. It had been the practice from time immemorial to place the grist in one end of the bag, and a large stone in the other end to balance it, and so throw it across the horse's back. But Johannes on the present occasion managed to get the grist divided between the two ends of the bag, so that there was no need of the stone. Full of the new discovery in gravitation, he ran to his father and cried out,—

"Oh, daddy, come and see! there ain't no use for the stone."

The old gentleman calmly surveyed the device, and with a severely-reproachful aspect remarked to his exulting son,—

"Johannes, your fader, your grandfader, and your great-grandfader all went to de mill wid de stone in one end of de bag und de grist in de odder. Und you, a mere poy, sets yourself up to know more as dey do. Yust put dat stone in de bag, and never lets me hear no more of such foolishness as dat."

MRS. BRUNDY'S DREAM.

Brundy has left his wife, after two weeks of married life. Brundy is a little man, and his wife weighs two hundred and forty pounds, and was the relict of the late Peter Potts. One morning Brundy was surprised, on awakening, to find his wife sitting up in bed and crying as if her heart would break. He asked the cause of her tears, but received no reply, and began to surmise that there must be some dreadful secret weighing on her mind. He begged that she would tell him the cause of her grief, and promised to do his utmost to avert it. After some coaxing, she related the following sorrowful experience:

"I just had a distressing dream. I thought that I was single, and as I walked through a well-lighted street I came to a store that had a sign in front advertising husbands for sale. Curious to know more about this business, I went in, and saw, ranged along the wall on both sides, men with prices affixed to them. Such beautiful men,— some for a thousand dollars, some for five hundred dollars, and so on, down to one hundred and fifty dollars. I did not buy any, as I had not money enough."

Brundy placed his arm lovingly around her, and asked,—

"And, my dear, did you see any men there like me?"

"Ye-yes," cried Mrs. Brundy, breaking out into fresh sobs, "l-lots like you: they were t-tied up in bunches, like asparagus, and sold for t-ten cents a bunch."

Brundy is now anxiously inquiring of his lawyer if he has sufficient grounds for a divorce.

WHY MR. DICKSON WITHDREW.

Mr. Dickson, a colored barber in a large New-England town, was shaving one of his customers, a respectable citizen, one morning, when a conversation occurred between them respecting Mr. Dickson's former connection with a colored church in that place.

"I believe you are connected with the church in Elm Street, are you not, Mr. Dickson?" said the customer.

"No, sah, not at all."

"What! are you not a member of the African Church?"

"Not this year, sah."

"Why did you leave their communion, Mr. Dickson, if I may be permitted to ask?"

"Well, I'll tell you, sah," said Mr. Dickson, stropping a concave razor on the palm of his hand. "It war just like dis. I jined de church in good fait'; I give ten dollars towards de stated gospill de fus' year, and de church-people call me '*Brudder* Dickson;' de second year my business not so good, and I give only *five* dollars. Dat year de people call me '*Mr.* Dickson. Dis razor hurt you sah?"

"No; the razor does very well."

"Well, sah, de third year I feel berry poor; hab sickness in my family; and I didn't gib *noffin* fer preachin'. Well, sah, arter dat dey call me '*dat ole nigger Dickson*,' and I left 'em."

THE DUTCHMAN'S NOTE.

Two German settlers in Pennsylvania, who were not well posted in finance, adopted the following original method of solving a pecuniary problem. Peter had occasion to borrow a hundred dollars from his neighbor John, to pay for some new land. John readily consented to make the loan, and counted out the sum in hard dollars; after which they seated themselves before two mugs of beer, each with pipe in mouth. After smoking for a while, it occurred to Peter that in similar transactions he had heard of a *note* being passed between borrower and lender, and he suggested this to John. The latter agreed that the idea was a correct one. Pen and ink were produced, and a paper drawn up, to the effect that John had loaned Peter one hundred dollars, which Peter would repay to John in three months. So far all went right; but here a difficulty arose. What was to be done with the document? Who was to take charge of it? Here was a dilemma. Finally a bright idea came to John.

"You haves de money to pay, Peter, so you must take dis paper, so as you can see as you haf to pay it."

This reasoning was conclusive, and Peter pocketed the note. Three months afterwards he punctually reappeared, and paid the money. The mugs and pipes were again produced, and the question arose, what was now to be done with the note. Peter settled the quandary, by handing the document to John, with the remark,—

"You must take de note now, so as you can see de money haf been paid."

CAPITAL AND EXPERIENCE.

A bright German gentleman, retired from business, relates the following anecdote.

"Going down to New York the other night on the boat," said he, "I got chatting with a German acquaintance, and asked him what he was doing.

"'Vell, he replied, 'shoost now I am doing nodings; but I have made arrangements to go into pizness.'

"'Glad to hear it. What are you going into?'

"'Vell, I goes into partnership mit a man.'

"'Do you put in much capital?'

"'No; I doesn't put in no gabital.'

"'Don't want to risk it, eh?'

"'No, but I puts in de experience.'

"'And he puts in the capital?'

"'Yes, dot is it. We goes into pizness for dree year; *he* puts in de gabital, *I* puts in de experience. At the *end* of de dree year *I* will have de gabital, and *he* will have de experience.'"

A DISGUSTED LOBSTER.

"Bridget, what did your mistress say she would have for dinner?"

"Broil the lobster."

"Are you sure, Bridget?"

"Entirely; get the gridiron."

Mary got the gridiron and placed it on the fire. She then placed the live lobster on the gridiron.

Intermission of five minutes, after which the dialogue was resumed, as follows:

"Did you broil that lobster, Mary?"

"Niver a broil! The more I poked the fire, the more he walked off. The baste's haunted; I'll try no more. No good will come from cookin' a straddle-bug like that."

"And where is the lobster?"

"Faix, the last I saw of him, he was goin' out of the door with his tail at half-mast, like a wild maniac that he is!"

PRAYER AND PRACTICE.

An old darky who was asked if, in his experience, prayer was ever answered, replied, "Well, sah, some pra'rs is ansud, an' some isn't: 'pends on w'at you axes fo'. Jest arter de wah, w'en it was mighty hard scratchin' fo' de cullud breddern, I 'bsarved dat w'eneber I pway de Lord to sen' one o' Marse Peyton's fat turkeys fo' de old man, dere was no notis took of de partition; but w'en I pway dat He would sen' de old man fo' de turkey, de matter was 'tended to befo' sun-up nex' mornin', dead sartin."

SUSPENSION OF SPECIE PAYMENTS.

JOHN P. KENNEDY.

[The author of the following sketch, John Pendleton Kennedy, a very popular writer of half a century ago, was born at Baltimore in 1795, was a soldier in the War of 1812, served three terms in the House of Representatives, and was appointed Secretary of the Navy in 1852. Of his novels, the most popular were "Swallow Barn" and "Horseshoe Robinson." Among his other works is the "Annals of Quodlibet," an amusing political satire, ascribed to the editorial hand of Solomon Secondthoughts, Schoolmaster. From this we select a chapter satirizing a condition of affairs happily no longer existing in our country, that of "wild-cat" banking, in which there was an abundance of "money," but a very short allowance of cash.]

It falls to my lot, at this stage of my history, to be constrained to record an event the most astounding, the most awful, the most unexpected, the most treacherous, the most ungrateful, the most flagitious—yea, the most super-eminently flagitious—that the history of mankind affords. Notwithstanding that laudatory and political ejaculation which The Hero and Sage breathed out in the evening of his brilliant career, like the last notes of the swan, "I leave this great people prosperous and happy,"—notwithstanding that flattering canzonet with which he who pledges himself to walk in the Hero and Sage's footsteps began his illustrious course, singing as it were the morning carol of the lark,—"we present an aggregate of human prosperity surely not elsewhere to be found,"—the echo of these sweet sounds had not died away upon the tympana of our ravished ears before these banks, these gentle pet banks, these fostered, favored, sugar-plum and candy-fed pet banks, with all their troop of curtailed, combed, and pampered paragon sister banks, one and all, without pang of remorse, without one word of warning, without even, as far as we could see, one tingle of a suppressed and struggling blush, incontinently suspended specie payments! *O curas hominum! Quantum est in rebus inane!*

Shall I tell it? Even the Patriotic Copperplate Bank of Quodlibet was compelled to follow in this faithless path Not at once, I confess,—not off-hand, and with such malice prepense as the others,—for Nicodemus Handy had a soul above such black ingratitude,—but after a pause, and, let the truth be told in extenuation, because he could not help it.

The Hon. Middleton Flam was sent for upon the first tidings of this extraordinary kicking in the traces by these high-mettled institutions,—tidings which reached Quodlibet, *via* the canal, about eleven o'clock one morning in May. The directors were summoned into council. What was to be done? was the general question. Anthony Hardbottle, of the firm of Barndollar and Hardbottle,—a grave man and a thoughtful, a man without flash, who seldom smiles; a lean man, hard-favored and simple in his outgoings and incomings; a man who has never sported, as long as I have known him, any other coat than that of a snuff-brown with covered buttons, and who does not wear out above one pair of shoes in a year; a man who could never be persuaded to give so far in to the times as to put on a black cravat, but has always stuck to the white,—such a man, it may be easily imagined, was not to be carried away by new-fangled notions: he was there at the Board, in place of Theodore Fog, who was compelled two years before to withdraw his name as a candidate for re-election. This same Anthony Hardbottle, speaking under the dictates of that cautious wisdom natural to him as a merchant, answered this question of "What was to be done?" by another, equally laconic and pregnant with meaning: "How much cash have we on hand?"

"One hundred and seven dollars and thirty-seven and a half cents in silver," replied Nicodemus, "and five half-eagles in gold, which were brought here by our honorable president and placed on deposit after he had used them in the last election for the purpose of showing the people what an admirable currency we were to have as soon as

Mr. Benton should succeed in making it float up the stream of the Mississippi."

Again asked Anthony Hardbottle, "What circulation have you abroad?"

"Six hundred thousand dollars," replied Nicodemus, "and a trifle over."

"Then," said Anthony, "I think we had better suspend with the rest."

"Never," said the Hon. Middleton Flam, rising from his seat and thumping the table violently with his hand. "Never, sir, whilst I am president of this bank, and there is a shot in the locker!"

"Bravo! Well said! admirably said! spoke as a Quodlibetarian ought to speak!" shouted Dr. Thomas G. Winkleman, the keeper of the soda-water pavilion. "I have fifteen dollars in fivepenny bits; they are at the service of the Board; and while I hold a piece of coin, the Patriotic Copperplate Bank shall never be subjected to the reproach of being unable to meet its obligations. Anthony Hardbottle, as a Democrat, I am surprised at you."

"I can't help it," replied Anthony: "in my opinion, our issues are larger than our means."

"How, larger, sir?" demanded Mr. Sniffers, the president of the New-Light, with some asperity of tone. "Haven't we a batch of brand-new notes, just signed and ready for delivery? Redeem the old ones with new. Why should we suspend?"

"Gentlemen, I will put the question to the Board," interposed Mr. Flam, fearful lest a quarrel might arise if the debate continued. "Shall this bank suspend specie payments? Those in favor of this iniquitious proposition will say, Ay."

No one answered. Anthony Hardbottle was intimidated by the president's stern manner.

"Those opposed to it will say, No."

"No!" was the universal acclamation of the Board, with the exception of Anthony Hardbottle, who did not open his lips.

"Thank you, gentlemen," said Mr. Flam, "for this generous support. I should have been compelled by the adoption of this proposition, much as I esteem this Board, much as I value your good opinion, to have returned the commission with which you have honored me as your president. Our country first, and then ourselves. The Democracy of Quodlibet never will suspend!"

At this moment, confused noises were heard in the banking-room, which adjoined that in which the directors were convened. Mr. Handy immediately sprang from his chair and went into this apartment.

There stood about thirty persons, principally boatmen from the canal. At their head, some paces advanced into the bank, was Flanigan Sucker. One sleeve of Flan's coat was torn open from the shoulder to the wrist; his shirt, of a very indefinite complexion, was open at the breast, disclosing the shaggy mat of hair that adorned this part of his person; his corduroy trousers had but one suspender to keep them up, thus giving them rather a lop-sided set. His face was fiery red; and his hat, which was considerably frayed at the brim, was drawn over one ear, and left uncovered a large portion of his forehead and crown, which were embellished by wild elf-locks of carroty hue.

"Nicodemus," said Flan, as soon as the cashier made his appearance, "we have come to make a run upon the bank; they say you've busted your biler." Then, turning to the crowd behind him, he shouted, "Growl, Tigers!—Yip!—No?—You don't!"

As Flan yelled out these words, a strange muttering sound broke forth from the multitude.

"What put it into your drunken noddle that we have broke?" inquired Mr. Handy, with great composure, as soon as silence was restored.

"Nim Porter sez, Nicodemus, that you're a gone horse, and that if you ain't busted up you will be before night. So we have determined on a run."

Nim Porter, who was standing in the rear of the crowd, where he had come to see how matters were going on, now stepped forward. Nim is the fattest man in Quodlibet, and wears more gold chains across his waistcoat than I ever saw at a jeweller's window. He is the most dressy and good-natured man we have; and on this occasion there he stood with a stiff starched linen roundabout jacket on as white as the driven snow, with white drilling pantaloons just from the washerwoman, and the most strutting ruffle to his shirt that could have been manufactured out of cambric. In all points he was unlike the crowd of persons who occupied the room. "I said nothing of the sort," was Nim's reply; "and I am willing now to bet ten to one that he can't produce a man here to say I said so."

"D—n the odds!" cried Flan. "Nicodemus, we are resolved upon a run: so shell out!"

"Begin when it suits you!" said Mr. Handy. "Let me have your note, and I will give you either silver or gold, as you choose."

"Yip!—No?—You don't!" cried Flan, with a screeching and varied intonation which he was in the habit of giving to these cant words, and accompanying them with abundance of grimace. "D—n the odds about notes!—shell out anyhow. We have determined on a run,—a genuine, Dimmycratic sortie."

"Have you none of our paper?" again inquired Mr. Handy.

"Devil a shaving, Nicodemus," replied Flan. "What's the odds?"

"But I have," said a big, squinting boatman, as he walked up to our cashier and untied his leather wallet. There's sixty dollars; and I'll thank you for the cash."

"And I have twenty-five more," cried out another.

"And I twice twenty-five," said a gruff voice from the midst of the crowd.

All this time, the number of persons outside was increasing, and very profane swearing was heard about the door. Mr. Handy stepped to the window to get a view of the assemblage, and seeing that nearly all the movable part of Quodlibet was gathering in front of the building, he retired with some trepidation into the directors' room and informed Mr. Flam and the Board of what was going on. They had a pretty good suspicion of this before Mr. Handy returned, for they had distinctly heard the uproar. Mr. Handy no sooner communicated the fact to them, than Mr. Flam, with considerable perturbation in his looks, rose and declared that Quodlibet was in a state of insurrection ; and, as every one must be aware that in the midst of a revolution no bank could be expected to pay specie, he moved, in consideration of this menacing state of affairs, that the Patriotic Copperplate Bank of Quodlibet suspend specie payments forthwith, and continue the same until such time as the re-establishment of the public peace should authorize a resumption. This motion was gracefully received by the Board, and carried without a division. During this interval, the conspirators having learned, through their leader, Flan Sucker, that the Hon. Middleton Flam was in the house, forthwith set up a violent shouting for that distinguished gentleman to appear at the door. It was some moments before our representative was willing to obey this summons; the Board of

Directors were thrown into a panic, and with great expedition got out of the back window into the yard and made their escape, thus leaving the indomitable and unflinching president of the bank, a man of lion heart, alone in the apartment; whilst the yells and shouts of the multitude were ringing in his ears with awful reduplication.   He was not at a loss to perform his duty, but, with a dignified and stately movement, stalked into the banking-room, approached the window that looked upon the street, threw it open, and gave himself in full view to the multitude.

There was a dreadful pause; a scowl sat upon every brow; a muttering silence prevailed.   As Tacitus says, "Non tumultus, non quies, sed quale magni metus et magnæ iræ silentium est."   Mr. Flam raised his arm, and spoke in this strain:

"Men of Quodlibet,—what madness has seized upon you?   Do you assemble in front of this edifice to make the day hideous with howling?   Is it to insult Nicodemus Handy, a worthy New-Light, or is it to affright the universe by pulling down these walls?   Shame on you, men of Quodlibet!   If you have a vengeance to wreak, do not inflict it upon us.   Go to the Whigs, the authors of our misfortune.   They have brought these things upon us. Year after year have we been struggling to give you a constitutional currency,—the real Jackson gold——"

"Three cheers for Middleton Flam!" cried out twenty voices, and straightway the cheers ascended on the air; and in the midst was heard a well-known voice, "Yip!— No?—You don't!   Go it, Middleton!"

"Yes, my friends," proceeded the orator, "whilst we have been laboring to give you the solid metals, whilst we have been fighting against this PAPER MONEY PARTY, and have devoted all our energies to the endeavor to prostrate the influence of these RAG BARONS, these MONOPOLISTS, these

CHAMPIONS OF VESTED RIGHTS AND CHARTERED PRIVILEGES,
the WHIGS, we have been foiled at every turn by the power
of their unholy combinations of associated wealth. They
have filled your land with banks, and have brought upon
us all the curses of *over-trading* and *over-speculating*, until
the people are literally on their faces at the footstool of
the Money Power. [Tremendous cheering.] Our course
has been resolute and unwaveringly patriotic. We have
stood in the breach and met the storm; but all without
avail. Between the rich and the poor lies a mighty gulf.
The rich man *has*, the poor man *wants*. Of that which
the rich hath, does he give to the poor? Answer me, men
of Quodlibet."

"No!" arose, deep-toned, from every throat.

"Then our course is plain. Poor men, one and all, rally
round our Democratic banner. Let the aristocrats know
and feel that you will not bear this tyranny."

"We will! we will!" shouted Flan Sucker. "Go it,
Middleton! Yip!—No?—You don't!"

"Gentlemen," continued Mr. Flam, "this bank of ours
is purely DEMOCRATIC. It is an exception to all other
banks; it is emphatically the poor man's friend; nothing
can exceed the skill and caution with which it has been
conducted. Would that all other banks were like it! We
have, comparatively, but a small issue of paper afloat; we
have a large supply of specie. You perceive, therefore,
that we fear no run. You all saw with what alacrity our
cashier proffered to redeem whatever amount our respectable fellow-citizen, that excellent Democrat, Mr. Flanigan
Sucker, might demand. [Cheers, and a cry of "Yip!—
No?—You don't!"] Mr. Sucker was satisfied, and did not
desire to burden himself with specie. Gentlemen, depend
upon *me*. When there is danger, if such a thing could be
to this New-Light Democratic Bank, I will be the first to

give you warning. [Cheers, and "Hurrah for Flam."]
Born with an instinctive love of the people, I should be
the vilest of men if I could ever forget my duty to them.
[Immense cheering, and cries of "Flam forever!"] Take
my advice, retire to your homes, keep an eye on the Whigs
and their wicked schemes to bolster up the State banks,
make no run upon this institution,—it is an ill bird that
defiles his own nest,—and before you depart, gentlemen,
let me inform you that, having the greatest regard to
your interest, we have determined upon a temporary suspension as a mere matter of caution against the intrigues
of the Whigs, who, we have every reason to believe, actu-
ated by their implacable hatred of the New-Light Democracy, will assail this your favorite bank with a malevolence
unexampled in all their past career. [Loud cheers, and
cries of "Stand by the bank."] But, Quodlibetarians,
rally, and present a phalanx more terrible than the
Macedonian to the invader. You can; I am sure you
will; and therefore I tell you your bank is safe."

"We can! we will!" rose from the whole multitude,
accompanied with cheers that might vie with the bursting
of the ocean surge.

"Gentlemen," added Mr. Flam, "I thank you for the
manifestation of this patriotic sentiment. It is no more
than I expected of Quodlibet. In conclusion, I am requested, my good friends, by Mr. Handy, to say that,
having just prepared some notes on a *superior* paper, he
will redeem at the counter any old ones you may chance
to hold, in that new emission; and I can with pride assure
you that this late supply is equal, perhaps, to anything
that has ever been issued in the United States. With
my best wishes, gentlemen, for your permanent prosperity
under the new and glorious dynasty of that distinguished
New-Light Democrat whom the unbought suffrages of

millions of freemen have called to the supreme executive chair [cheers], and under whose lead we fondly indulge the hope of speedily sweeping from existence this pestilential brood of Whig banks, I respectfully take my leave."

Having concluded this masterly appeal to the reason and good sense of the people, Mr. Flam withdrew, under nine distinct rounds of applause.

THE SKELETON IN THE CLOSET.

EDWARD EVERETT HALE.

[The prolific author of "The Man without a Country" has frequently tried his hand at humorous writing, and generally with good effect, preserving in this as in his more serious work that marked realism which is so meritorious a feature of his style. The following story is told with that practical detail which gives the air of probability to descriptions of actual events. It deals with a subject which is, happily, a thing of the past,—the wire hoop-skirt and the extreme difficulty of getting rid of this indestructible affair after it had served its purpose. Most of us remember what a nuisance the wire skeleton became when it was consigned to the side-walk or the back yard, in despair of getting rid of it otherwise, but few have experienced the troubles which befell Mr. Darragh, of the Confederate States Civil Service, through the total depravity of the skeleton skirt. He begins by telling how the Confederacy ran out of hoop-skirts, how several blockade-runners laden with them were captured, and how all efforts to manufacture them proved failures. He succeeded in getting a supply, sufficient for the ladies and the servants of his family, through the lines, twisted into a figure-8 form at the bottom of his trunks. The old wire skirts which these replaced, and these as they became worn out, were disposed of in methods which proved disastrous to the Confederacy; and "thereby hangs our tale." We take up the story at this point.]

I was up in the cedar closet one day, looking for an old parade-cap of mine, which I thought, though it was my

third-best, might look better than my second-best, which
I had worn ever since my best was lost at the Seven Pines.
I say, I was standing on the lower shelf of the cedar
closet, when, as I stepped along in the darkness, my right
foot caught in a bit of wire, my left did not give way in
time, and I fell, with a small wooden hat-box in my hand,
full on the floor. The corner of the hat-box struck me
just below the second frontal sinus, and I fainted away.

When I came to myself I was in the blue chamber;
I had vinegar on a brown paper on my forehead; the
room was dark, and I found mother sitting by me, glad
enough indeed to hear my voice and to know that I knew
her. It was some time before I fully understood what
had happened. Then she brought me a cup of tea, and I,
quite refreshed, said I must go to the office.

"Office, my child!" said she. "Your leg is broken above
the ankle; you will not move these six weeks. Where do
you suppose you are?"

Till then I had no notion that it was five minutes since
I went into the closet. When she told me the time, five
in the afternoon, I groaned in the lowest depths. For in
my breast-pocket in that innocent coat which I could now
see lying on the window-seat were the duplicate despatches
to Mr. Mason for which, late the night before, I had got
the Secretary's signature. They were to go at ten that
morning to Wilmington, by the Navy Department's special
messenger. I had taken them to insure care and certainty.
I had worked on them till midnight, and they had not
been signed till near one o'clock. Heavens and earth! and
here it was five o'clock! The man must be half-way to
Wilmington by this time. I sent the doctor for Lafarge,
my clerk. Lafarge did his prettiest in rushing to the
telegraph. But no! A freshet on the Chowan River, or
a raid by Foster, or something, or nothing, had smashed

the telegraph-wire for that night. And before that de-spatch ever reached Wilmington the navy's agent was in the offing in the Sea-Maid.

"But perhaps the duplicate got through?" No, breath-less reader, the duplicate did not get through. The dupli-cate was taken by Faucon, in the Ion. I saw it last week in Dr. Lieber's hands, in Washington. Well, all I know is that, if the duplicate had got through, the Confederate government would have had in March a chance at eighty-three thousand two hundred and eleven muskets which, as it was, never left Belgium. So much for my treading into that blessed piece of wire on the shelf of the cedar closet up-stairs.

"What was the bit of wire?"

Well, it was not telegraph-wire. If it had been, it would have broken when it was not wanted to. Don't you know what it was? Go up in your own cedar closet, and step about in the dark, and see what brings up round your ankles. Julia, poor child, cried her eyes out about it. When I got well enough to sit up, and as soon as I could talk and plan with her, she brought down seven of those old things, antiquated Belmonts and Simplex Ellip-tics, and horrors without a name, and she made a pile of them in the bedroom, and asked me in the most penitent way what she should do with them.

"You can't burn them," said she. "Fire won't touch them. If you bury them in the garden, they come up at the second raking. If you give them to the servants, they say, 'Thank'e, missus,' and throw them in the back pas-sage. If you give them to the poor, they throw them into the street in front, and do not say, 'Thank'e.' Sarah sent seventeen over to the sword-factory, and the foreman swore at the boy and told him he would flog him within an inch of his life if he brought any more of his sauce there; and so—and so," sobbed the poor child, "I just rolled up these wretched things and laid them in the cedar closet, hoping, you know, that some day the government would want something, and would advertise for them. You know what a good thing I made out of the bottle-corks."

In fact, she had sold our bottle-corks for four thousand two hundred sixteen dollars of the first issue. We afterwards bought two umbrellas and a corkscrew with the money.

Well, I did not scold Julia. It was certainly no fault of hers that I was walking on the lower shelf of her cedar closet. I told her to make a parcel of the things, and the first time we went to drive I hove the whole shapeless heap into the river, without saying mass for them.

[He got out on crutches at last. The war authorities were then hopefully at work. An important military enterprise was in the wind.]

I made an excuse to go home earlier than usual, rode down to the house in the major's ambulance, I remember, and hopped in, to surprise Julia with the good news, only to find that the whole house was in that quiet uproar which shows that something bad has happened of a sudden.

"What is it, Chloe?" said I, as the old wench rushed by me with a bucket of water.

"Poor Mr. George! I 'fraid he's dead, sah!"

And there he really was,—dear, handsome, bright George Schaff,—the delight of all the nicest girls of Richmond; he lay there on Aunt Eunice's bed on the ground-floor, where they had brought him in. He was not dead; and he did not die. He is making cotton in Texas now. But he looked mighty near it then. "The deep cut in his

II.—*v*

head" was the worst I then had ever seen, and the blow
confused everything. . . .

That evening we heard that everything had gone wrong
in the surprise. There we had been waiting for one of
those early fogs, and at last the fog had come. And Jubal
Early had, that morning, pushed out every man he had
that could stand; and they laid for three mortal hours
within I don't how near the picket-line at Fort Powhatan,
only waiting for the shot which John Streight's party
were to fire at Wilson's wharf as soon as somebody on our
left centre advanced in force on the enemy's line above
Turkey Island, stretching across to Nansemond. I am not
in the War Department, and I forget whether he was to
advance *en barbette* or by *échelon* of infantry. But he was
to advance somehow, and he knew how; and when he
advanced, you see, that other man lower down, was to
rush in, and as soon as Early heard him he was to surprise Powhatan, you see; and then, if you have understood me, Grant and Butler and the whole rig of them
would have been cut off from their supplies, would have
had to fight a battle for which they were not prepared,
with their right made into a new left, and their old left
unexpectedly advanced at an oblique angle from their
centre, and would not that have been the end of them?

Well, that never happened. And the reason it never
happened was that poor George Schaff, with the last fatal
order for this man whose name I forget, undertook to save
time by cutting across behind my house from Franklin to
Green Streets. You know how much time he saved: they
waited all day for that order. George told me afterwards
that the last thing he remembered was kissing his hand to
Julia, who sat at her bedroom window. He thought she
might be the last woman he ever saw this side of heaven.
Just after that, it must have been, his horse—that white

Messenger colt old Williams bred—went over like a log, and poor George was pitched fifteen feet head-foremost against a stake there was in that lot. Julia saw the whole. She rushed out with all the women, and had just brought him in when I got home. And that was the reason that the great promised combination of December, 1864, never came off at all.

[The horse was dead as a stone. And he had been flung by catching his feet in one of those old wire skirts which Chloe had thrown out when she received her new one.]

This time I made a row about it. I felt too badly to go into a passion. But before the women went to bed they were all in the sitting-room together. I talked to them like a father. I did not swear. I had got over that for a while, in that six weeks on my back. But I did say the old wires were infernal things, and that the house and premises must be made rid of them. The aunts laughed, —though I was so serious,—and tipped a wink to the girls. The girls wanted to laugh, but were afraid to. And then it came out that the aunts had sold their old hoops, tied as tight as they could tie them, in a great mass of rags. They had made a fortune by the sale,—I am sorry to say it was in other rags, but the rags they got were new instead of old; it was a real Aladdin bargain. The new rags had blue backs, and were numbered, some as high as fifty dollars. The rag-man had been in a hurry, and had not known what made the things so heavy. I frowned at the swindle, but they said all was fair with a peddler, and I own I was glad the things were well out of Richmond.

[The aunts having got rid of theirs, the girls, at his suggestion, tied theirs up in a paper parcel, with plenty of red tape and red wax, and marked it "Secret Service." He intended to throw this overboard, but changed his mind after a conversation with some naval officers.]

We were talking about the disappointment of the combined land-attack. I did not tell what upset poor Schaff's horse; indeed, I do not think those navy men knew the details of the disappointment. O'Brien had told me in confidence what I have written down probably for the first time now. But we were speaking in a general way of the disappointment. Norton finished his cigar rather thoughtfully, and then said, "Well, fellows, it is not worth while to put in the newspapers, but what do you suppose upset our grand naval attack the day the Yankee gunboats skitted down the river so handsomely?"

"Why," said Allen, who is Norton's best-beloved friend, "they say you ran away from them as fast as they did from you."

"Do they?" said Norton, grimly. "If you say that I'll break your head for you. Seriously, men," continued he, "that was a most extraordinary thing. You know I was on the ram. But why she stopped when she did I knew as little as this wine-glass does; and Callender himself knew no more than I. We had not been hit. We were all right as a trivet, for all we knew, when skree! she began blowing off steam, and we stopped dead, and began drifting down under those batteries. Callender had to telegraph to the little Mosquito, or whatever Walter called his boat, and the spunky little thing ran down and got us out of the scrape. Walter did it right well; if he had had a monitor under him he could not have done better. Of course we all rushed to the engine-room. What in thunder were they at there? All they knew was they could get no water into her boiler.

"Now, fellows, this is the end of the story. As soon as the boilers cooled off, they worked all night on those supply-pumps. May I be hanged if they hadn't sucked in, somehow, a long string of yarn, and cloth, and, if you will believe me, a wire of some woman's crinoline. And that French folly of a sham Empress cut short that day the victory of the Confederate navy, and old Davis himself can't tell when we shall have such a chance again."

[The chance never came. The 3d of April, and the end of the Confederacy, rolled round in due time. But the "Secret Service" package of hoop-skirts was not thrown into the river, but left on the table to do more mischief, for when it was designed to send some Gulf coast maps to the flying President of the Confederacy, another serious error occurred.]

As I live, we had sent the girls' old hoops to the President in his flight. And when the next day we read how he used them, and how Prichard arrested him, we thought if he had only had the right parcel he would have found the way to Florida.

This is really the end of this memoir. But I should not have written it, but for something that happened just now on the piazza. You must know, some of us wrecks are up here at the Berkeley baths. My uncle has a place near here. Here came to-day John Sisson, whom I had not seen since Memminger ran and took the clerks with him. Here we had before both the Richards brothers, the great paper men, you know, who started the Edgerly works in Prince George's County just after the war began. After dinner, Sisson and they met on the piazza. Queerly enough, they had never seen each other before, though they had used reams of Richards's paper in correspondence with each other and the Treasury had used tons of it in the printing of bonds and bank-bills. Of course we all fell to talking of old times,—old they seem now, though it is not a year ago. "Richards," said Sisson, at last, "what became of that last order of ours for water-lined, pure linen govern-

ment calendered paper of *sureté?* We never got it, and I
never knew why."

"Did you think Kilpatrick got it?" said Richards, rather
gruffly.

"None of your chaff, Richards. Just tell where the
paper went, for in the loss of that lot of paper, as it
proved, the bottom dropped out of the Treasury tub.
On that paper was to have been printed our new issue of
ten per cent. convertible, you know, and secured on that
up-country cotton which Kirby Smith had above the big
raft. I had the printers ready for near a month, waiting
for that paper. The plates were really very handsome.
I'll show you a proof when we go up-stairs. Wholly
new they were, made by some Frenchman we got, who
had worked for the Bank of France. I was so anxious to
have the thing well done that I waited three weeks for
that paper, and, by Jove, I waited just too long. We
never got one of the bonds off; and that was why we had
no money in March."

Richards threw his cigar away. I will not say he swore
between his teeth, but he twirled his chair round, brought
it down on all fours, both his elbows on his knees and his
chin in both hands.

"Mr. Sisson," said he, "if the Confederacy had lived, I
would have died before I ever told what became of that
order of yours. But now I have no secrets, I believe, and
I care for nothing. I do not know how it happened.
We knew it was an extra nice job. And we had it on an
elegant new French Fourdrinier, which cost us more than
we shall ever pay. The pretty thing ran like oil the day
before. That day, I thought all the devils were in it.
The more power we put on the more the rollers screamed;
and the less we put on the more sulkily the jade stopped.
I tried it myself every way; back current I tried; for-

ward current; high feed; low feed; I tried it on old stock, I tried it on new; and, Mr. Sisson, I would have made better paper in a coffee-mill! We drained off every drop of water. We washed the tubs free from size. Then my brother, there, worked all night with the machinists, taking down the frame and the rollers. You would not believe it, sir, but that little bit of wire,"—and he took out of his pocket a piece of this hateful steel, which poor I knew so well by this time,—" that little bit of wire had passed in from some hoop-skirt, passed the pickers, passed the screens, through all the troughs, up and down through what we call the lacerators, and had got itself wrought in, where, if you know a Fourdrinier machine, you may have noticed a brass ring riveted to the cross-bar, and there this cursed little knife—for you see it was a knife by that time—had been cutting to pieces the endless wire web every time the machine was started. You lost your bonds, Mr. Sisson, because some Yankee woman cheated one of my rag-men."

On that story I came up-stairs. Poor Aunt Eunice! She was the reason I got no salary on the first of April. I thought I would warn other women by writing down the story.

That fatal present of mine, in those harmless hour-glass parcels, was the ruin of the Confederate navy, army, ordnance, and treasury; and it led to the capture of the poor president, too.

But, heaven be praised, no one shall say that my office did not do its duty!

AWKWARD SITUATIONS.

VARIOUS.

[Our present Half-hour reading consists of a series of amusing sketches, headed by the interesting evolutions of John Phœnix's mule, with its effective method of sweeping the field. George H. Derby was born in Massachusetts in 1823, became a soldier, and died in 1861.]

MULE ARTILLERY.

OUT in a certain Western fort, some time ago, the major conceived the idea that artillery might be used effectively in fighting with the Indians by dispensing with gun-carriages and fastening the cannon upon the backs of mules. So he explained his views to the commandant, and it was determined to try the experiment. A howitzer was selected, and strapped upon an ambulance-mule, with the muzzle pointed towards the tail. When they had secured the gun, and loaded it with ball cartridge, they led that calm and steadfast mule out on the bluff, and set up a target in the middle of the river to practise at. The rear of the mule was turned toward the target, and he was backed gently up to the edge of the bluff. The officers stood around in a semicircle, while the major went up and inserted a time-fuse in the touch-hole of the howitzer. When the fuse was ready, the major lit it and retired. In a minute or two, the hitherto-unruffled mule heard the fizzing back there on his neck, and it made him uneasy. He reached his head around to ascertain what was going on, and, as he did so, his body turned, and the howitzer began to sweep around the horizon. The mule at last became excited and his curiosity became more and more intense, and in a second or two he was standing with his four legs in a bunch, making six revolutions a minute, and the howitzer, understand, threatening sudden death to every man within half a mile. The commandant was observed to climb suddenly up a tree; the lieutenants were seen sliding over the bluff into the river, as if they didn't care at all about the price of uniforms; the adjutant made good time toward the fort; the sergeant began to throw up breast-works with his bayonet, and the major rolled over the ground and groaned. In two or three minutes there was a puff of smoke, a dull thud, and the mule,—oh! where was he? A solitary jackass might have been seen turning successive back summersaults over the bluff, only to rest at anchor, finally, with his howitzer at the bottom of the river, while the ball went off toward the fort, hit the chimney of the major's quarters, and rattled the adobe bricks down into the parlor and frightened the major's wife into convulsions. They do not allude to it now, and no report of the results of the experiment was ever sent to the War Department.

GEORGE H. DERBY (JOHN PHŒNIX).

A POUND OF BUTTER.

One winter evening, a country store-keeper in the Green Mountain State was about closing up for the night, and, while standing in the snow outside putting up the window-shutters, saw, through the glass, a lounging, worthless fellow within grab a pound of fresh butter from the shelf and conceal it in his hat.

The act was no sooner detected than the revenge was hit upon, and a very few minutes found the Green Mountain store-keeper at once enjoying his appetite for fun to the fullest extent and paying off the thief with a facetious sort of torture for which he would have gained a premium from the old Inquisition.

"I say, Seth," said the store-keeper, coming in and closing the door after him, slapping his hands over his shoulders and stamping the snow off his feet.

Seth had his hand on the door, his hat on his head, and the roll of butter in his hat, anxious to make his exit as soon as possible.

"I say, Seth, sit down; I reckon, now, on such a cold night as this, a little something warm would not hurt a fellow."

Seth felt very uncertain; he had the butter, and was exceedingly anxious to be off; but the temptation of something warm sadly interfered with his resolution to go. This hesitation, however, was soon settled by the right owner of the butter taking Seth by the shoulders and planting him in a seat close to the stove, where he was in such a manner cornered in by the boxes and barrels that, while the grocer stood before him, there was no possibility of getting out, and right in this very place, sure enough, the store-keeper sat down.

"Seth, we'll have a little warm Santa Cruz," said the Green Mountain grocer: so he opened the stove door and stuffed in as many sticks as the place would admit; "without it, you'd freeze going home such a night as this."

Seth already felt the butter settling down closer to his hair, and he jumped up, declaring he must go.

"Not till you have something warm, Seth. Seth, come, I've got a story to tell you." And Seth was again rushed into his seat by his cunning tormentor.

"Oh! it's so hot here!" said the petty thief, attempting to rise.

"Sit down; don't be in such a hurry," replied the grocer, pushing him back into the chair.

"But I've the cows to fodder, and the wood to split, and I must be going," said the persecuted chap.

"But you mustn't tear yourself away, Seth, in this

manner. Sit down; let the cows take care of themselves, and keep yourself cool; you appear to be a little fidgety," said the roguish grocer, with a wicked leer.

The next thing was the production of two smoking glasses of hot toddy, the very sight of which, in Seth's present situation, would have made the hair stand erect upon his head, had it not been well oiled and kept down by the butter.

"Seth, I will give you a toast, now, and you can butter it yourself," said the grocer, with air of such consummate simplicity that poor Seth believed himself unsuspected. "Seth, here's a Christmas goose, well roasted, eh? I tell you, it's the greatest eating in creation. And, Seth, don't you never use hog's fat, or common cooking-butter to baste it with. Come, take your butter,—I mean, Seth, take your toddy."

Poor Seth now began to smoke as well as melt, and his mouth was hermetically sealed up as though he had been born dumb. Streak after streak of the butter came pouring from under his hat, and his handkerchief was already soaked with the greasy overflow. Talking away as if nothing was the matter, the fun-loving grocer kept stuffing wood into the stove, while poor Seth sat upright, with his back against the counter and his knees touching the red-hot furnace in front.

"Cold night, this," said the grocer. "Why, Seth, you seem to perspire as if you were warm. Why don't you take your hat off? Here, let me put your hat away."

"No," exclaimed poor Seth at last. "No, I must go. Let me out; I ain't well; let me go."

A greasy cataract was now pouring down the poor man's face and neck, and soaking into his clothes, and trickling down his body into his boots, so that he was literally in a perfect bath of oil.

"Well, good-night, Seth," said the humorous Vermonter, "if you will go," and added, as the man darted out of the door, "I say, Seth, I reckon the fun I have had out of you is worth ninepence, so I shan't charge you for that pound of butter in your hat."

Anonymous.

THE CHIEF JUSTICE'S DILEMMA.

On a recent occasion Chief-Justice Waite, of the Supreme Court, had a distressing experience. Like many great men, he is very absent-minded. Having an imperative engagement at Baltimore, he adjourned the court, and leisurely proceeded to the railroad-dépôt. On reaching it, he found that he had but ten minutes in which to get a ticket and a seat on the train. But, to his surprise, he as quickly discovered he had only a few pennies in his pocket. He had neglected to provide himself with cash for the journey. There was no one present whom he knew. His engagement was important. What was to be done? He advanced to the ticket-window, smiled in his pleasantest manner, and asked the ticket-agent if he knew him.

"No, I don't," snarled the agent; "and, what is more, I don't want to. What do you want?"

"A ticket to Baltimore and return. I am the Chief Justice of the Supreme Court, but have no money with me. It is purely accidental. I can give you my personal check."

"Oh, I know you; I know all the bloods; but that dodge won't work at this office. I have just had two members of the Cabinet trying to 'bilk' me out of tickets, and no Chief-Justice dodge gets me. Take your face from the window, and make way for people who have money."

The Chief Justice glared. He could not fine the young

man for contempt of court. The case was beyond his juris-
diction. But he felt meaner than if he had been a real
fraud. He blushed and perspired so that the agent was
confirmed in his opinion. The Chief Justice dashed out
of the station to see if he could find some one to identify
him. He had only five minutes left. It was too short a
time to reach the Capitol. He saw no familiar face.
Across the street was a saloon and eating-house. He
made a hasty rush across, but checked himself at the
door. What if he should be seen going into a common
rum-shop? What if some one inside should know him?
But there was no time to spare. Spying a private entrance, he dashed in and accosted the proprietor in frantic
haste,—"Do you know me?"

"Bet yer head I do, yer honor," said the short-haired,
freckle-faced man behind the bar. "Ye're the boss av the
Shupreme Coort. I see ye every day goin' by here on the
cars."

"Will you cash my check? I have no time to explain."
Here the Chief Justice grabbed a piece of paper upon a
desk near by and began to write hurriedly.

"Shure an I will, yer honor. I've seen ould byes on a
tear before get out o' money. Trust me, sorr. Is it a
twenty ye want? Here it is. Will ye have a drop before
ye run?"

But, before any further explanation could be made, the
Chief Justice had grabbed the money and was running
across the street. In some way the ticket-agent had
learned of his blunder during the judge's absence, and was
all politeness when he saw the money. Mr. Waite barely
made the train, but he had not had such a shock to his
dignity during his whole term upon the bench of the
Supreme Court.

Anonymous.

THE SOLDIER'S BUGLE.

"Mr. Hoffenstein," said Herman, as he folded up a pair of pants and placed them on a pile, "if you don't haf any objections, I would like to get from the store avay von efening and go mit de soldiers to de Spanish fort."

"Vell, Herman, I dinks you had better keep away from de soldiers," replied Hoffenstein, "und stay mit de store, because, you know, you don't can put any dependence mit de soldiers. I vill dell you vhy.

"Von day vile I vas in Vicksburg, during de var, a cock-eyed soldier came in my store mit an old bugle in his hand, und he looks around. I asks him vat he vants, und he buys a couple of undershirts; den he tells me to keep his bundle und de bugle behind de counter until he comes back. Afder de soldier vent de store out, some more come in und valk around, vile dey look at de goods.

"'Shentlemen,' I says, 'do you vant anyding?'

"'Ve are shoost looking to see vot you haf,' said one uf dem; und after a vile anodder says, 'Bill, shoost look dere at de bugle: de very ding de captain told us to get. You know we don't haf any bugle in de company for dree monts. How much do you ask for dot bugle?'

"I dells dem dat I can't sell de bugle, because it belongs to a man vot shust vent out.

"'I vill gif you fifty dollars for it,' says the soldier, pulling his money out.

"I dells dem I don't can sell it, because it vasn't mine."

"'I will give you a hundred dollars,' he said.

"Den he offers me von hundred und twenty-five dollars. My g-r-r-acious, Herman, I vants to sell de bugle so bad dat I vistles! De soldier dells me vile dey vos leaving de store if I buy de bugle from de man vot owns it, dey vill gif me von hundred und dwenty-five dollars for it. I dell dem I vill do it. I sees a chance, you know, Herman, to make some money by de oberation.

" Ven de cock-eyed soldier comes in, he says,—

" ' Git me my bundle und bugle; I got to go to de camp.'

" I says, ' My frient, don't you vant to sell your bugle?'

" He dell me ' No;' und I says,—

" ' My little boy Leopold vot plays in de store, sees de bugle, und he goes all around crying shust as loud as he can, because he don't can get it. Six dimes I dakes him in de yard und vips him, und he comes right back und cries for de bugle. It shows, you know, how much drouble a man vill haf mit a family. I vill gif you ten dollars for it shust to please little Leopold.'

" De soldier von't dake it, und at last I offers him fifty dollars, und he says,—

" ' Vell, I vill dake fifty, because I can't vaste any more time; I haf to go to de camp.'

" Afder he goes avay, I goes to de door und vatches for de soldiers vot vant de bugle. I sees dem passing along de street, und I says,—

" ' My frients, I haf got de bugle;' und dey says,—

" ' Vell, vy don't you blow it?'

" My gr-r-acious, Herman, vot you dink! All dem soldiers belong to de same crowd, und dey make de trick to swindle me. Levi Cohen, across de street, he finds it out, und efery day he gets boys to blow horns in front of my store, so as to make me dink how I vas swindled. Herman, I dink you had better stay mit de store."

, Anonymous.

VAGRANT VERSES.

ANONYMOUS.

[From the many anonymous poems of humor which have grown in
the garden of modern literature we cull a small bouquet, each blossom
with its own peculiar aroma of wit, and the whole garland fragrant
with the perfume of humor.]

FIRST APPEARANCE IN TYPE.

Ah, here it is! I'm famous now,—
  An author and a poet.
It really is in print. Hurrah!
  How proud I'll be to show it!
And gentle Anna!—what a thrill
  Will animate her breast,
To read these ardent lines, and know
  To whom they are addressed!

Why, bless my soul! here's something wrong!
  What can the paper mean
By talking of the "graceful brook"
  That "*ganders* o'er the green"?
And here's a *t* instead of *r*,
  Which makes it "tippling rill,"
We'll seek the "shad" instead of "shade,"
  And "hell" instead of "hill."

"Thy looks so"—what?—I recollect;
  'Twas "sweet," and then 'twas "kind;"
And now, to think! the stupid fool
  For "bland" has printed "blind."
Was ever such provoking work?
  ('Tis curious, by the bye,
That anything is rendered blind
  By giving it an *i*.)

The color of the " rose" is " nose,"
   " Affection" is " affliction ;"
(I wonder if the likeness holds
   In fact as well as fiction ?)
" Thou art a friend ?"   The *r* is gone :
   Who ever would have deemed
That such a trifling thing could change
   A friend into a fiend ?

" Thou art the same," is rendered " lame ;"
   It really is too bad !
And here, because an *i* is out,
   My lovely " maid" is " mad."
They drove her blind by poking in
   An *i*,—a process new,—
And now they've gouged it out again,
   And made her crazy, too.

I'll read no more.   What shall I do ?
   I'll never dare to send it.
The paper's scattered far and wide,—
   'Tis now too late to mend it.
O fame ! thou cheat of human life,
   Why did I ever write ?
I wish my poem had been burnt
   Before it saw the light.

Was ever such a horrid hash,
   In poetry or prose ?
I've said she was a " fiend," and praised
   The color of her " nose."
I wish I had that printer here
   About a half a minute :
I'd bang him to his heart's content,
   And with an *h* begin it.

PETER'S RIDE TO THE WEDDING.

Peter would ride to the wedding, he would;
   So he mounted his ass,—and his wife
She was to ride behind, if she could,
"For," says Peter, "the woman she should
   Follow, not lead, through life."

"He's mighty convenient, the ass, my dear,
   And proper and safe; and now
You hold by the tail, while I hold by the ear,
And we'll ride to the kirk in time, never fear,
   If the wind and the weather allow."

The wind and the weather were not to be blamed,
   But the ass had adopted the whim
That two at a time was a load never framed
For the back of one ass, and he seemed quite ashamed
   That two should stick fast upon him.

"Come, Dobbin," says Peter, "I'm thinking we'll trot."
   "I'm thinking we won't," says the ass,
In language of conduct, and stuck to the spot
As if he had shown he would sooner be shot
   Than lift up a toe from the grass.

Says Peter, says he, "I'll whip him a little;"
   "Try it, my dear," says she;
But he might just as well have whipped a brass kettle:
The ass was made of such obstinate mettle
   That never a step moved he.

"I'll prick him, my dear, with a needle," said she,
   "I'm thinking he'll alter his mind."
The ass felt the needle, and up went his heels:
"I'm thinking," says she, "he's beginning to feel
   Some notion of moving—behind."

"Now lend me the needle, and I'll prick his ear,
    And set t'other end, too, agoing."
The ass felt the needle, and upward he reared;
But kicking and rearing was all it appeared,
    He had any intention of doing.

Says Peter, says he, "We get on rather slow;
    While one end is up t'other sticks to the ground;
But I'm thinking a method to move him I know:
Let's prick head and tail together, and so
    Give the creature a start all around."

So said, so done; all hands were at work,
    And the ass he did alter his mind,
For he started away with so sudden a jerk
That in less than a trice he arrived at the kirk,
    But he left all his lading behind.

SOCRATES SNOOKS.

Mr. Socrates Snooks, a lord of creation,
The second time entered the marriage relation:
Xantippe Caloric accepted his hand,
And they thought him the happiest man in the land.
But scarce had the honeymoon passed o'er his head,
When one morning to Xantippe Socrates said,
"I think, for a man of my standing in life,
This house is too small, as I now have a wife:
So, as early as possible, carpenter Carey
Shall be sent for to widen my house and my dairy."

"Now, Socrates, dearest," Xantippe replied,
"I hate to hear everything vulgarly *my'd*;

Now, whenever you speak of your chattels again,
Say, *our* cow-house, *our* barn-yard, *our* pig-pen."
"By your leave, Mrs. Snooks, I will say what I please
Of *my* houses, *my* lands, *my* gardens, *my* trees."
"Say *our*," Xantippe exclaimed, in a rage.
"I won't, Mrs. Snooks, though you ask it an age."

O woman! though only a part of man's rib,
If the story in Genesis don't tell a fib,
Should your naughty companion ever quarrel with you,
You are certain to prove the best man of the two.
In the following case this was certainly true;
For the lovely Xantippe just pulled off her shoe,
And, laying about her on all sides at random,
The adage was verified, "Nil desperandum."

Mr. Socrates Snooks, after trying in vain
To ward off the blows that descended like rain,
Concluding that valor's best part was discretion,
Crept under the bed like a terrified Hessian;
But the dauntless Xantippe, not one whit afraid,
Converted the siege into a blockade.

At last, after reasoning the thing in his pate,
He concluded 'twas useless to strive against fate;
And so, like a tortoise protruding his head,
Said, "My dear, may we come out from under *our* bed?"
"Ha! ha!" she exclaimed, "Mr. Socrates Snooks,
I perceive you agree to my terms by your looks:
Now, Socrates, hear me, from this happy hour,
If you'll only obey me, I'll never look sour."
'Tis said, the next Sabbath, ere going to church,
He chanced for a clean pair of trousers to search;
Having found them, he asked, with a few nervous twitches,
"My dear, may we put on our new Sunday breeches?"

A MODEST WIT.

A supercilious nabob of the East,—
 Haughty, being great,—purse-proud, being rich,—
A governor, or general, at the least,
 I have forgotten which,—
Had in his family a humble youth,
 Who went to England in his patron's suite,
An unassuming boy, and yet in truth
 A lad of decent parts and good repute.

This youth had sense and spirit;
 But yet, with all his sense,
 Excessive diffidence
Obscured his merit.

One day at table, flushed with pride and wine,
 His honor, proudly free, severely merry,
Conceived it would be vastly fine
 To crack a joke upon his secretary.
" Young man," he said, " by what art, craft, or trade
 Did your good father gain a livelihood?"
" He was a saddler, sir," Modestus said,
 " And in his time was reckoned good."

" A saddler, eh! and taught you Greek,
 Instead of teaching you to sew!
Pray, why did not your father make
 A saddler, sir, of you?"

Each parasite then, as in duty bound,
The joke applauded, and the laugh went round.
 At length Modestus, bowing low,
Said (craving pardon, if too free he made),
 " Sir, by your leave, I fain would know
Your father's trade!"

"My father's trade? Bless me, that's too bad!
My father's trade? Why, blockhead, are you mad?
My father, sir, did never stoop so low:
He was a gentleman, I'd have you know."

"Excuse the liberty I take,"
  Modestus said, with archness on his brow,
"Pray, why did not your father make
  A gentleman of you?"

DEACON HEZEKIAH.

Oh, Hezekiah's a pious soul,
With his phiz as long as a hickory pole,
And he wouldn't smile if you'd give him the whole
  Of the gold in California.
There he sits, like a cloud, in his Sunday pew,
With his book in his hand, in his long-tailed blue,
And you'd better take care, or he'll look you through,
  With a glance that says, "I scorn ye."

He is very straight, and narrow, and tall,
From the crown to the hem of his overall;
And he sings the psalm with a woful drawl,
  And a mouth like a clam's when it's crying;
But when Monday comes he is up with the sun;
His *religion* is over, his work begun,
And you'd think that there wasn't a world but one,
  And he hadn't a thought of dying.

You would think he was sorry he'd lost a day,
As he rushes and rattles and drives away,
As he gives the poor orphan a crusty "nay,"
  And the widow a vinegar greeting;

And he bargains, and sells, and collects his rent,
Nor tears nor petitions can make him relent,
Till he gets in his pocket each doubtful cent,
    Though he wouldn't be *seen* a-cheating!

And Tuesday, and Wednesday, and all the week,
He doesn't know Gentile, nor Jew, nor Greek,
Nor care whom he robs of the last beefsteak,
    Nor the last poor hope of fire.
But Hezekiah is pious, *very!*
For who in the world ever saw him merry?
And he looks as forlorn as a dromedary,
    And his voice, of itself, is a choir.

A FOOLISH LITTLE MAIDEN.

A foolish little maiden bought a foolish little bonnet,
With a ribbon, and a feather, and a bit of lace upon it;
And, that the other maidens of the little town might know
    it,
She thought she'd go to meeting the next Sunday, just to
    show it.

But, though the little bonnet was scarce larger than a dime,
The getting of it settled proved to be a work of time:
So, when 'twas fairly tied, all the bells had stopped their
    ringing,
And when she came to meeting, sure enough, the folks
    were singing.

So this foolish little maiden stood and waited at the door,
And she shook her ruffles out behind, and smoothed them
    down before.
"Hallelujah, hallelujah!" sang the choir above her head,—
"Hardly knew you! hardly knew you!" were the words
    she thought they said.

This made the little maiden feel so very, very cross
That she gave her little mouth a twist, her little head a
  toss;
For she thought the very hymn they sang was all about
  her bonnet,
And the ribbon, and the feather, and the bit of lace upon
  it.

And she would not wait to listen to the sermon nor the
  prayer,
But pattered down the silent street, and hurried up the
  stair,
Till she reached her little bureau, and, in a bandbox
  on it,
Had hidden safe from critic's eye her foolish little bonnet.

Which proves, my little maidens, that each of you will
  find
In every Sabbath service but an echo of your mind;
And the little head that's filled with silly little airs
Will never get a blessing from sermon or from prayers.

BACHELOR'S HALL.

Bachelor's Hall!   What a quare-lookin' place it is!
 Save me from such all the days o' my life!
Sure but I think what a burnin' disgrace it is
 Niver at all to be gettin' a wife!

Pots, dishes, an' pans, an' such grasy commodities,
 Ashes and praty-skins, kiver the floor;
The cupboard's a storehouse of comical oddities,—
 Things that had niver been neighbors before.

Say the ould bachelor, gloomy an' sad enough,
  Placin' his tay-kettle over the fire;
Soon it tips over,—Saint Patrick! he's mad enough,
  If he were prisent, to fight with the squire!

He looks for the platter; Grimalkin is scourin' it,—
  Sure, at a baste like that, swearin's no sin;
His dish-cloth is missin',—the pigs are devourin' it:
  Thunder and turf! what a pickle he's in!

When his meal's over, the table's left sittin' so;
  Dishes, take care o' yourselves if ye can,—
Niver a drop o' hot water will visit ye:
  Och! let him alone for a baste of a man!

Now, like a pig in a mortar-bed wallowin',
  Say the ould bachelor kneadin' his dough;
Troth, if his bread he could ate without swallowin',
  How it would help his digestion, you know!

Late in the avenin' he goes to bed shiverin';
  Niver a bit is the bed made at all;
He crapes like a terrapin under the kiverin':
  Bad luck to the picture of Bachelor's Hall!

A COCKNEY WAIL.

The great Pacific journey I have done,
  In many a town and tent I've found a lodgement;
I think I've travelled to the setting sun,
  And very nearly reached the day of judgment:
Like Launcelot, in the quest of Holy Grail,
  From Western Beersheba to Yankee Dan
I've been a seeker; yet I sadly fail
  To find the genuine type American.

Where is the object of my youthful wonder
　　Who met me in the pages of Sam Slick?—
Who opened every sentence with " By thunder!"
　　And whittled always on a bit of stick?
The more the crowd of friends around me thickens,
　　The less my chance to meet him seems to be:
Why did he freely show himself to Dickens,
　　To Dixon, Sala, Trollope,—not to me?

No one accosts me with the words,—"Wa'al, stranger!"
　　Greets me with "festive cuss," or shouts, "old hoss;"
No grim six-shooter threatens me with danger
　　If I don't quickly "pass the butter, boss."
I, too, have sat, like every other fellow,
　　In many a railway, omnibus, street-car;
No girl has spiked me with a fierce umbrella,
　　And said, "You git; I mean to sit right thar!"

Gone are the Yankees of my early reading,
　　Faded the Yankee land of eager quest;
I meet with culture, courtesy, good breeding,
　　Art, letters, men and women of the best.
O fellow-Britons, all my hopes are undone;
　　Take counsel of a disappointed man;
Don't come out here, but stay at home in London
　　And seek *in books* the true American.

BOB WHITE, THE QUAIL.

WILLIAM P. HAWES.

[William Post Hawes was born in New York in 1803. He was an
essayist of fine talent and with a warm and delicate sense of humor,
and contributed, under the *nom-de-guerre* of J. Cypress, Jr., many

amusing and brilliant sporting-sketches to the periodicals of his day. Two volumes of his sketches were collected and published in 1842, shortly after his death, under the titles of "Sporting Scenes" and "Sundry Sketches."]

OCTOBER has arrived, and has entered into the kingdom prepared for him by his summery brethren departed. A kingdom, truly, within a republic, but mild, magnificent, *pro bono publico*, and full of good fruits; so that not a democrat, after strictest sect of St. Tammany, but bows the knee. Hail! O king! His accomplished artists are preparing royal palaces among the woods and fields and on the hill-sides, painting the mountains and arching the streams with glories copied from the latest fashion of rainbows. His keen morning winds and cool evening moons, assiduous servants, are dropping diamonds upon the fading grass and tree-tops, and are driving in the feathery tenants of his marshes, bays, and brakes. Thrice happy land and water lord! See how they streak the early sky, piercing the heavy clouds with the accurate wedge of their marshalled cohorts, shouting *pæans* as they go,—and how they plunge into well-remembered waters, with an exulting sound, drinking in rest and hearty breakfasts! These be seges of herons, herds of cranes, droppings of sheldrakes, springs of teals, trips of widgeons, coverts of coots, gaggles of geese, sutes of mallards, and badelynges of ducks; all of which the profane and uninitiated, miserable herd, call flocks of fowl, not knowing discrimination! Meadow and upland are made harmonious and beautiful with congregations of plovers, flights of doves, walks of snipes, exaltations of larks, coveys of partridges, and bevies of quail. For all these vouchsafed comforts may we be duly grateful! but chiefly, thou sunburned, frost-browed monarch, do we thank thee that thou especially bringest to vigorous maturity and swift strength our own bird of our heart, our family chicken, *tetrao coturnix.*

The quail is peculiarly a domestic bird, and is attached to his birthplace and the home of his forefathers. The various members of the anatic families educate their children in the cool summer of the far north, and bathe their warm bosoms in July in the iced-water of Hudson's Bay; but when Boreas scatters the rushes where they builded their bedchambers, they desert their fatherland, and fly to disport in the sunny waters of the south. They are cosmopolitans entirely, seeking their fortunes with the sun. So, too, heavy-eyed, wise, Master Scolopax fixes his place of abode, not among the hearths and altars where his infancy was nurtured, but he goeth *a-skaaping* where best he may run his long bill into the mud, tracking the warm brookside of juxtacapricornical latitudes. The songsters of the woodland, when their customary crops of insects and berries are cut off in the fall, gather themselves together to renew their loves and get married in more genial climes.   Even black-gowned Mr. Corvus—otherwise called Jim Crow—in autumnal fasts contemplateth Australian carcasses. Presently the groves so vocal, and the sky so full, shall be silent and barren. The "melancholy days" will soon be here.   Only thou, dear Bob White,—not of the Manhattan,—wilt remain. Thy cousin, *tetrao umbellus,* will not be far off, it is true; but he is mountainous and precipitous, and lives in solitary places, courting rocky glens and craggy gorges, misandronist. Where the secure deer crops the young mosses of the mountain-stream and the bear steals wild honey, there drums the ruffled strutter on his ancient hemlock log. Ice cools not his blood, nor the deep snow-drift whence he, startled, whirs impetuous to the solemn pines and his hiding-places of laurel and tangled rhododendron, laugh-

ing at cheated dogs and wearied sportsmen. A bird to
set traps for. Unfamiliar, rough, rugged hermit. Dry
meat. I like him not.

The quail is the bird for me. He is no rover, no emi-
grant. He stays at home, and is identified with the soil.
Where the farmer works, he lives, and loves, and whistles.
In budding spring-time and in scorching summer, in
bounteous autumn and in barren winter, his voice is
heard from the same bushy hedge fence and from his
customary cedars. Cupidity and cruelty may drive him
to the woods and to seek more quiet seats; but be merciful and kind to him, and he will visit your barn-yard, and
sing for you upon the boughs of the apple-tree by your
gate-way. But when warm May first wooes the young
flowers to open and receive her breath, then begin the
loves and jealousies and duels of the heroes of the bevy,—
duels too often, alas! bloody and fatal; for there liveth
not an individual of the gallinaceous order braver, bolder,
more enduring than a cock-quail fighting for his ladye-
love. Arms, too, he wieldeth such as give no vain blows,
rightly used. His mandible serves for other purposes
than mere biting of grasshoppers and picking up Indian
corn. While the dire affray rages, Miss Quailiana looketh
on from her safe perch on a limb above the combatants,
impartial spectatress, holding her love under her left wing,
patiently, and, when the vanquished craven finally bites
the dust, descends and rewards the conquering hero with
her heart and hand.

Now begin the cares and responsibilities of wedded life.
Away fly the happy pair to seek some grassy tussock,
where, safe from the eye of the hawk and the nose of the
fox, they may rear their expected brood in peace, provi-
dent, and not doubting that their *espousals* will be blessed
with a numerous offspring. Oats harvest arrives, and the

fields are waving with yellow grain. Now be wary, O kind-
hearted cradler, and tread not into those pure-white eggs
ready to burst with life! Soon there is a peeping sound
heard, and, lo! a proud mother walketh magnificently in
the midst of her children, scratching and picking and
teaching them how to swallow. Happy she, if she may
be permitted to bring them up to maturity and uncom-
pelled to renew her joys in another nest.

The assiduities of a mother have a beauty and a sacredness about them that command respect and reverence in
all animal nature, human or inhuman,—what a lie does
that word carry!—except, perhaps, in monsters, insects,
and fish. I never yet heard of the parental tenderness of
a trout, eating up his little baby, nor of the filial gratitude
of a spider, nipping the life out of his gray-headed father
and usurping his web. But if you would see the purest,
the sincerest, the most affecting piety of a parent's love,
startle a young family of quails, and watch the conduct of
the mother. She will not leave you. No, not she. But
she will fall at your feet, uttering a noise which none but
a distressed mother can make, and she will run, and flutter,
and seem to try to be caught, and cheat your outstretched
hand, and affect to be wing-broken and wounded, and yet
have just strength to tumble along, until she has drawn
you, fatigued, a safe distance from her threatened children
and the young hopes of her heart; and then will she
mount, whirring with glad strength, and away through
the maze of trees you have not seen before, like a close-
shot bullet, fly to her skulking infants. Listen now. Do
you hear those three half-plaintive notes, quickly and
clearly poured out? She is calling the boys and girls
together. She sings not now, "Bob White!" nor "Ah,
Bob White!" That is her husband's love-call, or his
trumpet-blast of defiance. But she calls sweetly and softly

for her lost children. Hear them "peep! peep! peep!" at
the welcome voice of their mother's love! They are
coming together. Soon the whole family will meet again.
It is a foul sin to disturb them; but retread your devious
way, and let her hear your coming footsteps breaking
down the briers, as you renew the danger. She is quiet.
Not a word is passed between the fearful fugitives. Now,
if you have the heart to do it, lie low, keep still, and
imitate the call of the hen-quail. O mother! mother! how
your heart would die if you could witness the deception!
The little ones raise up their trembling heads, and catch
comfort and imagined safety from the sound. "Peep!
peep!" they come to you, straining their little eyes, and
clustering together, and answering, seem to say, "Where
is she? Mother! mother! we are here!"

I knew an Ethiopian once—he lives *yet* in a hovel on
the brush plains of Matowacs—who called a whole bevy
together in that way. He first shot the parent bird; and
when the murderous villain had ranged them in close
company, while they were looking over each other's necks,
and mingling their doubts and hopes and distresses, in a
little circle, he levelled his cursed musket at their unhappy
breasts, and butchered—"What! all my pretty ones! Did
you say all?" He did; and he lives yet! Oh, let me not
meet that nigger six miles north of Patchogue, in a place
where the scrub-oaks cover with cavernous gloom a sudden
precipice, at whose bottom lies a deep lake, unknown but
to the Kwaack and the lost deer-hunter. For my soul's
sake, let me not encounter him in the grim ravines of the
Callicoon, in Sullivan, where the everlasting darkness of
the hemlock forests would sanctify virtuous murder!

A NUTTING-ADVENTURE.

WILLIAM HAMILTON GIBSON.

[William Hamilton Gibson, an artist and author of fine ability, was born at Sandy Hook, Connecticut, in 1850. As an illustrator of books he stands in high repute. He has written "Camp Life," "Pastoral Days," and "Highways and Byways," all beautifully illustrated by himself.]

A PARTY of adventurous lads, myself among the number, were out for a glorious holiday. Each had his canvas bag across his shoulder, and we stole along the stone wall yonder, and entered the woods beneath that group of chestnuts. Two of us acted as outposts on picket-guard, and another, young Teddy Shoepegg by name, the best climber in the village, did the shaking. There were five busy pairs of hands beneath these trees, I can tell you; for each of us fully realized the necessity of making the most of his time, not knowing how soon the warning cry from our outposts might put us all to headlong flight, for the alarm, "Turner's coming!" was enough to lift the hair of any boy in town.

But luck seemed to favor us on that day. We "cleaned out" six big chestnut-trees, and then turned our attention to the hickories. There was a splendid tall shag-bark close by, with branches fairly loaded with the white nuts in their open shucks. They were all ready to drop, and when the shaking once commenced the nuts came down like a shower of hail, bounding from the rocks, rattling among the dry leaves, and keeping up a clatter all around. We scrambled on all-fours, and gathered them by quarts and quarts. There was no need of poking over the leaves for them; the ground was covered with their bleached shells, all in plain sight. While busily engaged, we noticed an ominous lull among the branches overhead.

"'Sst! 'sst!" whispered Shoepegg up above: "I see old Turner on his white horse down the road yonder."

"Coming this way?" also in a whisper from below.

"I dunno yet, but I jest guess you'd better be gittin' ready to leg it, fer he's hitchin' his old nag 't the side o' the road. *Yis*, sir, I b'leeve he's a-comin'. Shoepegg, you'd better be gittin' aout o' this." And he commenced to drop hap-hazard from his lofty perch. In a moment, however, he seemed to change his mind, and paused, once more on the watch. "Say, fellers," he again broke in, as we were preparing for a retreat, "he's gone off to'rd the cedars: he ain't comin' this way at *all*." So he again ascended into the tree-top, and finished his shaking in peace, and we our picking also. There was still another tree, with elegant large nuts, that we had all concluded to "finish up on." It would not do to leave it. They were the largest and thinnest-shelled nuts in town, and there were over a bushel in sight on the branch tips. Shoepegg was up among them in two minutes, and they were showered down in torrents as before. And what splendid, perfect nuts they were! We bagged them with eager hands, picked the ground all clean, and, with jolly chuckles at our luck, were just about thinking of starting for home with our well-rounded sacks, when a change came o'er the spirit of our dreams. There was a suspicious noise in the shrubbery near by, and in a moment more we heard our doom.

"Jest yeu look *eeah*, yeu boys," exclaimed a high-pitched voice from the neighboring shrubbery, accompanied by the form of Deacon Turner, approaching at a brisk pace, hardly thirty feet away. "Don't yeu think yeu've got jest abaout *enuff* o' them nuts?"

Of course a wild panic ensued, in which we made for the bags and dear life; but Turner was prepared and ready for the emergency, and, raising a huge old shot-gun, he levelled it and yelled, "Don't any on ye stir ner move, or I'll blow the heads clean off 'n the hull pile on ye. I'd shoot ye quicker'n lightnin'."

And we believed him, for his aim was true, and his whole expression was not that of a man who was trifling. I never shall forget the uncomfortable sensation that I experienced as I looked into the muzzle of that double-barrelled shot-gun, and saw both hammers fully raised, too. And I can see now the squint and the glaring eye that glanced along those barrels. There was a wonderful persuasive power lurking in those horizontal tubes: so I hastened to inform the deacon that we were "not going to run."

"Wa'al," he drawled, "it looked a leetle that *way*, I thort, a spell *ago;*" and he still kept us in the field of his weapon, till at length I exclaimed, in desperation,—

"Point that gun in some other way, will you?"

"Wa'al, *no!* I'm not fer p'intin' it ennywhar else jest *yit,*—not until you've sot them ar *bags* daown ag'in, jest whar ye *got* 'em, every *one* on ye." The bags were speedily replaced, and he slowly lowered his gun.

"Wa'al, naow," he continued, as he came up in our midst, "this is a putty bizness, *ain't* it? Bin havin' a putty likely sort o' time, teu, I sh'd jedge from the looks o' these 'ere *bags.* One—two—six on 'em; and I vaow they must be nigh on teu tew an' a half bushel in every pleggy *one* on 'em. Wa'al, naow,"—with his peculiar drawl,—"look eeah: you're a putty ondustrious lot o' *thieves*, I'm *blest* if ye ain't." But the deacon did all the talking, for his manœuvres were such as to render us speechless. "Putty likely place teu come a-nuttin', ain't it?" Pause. "Putty nice mess o' shell-barks ye got thar, I tell ye. Quite a sight o' *chestnuts* in *yourn*, ain't they?"

There was only one spoken side to this dialogue, but the pauses were eloquent on both sides, and we boys kept up a deal of tall thinking as we watched the deacon alternate his glib remarks by the gradual removal of the bags to the foot of a neighboring tree. This done, he seated himself upon a rock beside them.

"Thar," he exclaimed, removing his tall hat, and wiping his white-fringed forehead with a red bandanna handkerchief. "I'm much *obleeged.* I've bin a-watchin' on ye gittin' these 'ere nuts the hull arternoon. I thort as haow yeu might like to know it." And then, as though a happy thought had struck him, what should he do but deliberately spit on his hands and grasp his gun? "Look eeah," —a pause, in which he cocked both barrels,—"yew boys waz paowerful anxyis teu git *away* from eeah a spell ago. Naow yeu kin *git* ez lively ez you please. I hain't got nothin' more fer ye teu deu to-day." And bang! went one of the gun-barrels directly over our heads.

We *got;* and when once out of gun-range we paid the deacon a wealth of those rare compliments for both eye and ear that always swell the boy's vocabulary.

"All right," he yelled back in answer, as he transported the bags across the field. "Cum ag'in next year,—cum ag'in. Alluz welcome! alluz welcome!"

DIRECTIONS FOR COURTSHIP.

PHILIP FRENEAU.

[The following selection is not offered as an example of very choice humor, but rather as a specimen of the humorous literature of a century ago, and as the work of an author of considerable note in the

Revolutionary period. Philip Freneau was born at New York in 1752, of French descent. During the war he wrote many satirical and burlesque poems against the Tories, which were highly popular. Some of his serious poems possess a degree of merit. He became editor of a newspaper which violently assailed the administration of Washington. He died in 1832.]

THE parson of our parish used to say, in his hours of convivial gayety, that nothing puzzled a man of true delicacy more than how to make the first advances to the woman he loves, with a becoming propriety of sentiment, language, and behavior.

I must confess I am somewhat of his opinion in this matter, and, having in my time observed many a promising alliance broken off by a mere idle inattention to what even a very moderate share of understanding ought always to dictate upon these occasions, I shall, for the benefit of those whom it may concern, set down a few easy rules, by the assistance of which people may at least prevent themselves from becoming personally ridiculous, if they cannot succeed to the utmost of their wishes in other respects.

When you take a serious liking to a young woman, never discover your passion to her by way of letter. It will either give the lady an idea that you are a bashful booby, or that you have not any address in conversation; both of which defects are sufficient to ruin you in the estimation of any woman of only tolerable good sense.

During the time of courtship be careful never to discourse with the lady upon serious subjects, or matters that are not strictly and immediately pertinent to the purpose you are upon. If she asks you what news, you must not tell her a long story out of the Dutch or English gazettes about the decline of trade, the fall of stocks, or the death of Mynheer Van der Possum. She looks for no such answers. You must rather relate a melancholy tale

of two or three young gentlemen of fortune and handsome expectations that have lately drowned themselves in
the Schuylkill, or thrown themselves headlong from their
third-story windows and been dashed to pieces upon the
pavement, for the sake of a certain inexorable fair one,
whose name you cannot recollect, but the beauty and
shafts of whose eyes these poor young gentlemen could
not possibly withstand. Such intelligence as this will
instantly put her into good humor. . . .

Have a care that you do not pester her with descriptions
of the Alps, the Apennines, and the river Po. A lady is
not supposed to know anything of such matters; besides,
you must be a very cold lover if these far-fetched things
can command your attention a moment in the company
of a fine woman. Whatever she thinks proper to assert,
it is your business to defend and prove to be true. If she
says *black* is *white*, it is not for men in your probationary
situation to contradict her. On the contrary, you must
swear and protest that she is right; and, in demonstrating
it, be very cautious of using pedantic arguments, making
nice logical distinctions, or affecting hard and unintelligible
terms. . . .

When you are courting a young lady, be careful never
to send her any presents that are very easily to be come
at, or such as particularly appertain to your own shop or
line of business. A certain French tobacconist of some
fortune fell in love with a girl of considerable merit and
beauty, but, having never turned his attention much to
the gay world, he was not so well acquainted with what
is called the etiquette of polite life as Frenchmen in general are. By way of introducing himself to the lady, he
sent her his compliments, a letter full of love, and a
basket of *cut tobacco*, to the chewing and smoking of which
he himself was extravagantly addicted, and therefore very

rationally concluded that the whole world ought to do the same.

The lady returned the tobacco by the same servant that brought it, with some expressions of contempt and indignation, as the present seemed to imply that she was fond of smoking and chewing this very vulgar and nauseous weed. The Frenchman, fired with resentment upon seeing his ill-judged present returned, then sat down and wrote the following billet by way of answer:

" Vat! you send home the tabac?—den vat shall I send in reverse [return]? You will have me send my own heart? Dat I cannot en present. Adieu."

He soon after inquired of one of the lady's relations what she was particularly fond of. Some one answered, *soft cheese.*

He accordingly procured a large cheese of an excellent quality, and, to show that he was in every sense her slave, carried it to her himself upon his shoulder. The lady, you may be sure, could do no less than smile.

" Why you laugh, lady? Mademoiselle, en vérité, you be in one très-agreeable good humor, pardie!"

" I am laughing," said the lady, " to think you are turned cheesemonger."

It is almost needless to say that both he and his cheese were instantly dismissed the house forever.

If it can possibly be avoided, never, in the hours of courtship, let your discourse turn upon anything relative to *female anatomy.* Few young ladies can ever forgive the man who is found guilty of only insinuating in company that the sex have anything to do with materiality. Whatever, therefore, be your private opinion, you must, while in their society, be an absolute immaterialist in regard to the rational female world. Perhaps an instance may sufficiently illustrate my meaning.

A certain juvenile young lady of acknowledged good sense and beauty some time ago had the misfortune to fall out of her coach, and broke no less than three of her ribs on the left side, dislocated one of her hips, and considerably injured her left shoulder, etc. This was for some days a topic of public conversation. Dick Pretty-man, whom I have mentioned upon another occasion, was at that time paying his attentions to Miss Angelica Ever-green. Upon her inquiring of Dick, one afternoon, the particulars of this untoward accident, he was silly enough to blurt out in plain language, before a polite assembly of young females, that "the lady had fallen out of the coach topsy-turvy, had broken three of the best and strongest ribs in her whole body, had considerably damaged one of her hips, and that her legs, etc., had not escaped entirely without injury." The company blushed up to the eyes, unfurled their fans, and a general confusion took place, till one of the most resolute of the ladies peeped out from behind her fan, and exclaimed, "Fie, Mr. Prettyman! have you been bred up in a hog-sty, sir, to talk in this scandalous manner in the presence of ladies?"

He was then turned out of the room by unanimous consent; and this small inattention to a proper decorum in conversation had very nearly ruined his expectations. I remember it was not until after a long and sincere repentance that he reinstated himself in Miss Angelica's favor.

Now, had he been a man of sense and breeding, he would have related the disaster in this manner:

"The chariot was driving along with vast rapidity, pomposity, and an ineffable display of grandeur, when suddenly one of the rotatory supporters, commonly called wheels, struck a post, through the carelessness of the celestial charioteer, and completely overturned this most elegant and awful machine; that divine creature, Miss

Myrtilla Myrtlebones, then tumbled out upon the dusty pavement, which, I will be bold to say, never before received so heavenly and sky-bespangled a burden. Her guardian angel, it seems, was at that moment neglecting his duty. She fell, and—oh, lamentable!—that exquisitely delicate frame, which the immortal Jupiter himself had put together with such wonderful excess of art,—that heavenly frame, I say, was considerably disordered by so rude and severe a shock."

Such a representation of matters, though in reality giving very little information in itself, would have thrown the whole female circle into the most charming humor in the world; whereas the vulgar way in which Dick told it was only calculated for the ears of the surgeon.

THE COUNTRY OVEN.

HENRY COGSWELL KNIGHT.

[The author of the following mock-epic poem was born at Newburyport, Massachusetts, about 1788. He studied for the Episcopalian ministry, but much of his time was given to literature. His works consist of poems, which are elegant and scholarly, though not always highly-finished performances. Several of them, as the "Crusade" and the "Sciences in Masquerade," are of an amusingly satirical character. "The Oven," given below, sings a scene of the past whose counterpart few modern kitchens possess.]

I SING the Oven,—glowing, fruitful theme.
Happy for me that mad Achilles found,
And weak Ulysses erst, a servile bard,
That deigned their puny feats, else lost, to sing.

And happy that Æneas, feeble man!
Fell into hands of less emprise than mine;
Too mean the subject for a bard so high.
Not Dante, Ariosto, Tasso, dared
Sport their gross minds in so grand element.
Nor he, Dame Nature's master-journeyman,
Who nimbly wrought a comic tragedy,
As poet wooes a muse, one Shakespeare called;
Nor Milton who embattled devils sung,
Nor bold Sir Blackmore, who an epic built
Quick as can mason rear a chimney-stack,
Nor later these, Klopstock and Wieland famed,
Who sung, this King of Elves, that King of Kings,
Dared the prolific Oven blaze in song.

Expect not now of furnaces to hear,
Where Æolus dilates the liquid glass;
Nor where the THREE, testing their God could save,
Walked barefoot through the lambent heat, unseared;
Nor where the Hollanders, in nests of tow,
With mimic nature incubate their eggs;
For the Domestic Oven claims my powers.

Come, then, from kilns of flame, and tropic suns,
Each salamander Muse, and warm my brain.

Need I describe?—Who hath a kitchen seen,
And not an arched concavity called Oven?
Grand farinaceous nourisher of life!
See, hungry gapes its broad mouth for its food,
And hear the fagots crackling in its jaws,
Its palate glowing red with burning breath.
Do not approach too near; the engulfing draught
Will drink your respiration ere you list.

Glance now the fire-jambs round, and there observe
Utensils formed for culinary use.
Shovel and tongs, like ancient man and wife,

He with his arms akimbo, she in hoops.
There, dangling sausages in chains hang down,
As Sciences and Arts, distinct, allied,
Or, as in Union bound, our sister States.
Here, flayéd eels, strung pendent by the waist;
So swing aloof victims in heathen climes;
O Algier hearts! to mock at writhing pain.
And, high in smoke-wreaths, ponderous ham to cure;
So may each traitor to his country hang!
And, thick on nails, the housewife's herbs to dry;
Coltsfoot for pipe, and spearmint for a tea.
Upon the hearth the shrill-lunged cricket chirps
Her serenade, not waiting to be pressed,
And Sue, poking the cinders, smiles to point,
As fond associations cross the mind,
A gallant, ring, or trinket fashioned there.
And purring puss, her pied coat licked sleek,
Sits mousing for the crumbs, beside black Jack.
He, curious drone, with eyes and teeth of white,
And natural curl, who twenty falls has seen,
And cannot yet count four!—nor ever can,
Though tasked to learn, until his nose be sharp.
'Tis marvel if he thinks but when he speaks;
Else to himself why mutter loud and strange,
And scold, and laugh, as half a score were by?
In shape, and parts, a seed of Caliban!
He now is roasting earth-nuts by the coals,
And hissing clams, like martyrs mocking pain;
And sizzing apples, air-lanced with a pin;
While in the embers hops the parching corn,
Crack! crack! disploding with the heat, like bombs.
Craunching, he squats, and grins, and gulps his mug,
And shows his pompion-shell, with eyes and mouth,
And candle fitted, for the tail of kite,

To scare the lasses in their evening walk,—
For next day, and Thanksgiving-Eve will come.
  Now turn we to the teeming Oven; while,
A skilful midwife, comes the ancient Dame,
Her apron clean, and nice white cap of lawn.
With long, lean arm, she lifts the griding slice,
And inward slides it, drawing slowly out:
In semi-globes, and frustums of the cone,
Tanned brown with heat, come, smoking, broad high
        loaves;
And drop-cakes, ranged like cocks round stack of hay;
Circles and segments, pies and turn-overs,
For children's children, who stand teasing round,
Scorching their mouths, and dance like jugglers' apes,
Wishing the pie more cool, or they less keen.
Next, brown and wrinkled, like the good dame's brow,
Come russet-coated sweetings, pulp for milk;
A luscious dish,—would one were brought me now!
And *kisses*, made by Sue for suitor's pun.
And when the morrow greets each smiling face,
And from the church, where grateful hearts have poured,
Led by the Man of God, their thanks and prayers,
To Him who fills their granaries with good,
They hurry home, snuffing the spicy steams;
The pious matron, with full heart, draws forth
The spare-rib crisp, more savory from the spit!
Full pots of pease and beans,—vile, flatulent,—
And puddings, smoking to the raftered walls,
And sweet cup-custards, part of the dessert.
These all, concreted some, some subtilized,
And by the generative heart matured,
A goodly birth, the welcome time brings forth.
  Illustrious Oven, warmest, heartiest friend!
Destroy but thee, and where were festive smiles?

We, cannibals, might torrify and seethe,
Or dry blood-reeking flesh in the cold sun,
Or like the Arab on his racing horse,
Beneath the saddle swelter it for food.
　　And yet, ere thou give us, we must give thee.
Thus many an Oven barren is for life.
O poverty! how oft thy wishful eye
Rests on thine Oven, hungry as thyself!
Would I might load each Oven of the Poor
With what each palate craves,—a fruitless wish!
Yet seldom hear we Industry complain;
And no one should complain who hath two eyes,
Two hands, and mind and body sound and free.
And such, their powers to worthy ends applied,
Be pleased, indulgent Patroness, to feed.

UNCLE ZEKE'S CONSCIENCE.

T. L. McCREADY.

[*Harper's Magazine* is the source of the following story, one of the many excellent examples of humorous fiction which adorn the pages of that popular periodical. We may premise that Uncle Zeke resided on the western shore of the lower Chesapeake, in a tumble-down mansion, which yet, however, had about it many signs of comfort and comparative prosperity.]

THIS establishment is the residence of Mr. Ezekiel Foster, known of white folks and the younger fry of darkies as Uncle Zeke, but addressed by the older members of his church as Bro'r Zekel or Bro'r Foster. A sage and dignified old gentleman is Uncle Zeke, strictly polite to white ladies and "gemmen," but rather discouraging any familiarity on the part of "dem po' white trash, 'at

neber was no 'count 'fore de war, and ain't so much 'count
now." At church meetings his prayer is the loudest and
most earnest, and at the shouting exercises on Sunday
nights, when the old man strikes up the hymn,—

> " Rock o' my soul in de bosom ob Abraham,
> Rock o' my soul in de bosom ob Abraham,
> Rock o' my soul in de bosom ob Abraham,
>   Lord, Rock o' my soul,"—

his feet begin to move before the end of the first verse,
and at the close of the second he is jumping with a vigor
indicative of the highest internal happiness and peace.
Uncle Zeke always was remarkable for religious enthusiasm. His white wool curling close to his head, a fringe
of snowy whisker surrounding his coffee-colored face,
seamed and criss-crossed with wrinkles, and a benevolent
smile upon his lips, he might sit to a painter as a model
for an African bishop or for Uncle Tom.

And Uncle Zeke can talk, too. Step into his cabin,
having been properly introduced,—for Uncle Zeke is apt
to resent intrusion, and "don't make much 'count o'
strange white folks 'quirin' round,"—and the old man
shall spin you yarns like any man-o'-war's-man. With a
flask of whiskey (for Uncle Zeke is no believer in temper-
ance) or a bit of tobacco and a few civil words, you may
keep him telling stories the livelong day,—tales of the
old days when he and his were slaves; how his first wife
was taken from him. "Yes, sar; done sole her 'way, an'
'e chillun too. Pow'ful fine woman she was, Nancy; hear
ole marster say she done fotch de rise o' twel' hundred
dollars—ke! ke!" And the old man chuckles as he recalls
the pecuniary value of the abducted Nancy. He can tell
you, too, how in old times the river swarmed with fish
and was bottomed with oysters. "But sence de war de

boys dey done go iseterin' so much dey broke up all de
iseters, and 'pears like de fish dey done gone too. Well,
well, ole man done see it all." Or, if you wish to investi-
gate the workings of the negro mind and learn its superstitions and its reasoning powers, you can have no better
opportunity than in a talk with Uncle Zeke. Talk to him,
as I did one day, about spiritualism, and listen to the old
man's views on that point. " Well, now I tell you, Mis'
Long, you's got eddication an' all dat; but dere's a heap
o' curus tings in dis worl' can' no man make out. I done
had some queer 'sperences myself. I tell you some'in'
happen me when I's a chile. Ain' neber tole you disser
story 'fore, 'cause dem fool chillun allers been roun', an'
'pears like dey ain't got no 'spect for gray hairs; laugh at
ole man jus' like he's a young gal or boy. Well, well,
chillun is mighty curus, dat's sartin. Sarvent, Mis' Long,
I take a small piece tobacco, sence you's so kind; sarvent,
sar.

   " When I's a chile an' live to ole Maje Warner up in
Gloucester dere—ah! had pow'ful fine place, de maje;
flowers an' hot-house an' fruit, and eberyting o' de bes'
could be had for money. An' ole' Maje Warner he pow'ful
fond o' watermelons; ebery year done sot out a patch, an'
had de fus' melons in all de neighborhood. An' one year
melons dey was skase; mos' all de crop done fail; all de
neighbors got none, an' ole maje he on'y make out raise a
few.

   " Well, sar, one night de han's dey sont me in de patch
fur git some melon, an' I take four. Next mornin' old
marster call all de han's togedder, an' 'low he miss four
melon, an' dey mus' 'a' stole 'em. Den he ax each one,
' Boy, you take dem melon?' Ebery one say, 'No, sar.'
Den ole maje says, ' I gwine fine out 'bout dis ting.' An'
he sont in de chicken-yard an' cotch big rooster, an' put

him in de old kitchen, an' put big iron pot atop o' him.
Den he make ebery man put his han' on dat pot, an' ax
him if he stole dem melon. By an' by come my turn.
Ole maje say, ' Zeke, you steal dem melon?' I say, ' No,
sar.' And dat rooster he crow—ke! ke! Yes, sar, crow
right out, jus' like he was sayin', ' Zeke, you's a-lyin'.'
Den ole maje say, ' Zeke, you's de man.' I say, ' Yes, sar ;
no use fur 'ny it now.' An' den I cotch a lickin'. Now
how you s'pose dat ar rooster know I take dem melon?
Tell you, sar, is some tings white folks don' un'stan', nor
cullud pussons neider."

But there is one of his experiences Uncle Zeke can never
be persuaded to relate. No matter how he may be pressed,
he has but one invariable answer : " Oh, g' way, Mis' Long ;
dat all foo'shness ; don' like talk 'bout dat ar, noway."
And if the questioning be pushed too far old Zeke is apt
to turn crusty, and will break off the conference with,
" Mus' 'scuse me now, sir ; I got go iseterin'," and hobble
off to his canoe, muttering in high dudgeon : so, since the
old man will not tell the story himself, I must do the best
I can to relate it for him.

No man, however pure, can entirely escape the voice of
slander, and there are not wanting unregenerate and nar-
row-minded people who aver that Uncle Zeke, with all his
outward piety and obsequious respectfulness, is, as they
phrase it, " one grand old scoundrel." Certain it is that,
either in direct answer to prayer or in some equally
abnormal manner, the necessities of Mr. Foster are often
supplied with wonderful promptitude. Other darkies may
be prevented by hard weather from oystering for days
together, but Uncle Zeke always has a bushel or two to
carry to " de sto' " to exchange for groceries ; and his
canoe is often seen at night in suspicious proximity to
beds of planted oysters. He grows little corn, but some-

how never wants for meal; and, though fried chicken is no unusual dish at his table, his stock of fowls seems never to diminish. But let us not be too hard on Uncle Zeke's peculative peculiarities. Slavery was a wretched school of morality, and the man who saw all the fruits of his labor absorbed by another, naturally enough thought little harm of the abstraction of an occasional chicken or casual bit of meat.

[One gentleman, who came from New York and began farming in the neighborhood, found himself much the worse for the pilfering habits of the natives. His chickens, geese, turkeys, etc., vanished, and his corn-crib suffered severely. He concealed a spring-trap in the latter, but the thief was too cunning to be caught. The trap was found sprung and more corn missing. Mr. Smith thereupon set his wit to work to get even with his midnight visitant.]

At last a good-sized box arrived from New York, and the next day the local carpenter was ordered to fix two brass handles to the corn-crib,—one to be put along-side the door for convenience, as Mr. Smith publicly explained, of steadying one's self while turning the other. The second handle had a latch attached to it by which the door was secured on the inside, and was set in such a position that any one turning it must hold on by the other knob to prevent being thrown backward by the opening door. Both handles were profusely decorated with glass, and elicited much admiration from the hands, who submitted them to a critical examination. The carpenter's work being finished, Smith, in presence of all his colored employees, solemnly repeated, in front of the corn-crib, the first two lines of the second book of Virgil's Æneid, and announced that his corn was thenceforward secure. A box, stated to contain seeds, was that afternoon deposited in the crib, and during the early part of the succeeding night the proprietor of Bellevue secretly busied himself with a coil of insulated wire.

Numerous and diverse were the speculations among the darkies. Jim Oakley "'lowed Mis' Smith done 'witched dat ar corn-house, sho' 'nuff. Tell you, gemmen, you touch dem 'ere handles, evil spirit carry you 'way.—No such ting 's evil sperit! How you know dere no such ting? tush, boy; go see what de Bible say 'bout dem ting." Pete Lee "didn' b'lieve in no sperits; got a gun fix somewhar inside dat house; turn de handle an' de gun go off. Seen dem tings afore up-country, when I live in Goozleum." Another theorist averred that, "while Mis' Smith sayin' dat ar Scripter ober dem handles, he seen a white pigeon come a-sailin' roun' an' roun' an' roun', and done light on de peak o' de corn-house roof. High! tell you, sar, sumpin up, sho'."

Uncle Zeke, like the rest, was troubled in his mind, but, unlike his fellows, he determined to waste no time in speculation, but to seek his information direct from head-quarters. Prepared with half a bushel of oysters, as an excuse for conversation, he sought an interview with Mr. Smith, and boldly propounded his questions.

"Mis' Smith, what you bin a-doin' to dat ar crib o' yourn?"

"Why, Uncle Zeke, what do you want to know for?"

"Oh, nuffin, sar; sorter curus like. Hearn all de boys talkin' 'bout it; neber see nuffin like dat afore."

"Well, Uncle Zeke, I can't very well explain it to you; but I just advise you, don't go near that crib after dark, or you may see something you won't like." And Uncle Zeke departed, revolving many things in his mind.

It was midnight,—the hour when church-yards are said to yawn, not with exhaustion, but returning animation.

In front of the enchanted corn-house stood Brother Ezekiel, a lengthy pole in his hand and a capacious meal-bag over his shoulder. In silent meditation he stood for some five minutes, deliberating on the best place of attack. The great Newfoundland watch-dog bounded towards him, evidently in rejoicing welcome. Forth from his pocket the old man drew a savory bit of fried bacon, which the faithless Bos'en eagerly devoured. The refection ended, the dog lay contentedly on the ground, and watched the subsequent proceedings with the air of a totally disinterested observer.

" Clar' to goodness, now," muttered Uncle Zeke, " wish't I un'stood 'bout dis ting. Can' be no spring-trap like a las' time, kase how he gwine to spring froo de do'! Ke! ke! Done bodder Mis' Smith sho' 'nuff when he find dat ole rat-trap sprong an' nuffin cotch. High! Can' fool disser chile wid no traps. No, sar! done see too much for dat."

Uncle Zeke paused, scratched his head meditatively, and then resumed his soliloquy :

" Well, I declar', ef disser don' beat preachin'! Mus' be a gun in dar. Ef ain' no gun, den dar ain't nuffin dere,— all foo'shness. Anyway, I's gwine for try him."

Uncle Zeke threw his bag to the ground, stepped to one side of the house, and with his pole struck a sharp blow on the brass knob nearest him. Nothing followed. He pried against it with his stick, but still without effect. He went to the other side of the house and repeated his experiments on the second knob, but still all remained quiet.

Uncle Zeke now drew from his pocket a skeleton key, mounted the ladder, and in a trice had opened the padlock which held the door.

" Dar, now, jus' 's I t'ought. De boss done humbug dem fool nigger,—make um tink disser house 'witched. Ain't nuffin' dar, sho' 'nuff."

The old darky reached up and cautiously turned the handle. The door opened a little, and, casting away all fear, Uncle Zeke boldly reached for the other knob, to steady himself while he swung back the door.

Literally like a flash of lightning the electric discharge passed through him. The muscles of his fingers contracted, and he could not release his hold of the enchanted handles. At last his feet slipped from the ladder, and the weight of his body tore his hands adrift. Like a log the old man dropped to the ground, and lay groaning, praying, and generally bewildered.

"Oh, de lawsgoramity! Oh, my heabenly Marster! Who eber t'ought o' dat! My consc'ence done wake up! Heern 'bout it often, an' now I knows it. Oh, my heabenly Marster! ef you lets up on me dis time, Uncle Zeke neber touch nuffin no mo.' Clar' to goodness I's a change' man f'om dis day. B—r-r-r-r——" And what with the shock, the fright, and the fall, Uncle Zeke's senses seemed leaving him.

"Ezekiel," said a solemn voice. Instinctively Uncle Zeke answered, "Here me," and looked in the direction of the sound. Oh, horror! A figure clad in white was nearing him with slow and solemn steps. As the mysterious visitor approached, it seemed to rise until it towered to the height of at least ten feet. The wretched Ezekiel, on his hands and knees, his eyes protruding, and his jaw dropped, remained as if paralyzed.

Suddenly the phantom bowed itself, and its head descending with incredible swiftness smote the unfortunate Uncle Zeke senseless to the earth.

Three days later, as poor Uncle Zeke lay, racked with rheumatism and tormented with spiritual fear, upon his bed in the single room at his cabin, the door opened, and in walked Mr. Smith, of Bellevue.

"Good-morning, Uncle Zeke. Why, what's the matter with you, old man?"

"Oh, Mis' Smith! oh, Mis' Smith! I done had some turrible 'sperences lately. De angel ob de Lord done wrastle wid me, an' my consc'ence done woke, an' oh, my heabenly Marster, I's one sufferin' sinner. Mis' Smith, is you bin—is you done—is you m-miss anyting wid dat are c-corn-house o' yourn?"

"No, indeed, Uncle Zeke; nobody been near it. Everything all right now."

"An' nobody done touch de lock? Done lock ebery mornin'?"

"Yes, indeed. Why, who do you think would touch it, old man?"

Uncle Zeke answered not, but his lips moved convulsively as he muttered, "Knock me down fus', an' den lock de do' an' took de key! Now I *knows* it was de angel ob de Lord."

Needless to say that thenceforward Smith's premises were safe. Pigs might squeal, "Take me out, take me out;" barn and corn-crib might be left open; but the rumor of Uncle Zeke's terrible experience had gone abroad among the darkies, and not a man of them could have been induced for love or money to land on the shores of Bellevue after dark. Smith judiciously kept his counsel, and it was many months before he related to me how, with a powerful galvanic battery, he had shocked poor Uncle Zeke's nerves, and, with the aid of a mask and a sheet on a hickory pole, enacted an elongating ghost. But he seldom failed when he met Uncle Zeke to inquire into the state of his conscience, and the awakened and repentant African would roll his eyes piously upward and reply,—

"Much better, sar, t'ank de Lord. Ain' trouble me in long time now, sar."

But no persuasion has ever induced Uncle Zeke to relate the history of that awful night when his conscience awoke to trouble him, and the angel of the Lord appeared and smote him.

POLLY PEABLOSSOM'S WEDDING.

JOHN B. LAMAR.

[Who John B. Lamar is we are not able to state, but he has done his share of work for American humorous literature in the following amusing story of life in North Carolina some forty years ago.]

"MY stars! that parson is *powerful* slow a-coming! I reckon he wa'n't so tedious gitting to his own wedding as he is coming here," said one of the bridesmaids of Miss Polly Peablossom, as she bit her lips to make them rosy, and peeped into a small looking-glass for the twentieth time.

"He preaches enough about the shortness of a lifetime," remarked another pouting miss, "and how we ought to improve our opportunities, not to be creeping along like a snail, when a whole wedding-party is waiting for him, and the waffles are getting cold, and the chickens burning to a crisp."

"Have patience, girls. Maybe the man's lost his spurs, and can't get along any faster," was the consolatory appeal of an arch-looking damsel, as she finished the last of a bunch of grapes.

"Or perhaps his old fox-eared horse has jumped out of the pasture, and the old gentleman has to take it afoot," surmised the fourth bridesmaid.

The bride used industrious efforts to appear patient and

rather indifferent amid the general restiveness of her aids, and would occasionally affect extreme merriment; but her shrewd attendants charged her with being fidgety and rather more uneasy than she wanted folks to believe.

"Helloo, Floyd!" shouted old Captain Peablossom, out of doors, to his copperas-trousered son, who was entertaining the young beaux of the neighborhood with feats of agility in jumping with weights,—"Floyd, throw down them rocks, and put the bridle on old Snip, and ride down the road and see if you can't see Parson Gympsey, and tell him hurry along: we are all waiting for him. He must think weddings are like his meetings, that can be put off to the 'Sunday after the fourth Saturday in next month,' after the crowd's all gathered and ready to hear the preaching. If you don't meet him, go clean to his house. I 'spect he's heard that Bushy Creek Ned's here with his fiddle, and taken a scare."

As the night was wearing on, and no parson had come yet to unite the destinies of George Washington Hodgkins and "the amiable and accomplished" Miss Polly Peablossom, the former individual intimated to his intended the propriety of passing off the time by having a dance.

Polly asked her ma, and her ma, after arguing that it was not the fashion in her time, in North Car'lina, to dance before the ceremony, at last consented.

The artist from Bushy Creek was called in, and, after much tuning and spitting on the screws, he struck up "Money Musk;" and away went the country-dance, Polly Peablossom at the head, with Thomas Jefferson Hodgkins as her partner, and George Washington Hodgkins next, with Polly's sister Luvisa for his partner. Polly danced to every gentleman, and Thomas Jefferson danced to every lady; then up and down in the middle, and hands all round. Next came George Washington and his partner, who underwent the same process; and "so on through the whole," as Daboll's Arithmetic says.

The yard was lit up by three or four large light-wood fires, which gave a picturesque appearance to the groups outside. On one side of the house was Daniel Newnan Peablossom and a bevy of youngsters, who either could not or did not desire to get into the dance,—probably the former,—and who amused themselves by jumping and wrestling. On the other side, a group of matrons sat under the trees, in chairs, and discoursed of the mysteries of making butter, curing chickens of the pip and children of the croup, besides lamenting the misfortunes of some neighbor, or the indiscretion of some neighbor's daughter who had run away and married a circus-rider. A few pensive couples, eschewing the "giddy dance," promenaded the yard and admired the moon, or "wondered if all them little stars were worlds like this."   Perhaps they may have sighed sentimentally at the folly of the mosquitoes and bugs which were attracted round the fires to get their pretty little wings scorched and lose their precious lives; or they may have talked of "true love," and plighted their vows, for aught we know.

Old Captain Peablossom and his pipe, during the while, were the centre of a circle in front of the house, who had gathered around the old man's arm-chair to listen to his "twice-told tales" of "hair-breath 'scapes," of "the battles and sieges he had passed;" for, you must know, the captain was no "summer soldier and sunshine patriot:" he had burned gunpowder in defence of his beloved country.

At the especial request of Squire Tompkins, the captain narrated the perilous adventures of Newnan's little band among the Seminoles: how "bold Newnan" and his men lived on alligator-flesh and parched corn and marched barefooted through saw-palmetto; how they met Bowlegs and his warriors near Paine's Prairie, and what fighting was there. The amusing incident of Bill Cone and the terra-pin-shell raised shouts of laughter among the young brood, who had flocked around to hear of the wars. Bill (the "Camden Bard," peace to his ashes!), as the captain familiarly called him, was sitting one day against the logs of the breastwork, drinking soup out of a terrapin-shell, when a random shot from the enemy broke the shell and spilt his soup, whereupon he raised his head over the breastwork and sung out, "Oh, you villain! you couldn't do that again if you tried forty times." Then the captain, after repeated importunities, laid down his pipe, cleared his throat, and sung,—

> We marchéd on to our next station,
>   The Injens on before did hide,
> They shot and killed Bold Newnan's nigger,
>   And two other white men by his side.

The remainder of the epic we have forgotten.

After calling out for a chunk of fire and relighting his pipe, he dashed at once over into Alabama, in General Floyd's army, and fought the battles of Calebee and Otassee over again in detail. The artillery from Baldwin County blazed away, and made the little boys aforesaid think they could hear thunder, almost, and the rifles from Putnam made their patriotic young spirits long to revenge that gallant corps. And the squire was astonished at the narrow escape his friend had of falling into the hands of Weatherford and his savages, when he was miraculously rescued by Timpoochie Barnard, the Uchee chief.

At this stage of affairs, Floyd (not the general, but the ambassador) rode up, with a mysterious look on his countenance. The dancers left off in the middle of a set, and assembled around the messenger, to hear the news of the parson. The old ladies crowded up, too, and the captain and the squire were eager to hear. But Floyd felt the importance of his situation, and was in no hurry to divest himself of the momentary dignity.

"Well, as I rode on down to Boggy Gut, I saw——"

"Who cares what the devil you saw?" exclaimed the impatient captain. "Tell us if the parson is coming first, and you may take all night to tell the balance, if you like, afterwards."

"I saw——" continued Floyd, pertinaciously.

"Well, my dear, what did you see?" asked Mrs. Peablossom.

"I saw that some one had tooken away some of the rails on the cross-way, or they had washed away, or some-how——"

"Did anybody ever hear the like?" said the captain.

"And so I got down," continued Floyd, "and hunted some more, and fixed over the boggy place——"

Here Polly laid her hand on his arm and requested, with a beseeching look, to know if the parson was on the way.

"I'll tell you all about it presently, Polly. And when I got to the run of the creek, then——"

"Oh, the devil!" ejaculated Captain Peablossom. "Stalled again!"

"Be still, honey: let the child tell it his own way. He always would have his way, you know, since we had to humor him so when he had the measles," interposed the old lady.

Daniel Newnan Peablossom, at this juncture, facetiously lay down on the ground, with the root of an old oak for his pillow, and called out yawningly to his pa to "wake him when brother Floyd had crossed over the run of the creek and arrived safely at the parson's." This caused loud laughter.

Floyd simply noticed it by observing to his brother,

"Yes, you think you're mighty smart before all these folks!" and resumed his tedious route to Parson Gympsey's, with as little prospect of reaching the end of his story as ever.

Mrs. Peablossom tried to coax him to "jest" say if the parson was coming or not. Polly begged him, and all the bridesmaids implored. But Floyd "went on his way rejoicing." "When I came to the Piney Flat," he continued, "old Snip seed something white over in the baygall, and shied clean out o' the road, and——" Where he would have stopped would be hard to say, if the impatient captain had not interfered.

That gentleman, with a peculiar glint of the eye, remarked, "Well, there's one way I can bring him to a showing," as he took a large horn from between the logs, and rung a "wood-note wild," that set a pack of hounds to yelping. A few more notes, as loud as those that issued from "Roland's horn at Roncesvalles," was sufficient invitation to every hound, foist, and "cur of low degree," that followed the guests, to join in the chorus. The captain was a man of good lungs, and "the way he *did* blow was the way," as Squire Tompkins afterwards very happily described it; and, as there were in the canine choir some thirty voices of every key, the music may be imagined better than described. Miss Tabitha Tidwell, the first bridesmaid, put her hands to her ears and cried out, "My stars! we shall all git blowed away!"

The desired effect of abbreviating the messenger's story was produced, as that prolix personage in copperas pants was seen to take Polly aside and whisper something in her ear.

"Oh, Floyd, you are joking! you oughtn't to serve me so. An't you joking, bud?" asked Polly, with a look that seemed to beg he would say yes.

"It's true. as preaching," he replied: "the cake's all dough!"

Polly whispered something to her mother, who threw up her hands, and exclaimed, "Oh, my!" and then whispered the secret to some other lady, and away it went. Such whispering and throwing up of hands and eyes is rarely seen at a Quaker meeting. Consternation was in every face. Poor Polly was a very personification of "Patience on a monument, smiling at green and yellow Melancholy."

The captain, discovering that something was the matter, drove off the dogs, and inquired what had happened to cause such confusion. "What the devil's the matter now?" he said. "You all look as down in the mouth as we did on the Santafee when the quartermaster said the provisions had all give out. What's the matter? Won't somebody tell me? Old 'oman, has the dogs got into the kitchen and eat up all the supper? or what else has come to pass? Out with it!"

"Ah, old man, bad news!" said the wife, with a sigh.

"Well, what is it? You are all getting as bad as Floyd, terrifying a fellow to death."

"Parson Gympsey was digging a new horse-trough, and cut his leg to the bone with a foot-adze and can't come. Oh, dear!"

"I wish he had taken a fancy to 'a' done it a week ago, so we mout 'a' got another parson; or, as long as no other time would suit but to-day, I wish he had cut his derned eternal head off!"

"Oh, my! husband!" exclaimed Mrs. Peablossom. Bushy Creek Ned, standing in the piazza with his fiddle, struck up the old tune of

> "We'll dance all night, till broad daylight,
> And go home with the gals in the morning."

Ned's hint caused a movement towards the dancing-room among the young people, when the captain, as if waking from a revery, exclaimed, in a loud voice, "Oh, the devil! what are we all thinking of? Why, here's Squire Tompkins; he can perform the ceremony. If a man can't marry folks, what's the use of being squire at all?"

Manna did not come in better time to the children of Israel in the wilderness than did this discovery of the worthy captain to the company assembled. It was as vivifying as a shower of rain on corn that is about to shoot and tassel, especially to G. W. Hodgkins and his lady-love.

Squire Tompkins was a newly-elected magistrate, and somewhat diffident of his abilities in this untried department. He expressed a hint of the sort, which the captain only noticed with the exclamation, "Hoot toot!"

Mrs. Peablossom insinuated to her husband that in her day the "quality," or better sort of people, in North Ca'lina, had a prejudice ag'in' being married by a magistrate; to which the old gentleman replied, "None of your nonsense, old lady; none of your Duplin County aristocracy about here now. The better sort of people, I think you say! Now, you know North Ca'lina ain't the best State in the Union, nohow, and Duplin's the poorest county in the State. Better sort of people, is it? Quality, eh? Who the devil's better than we are? Ain't we honest? Ain't we raised our children decent, and learned them how to read, write, and cipher? Ain't I fou't under Newnan and Floyd for the country? Why, darn it! we are the very best sort of people. Stuff! nonsense! The wedding shall go on; Polly shall have a husband."

Mrs. P.'s eyes lit up, her cheek flashed, as she heard "the old North State" spoken of so disparagingly; but she was a woman of good sense, and reserved the castigation for a future curtain lecture.

Things were soon arranged for the wedding; and as the old wooden clock on the mantel-piece struck one, the bridal party were duly arranged on the floor, and the crowd gathered round, eager to observe every twinkle of the bridegroom's eye and every blush of the blooming bride.

The bridesmaids and their male attendants were arranged in couples, as in a cotillion, to form a hollow square, in the centre of which were the squire and betrothing parties. Each of the attendants bore a candle; Miss Tabitha held hers in a long brass candlestick which had belonged to Polly's grandmother, in shape and length somewhat resembling Cleopatra's Needle; Miss Luvisa bore a flat tin one; the third attendant bore such an article as is usually suspended on a nail against the wall; and the fourth had a curiously-devised something cut out of wood with a pocket-knife. For want of a further supply of candlesticks, the male attendants held naked candles in their hands. Polly was dressed in white, and wore a bay flower with its green leaves in her hair, and the whisper went round, "Now *don't* she look pretty?" George Washington Hodgkins rejoiced in a white satin stock and a vest and pantaloons of orange color; the vest was straight-collared, like a Continental officer's in the Revolution, and had eagle buttons on it. They were a fine-looking couple.

When everything was ready, a pause ensued, and all eyes were turned on the squire, who seemed to be undergoing a mental agony such as Fourth-of-July orators feel when they forget their speeches, or a boy at an exhibition when he has to be prompted from behind the scenes. The truth was, Squire Tompkins was a man of forms, but had always taken them from form-books, and never trusted his memory. On this occasion he had no "Georgia Justice" or any other book from which to read the marriage ceremony, and was at a loss how to proceed. He thought over everything he had ever learned "by heart," even to

> "Thirty days hath the month of September;
> The same may be said of June, April, November,"

but all in vain; he could recollect nothing that suited such an occasion. A suppressed titter all over the room admonished him that he must proceed with something, and, in the agony of desperation, he began,—

"Know all men by these presents that I——" Here he paused, and looked up to the ceiling, while an audible voice in a corner of the room was heard to say, "He's drawing up a deed to a tract of land," and they all laughed.

"In the name of God, Amen!" he began a second time, only to hear another voice, in a loud whisper, say, "He's making his will, now. I thought he couldn't live long, he looks so powerful bad."

> "Now I lay me down to sleep,
> I pray the Lord——"

was the next essay, when some erudite gentleman remarked, "He is not dead, but sleepeth."

"O yes! O yes!" continued the squire. One voice replied, "Oh, no! oh, no! don't let's;" another whispered, "No bail!" Some person out of doors sang out, "Come into court!" and the laughter was general. The bridesmaids spilt the tallow from their candles all over the floor, in the vain attempt to look serious. One of them had a red mark on her lip for a month afterwards, where she had bit it. The bridegroom put his hands in his pockets, and took them out again; the bride looked as if she would faint; and so did the squire.

But the squire was an indefatigable man, and kept trying. His next effort was—

"To all and singular the sher——" "Let's run! he's going to level on us," said two or three at once.

Here a gleam of light flashed across the face of Squire Tompkins. That dignitary looked around all at once, with as much satisfaction as Archimedes could have felt when he discovered the method of ascertaining the specific gravity of bodies. In a grave and dignified manner, he said, "Mr. Hodgkins, hold up your right hand." George Washington obeyed, and held up his hand. "Miss Polly, hold up yours." Polly in confusion held up her left hand. "The other hand, Miss Peablossom." And the squire proceeded, in a loud and composed manner, to qualify them: "You and each of you do solemnly swear, in the presence of Almighty God and the present company, that you will perform toward each other all and singular the functions of husband and wife, as the case may be, to the best of your knowledge and ability, so help you God!"

"Good as wheat!" said Captain Peablossom. "Polly, my gal, come and kiss your old father: I never felt so happy since the day I was discharged from the army and set out homeward to see your mother."

THE HOSPITAL FOR LIARS.

ANONYMOUS.

[From the columns of the *New York Times* we extract the following amusing sketch.]

MY DEAR FRIEND,—You will, no doubt, be glad to learn about the newly-established Infirmary at Lugville. I visited it a few days ago in company with Mr. Merkle, a Boston lawyer, whom I happened to meet upon the train. On the way down he gave me a most interesting account of the endowment of this institution by the late Lorin Jenks, to whose discriminating philanthropy the world owes a charity that is not less novel in its conception than noble and practical in its aim.

Mr. Lorin Jenks, as you know, was president of the Saco Stocking and Sock Mills. He was a bachelor, and a very remarkable man. He made a million dollars one day by observing women as they purchased hose in a cheap store in Tremont Row. Mr. Jenks noticed that females who hesitated a good while about paying fifty cents a pair for plain white stockings eagerly paid seventy-five cents for the same quality ornamented with red clocks at the ankles. It cost twenty-two cents a pair to manufacture the stockings. The red fisolle for the clocks cost a quarter of a cent.

"That observation," said Mr. Merkle, "was the foundation of Jenks's great fortune. The Saco mills immediately stopped making plain hosiery. From that time forth Jenks manufactured nothing but stockings with red clocks, which he retailed at sixty cents. I am told that there is not a woman under sixty-five in Massachusetts, Maine, or Vermont who does not own at least half a dozen pairs of poor Jenks's sixty-cent red clockers."

"That fact," said I, "would interest Mr. Matthew Arnold. It shows that sweetness and light——"

"Pardon me. It shows that Jenks was a practical man as well as a philosopher. Busy as he was during his life, he took great interest in politics, like all sensible citizens. He was also a metaphysician. He closely followed contemporary speculative thought, inclining, until shortly before his death, to the Hegelian school. Every midsummer he left the stocking-mill to run itself, and repaired joyfully to Concord to listen to the lectures in the apple-orchard. It is my private opinion that Messrs. Plato, Kant, & Co. bled him pretty heavily for the privilege; but at Concord Jenks acquired new ideas as to his duty to the race."

Mr. Merkle paused to hand his ticket to the conductor.

"During the last years of his life, inasmuch as he was known to be eccentric, philanthropic, and without a family, Jenks was much beset by people who sought to interest him in various schemes for the amelioration of the human race. A week before he died he sent for me.

"'Merkle,' said he, 'I want you to draw me a will so leathery that no shark in Pemberton Square can bite it in two.'

"'Well, says I, 'what is it now, Jenks?'

"'I wish,' said he, 'to devote my entire fortune to the endowment of an institution, the idea of which occurred to me at Concord.'

"'That's right,' said I, rather sharply. 'Put honest money made in red clock hose into the Concord windmill, —that's a fine final act for a summer philosopher.'

"'Wait a minute,' said Jenks, and I fancied I saw a smile around the corners of his mouth. 'It isn't the Concord school I want to endow, though I don't deny there may be certain expectations in and around the orchard. But why spend money in teaching wisdom to the wise?' And then he proceeded to unfold his noble plan for the foundation of an Infirmary for the Mendacious."

The train was hauling up at the platform of the Lugville station.

"A few days later," continued the lawyer, as we arose from our seats, "this far-seeing and public-spirited citizen died. By the terms of his will, the income of one million

five hundred thousand dollars in Governments, Massachusetts sixes, Boston and Albany stock, and sound first mort-
gages on New England property is devoted to the Infirmary, under the direction of thirteen trustees. How the
trust has been administered you will see for yourself in a
few minutes."

We were met at the door of the Infirmary by a pleasant-
faced gentleman, who spoke with a slight German accent
and introduced himself as the Assistant Superintendent.

"Excuse me," said he, politely, "but which of you is
the patient ?"

"Oh, neither," replied Merkle, with a laugh. "I am
the counsel for the board, and this gentleman is merely a
visitor who is interested in the workings of the Institution."

"Ah, I see," said the Assistant Superintendent. "Will
you kindly walk this way?"

We entered the office, and he handed me a book and
a pen. "Please inscribe your name," said he, "in the
Visitors' Book." I did so, and then turned to speak to
Merkle, but the lawyer had disappeared.

"Our system," said the Assistant Superintendent, "is
very simple. The theory of the Institution is that the
habit of mendacity, which in many cases becomes chronic,
is a moral disease, like habitual inebriety, and that it can
generally be cured. We take the liar who voluntarily
submits himself to our treatment, and for six months we
submit him to the forcing process. That is, we encourage
him in lying, surround him with liars, his equals and supe-
riors in skill, and cram him with falsehood until he is fairly
saturated. By this time the reaction has set in, and the
patient is usually starved for the truth. He is prepared
to welcome the second course of treatment. For the next
half-year the opposite method is pursued. The satiated
and disgusted liar is surrounded by truthful attendants,

encouraged to peruse veracious literature, and by force of lectures, example, and moral influence brought to understand how much more creditable it is to say the thing which is than the thing which is not. Then we send him back into the world; and I must say that cases of relapse are infrequent."

"Do you find no incurables?" I asked.

"Yes," said the Assistant Superintendent, "once in a while. But an incurable liar is better off in the infirmary than outside, and it is better for the outside community to have him here."

Somebody came in, bringing a new patient. After sending for the Superintendent, the Assistant invited me to follow him. "I will show you how our patients live and how they amuse themselves," he said. "We will go first, if you please, through the left wing, where the saturating process may be observed."

He led the way across the hall into a large room, comfortably furnished and occupied by two dozen or more gentlemen, some reading, some writing, while others sat or stood in groups engaged in animated talk. Indeed, had it not been for the iron bars at the windows, I might have fancied myself in the lounging-room of a respectable club. My guide stopped to speak to an inmate who was listlessly turning the leaves of a well-thumbed copy of "Baron Munchausen," and left me standing near enough to one of the groups to overhear parts of the conversation.

"My rod creaked and bent double," a stout, red-faced gentleman was saying, "and the birch spun like a teetotum. I tell you, if Pierre Chaveau hadn't had the presence of mind to grip the most convenient part of my trousers with the boat-hook, I should have been dragged into the lake in two seconds or less. Well, sir, we fought sixty-nine minutes by actual time-taking, and when I had

him in and had got him back to the hotel he tipped the
scale, the speckled beauty did, at thirty-seven pounds and
eleven-sixteenths, whether you believe it or not."

"Nonsense!" said a quiet little gentleman who sat opposite. "That is impossible."

The first speaker looked flattered at this, and colored with
pleasure. "Nevertheless," he retorted, "it's a fact, on my
honor as a sportsman. Why do you say it's impossible?"

"Because," said the other, calmly, "it is an ascertained
scientific fact, as every true fisherman in this room knows
perfectly well, that there are no trout in Mooselemagunti-
cook weighing under half a hundred."

"Certainly not," put in a third speaker. "The bottom
of the lake is a sieve,—a sort of schistose sieve formation,
—and all fish smaller than the fifty-pounders fall through."

"Why doesn't the water drop through, too?" asked the
stout patient, in a triumphant tone.

"It used to," replied the quiet gentleman, gravely, "until
the Maine Legislature passed an act preventing it."

My guide rejoined me, and we went on across the room.
"These sportsman liars," he said, "are among the mildest
and most easily cured cases that come here. We send
them away in from six to nine weeks' time, with the
habit broken up, and pledged not to fish or hunt any
more. The man who lies about the fish he has caught,
or about the intelligence of his red setter dog, is often in
all·other respects a trustworthy citizen. Yet such cases
form nearly forty per cent. of all our patients."

"What are the most obstinate cases?"

"Undoubtedly those which you will see in the Travellers' and Politicians' wards of the Infirmary. The more
benign cases, such as the fisherman liars, the society liars,
the lady-killer or *bonnes fortunes* liars, the Rocky Mountain
and frontier liars (excepting Texas cases), the railroad pros-

pectus liars, the psychical research liars, and the miscellaneous liars of various classes, we permit, during the first stage of treatment, to mingle freely with each other.   The effect is good.   But we keep the Travellers and the Politicians strictly isolated."

He was about to conduct me out of the room, by a door opposite that through which we had entered, when a detached phrase, uttered by a pompous gentleman arrested my attention :

"Scipio Africanus once remarked to me——"

"There couldn't be a better example," said my guide, as we passed out of the room, "of what we call the forcing system in the treatment of mendacity.   That patient came to us voluntarily about two months ago.   The form of his disease is a common one.   Perfectly truthful in all other respects, he cannot resist the temptation to claim personal acquaintance and even intimacy with distinguished individuals.   His friends laughed at him so much for this weakness that when he heard of the establishment of the Infirmary he came here, like a sensible man, and put himself under our care.   He is doing splendidly.   When he found that his reminiscences of Beaconsfield and Bismarck and Victor Hugo created no sensation here, but were, on the contrary, at once matched and capped by still more remarkable experiences narrated by other inmates, he was at first a little staggered.   But the habit is so strong, and the peculiar vanity that craves admiration on this score is so exacting, that he began to extend his acquaintance, gradually and cautiously, back into the past.   Soon we had him giving reminiscences of Talleyrand, of Thomas Jefferson, and of Lord Cornwallis.   Observe the psychologic effect of our system.   The ordinary checks on the performances of such a liar being removed, and no doubt, suspicion, nor even wonder being expressed at any of his anecdotes, he has gone back through Voltaire and William the Silent to Charlemagne, and so on. There happens to be in the institution another patient with precisely the same trouble. They are, therefore in active competition, and each serves to force the other back more rapidly. Not long ago I heard our friend in here describing one of Heliogabalus's banquets, which he had attended as an honored guest. 'Why, I was there, too!' cried the other liar. 'It was the night they gave us the boar's head stuffed with goose-giblets, and that delicious dry Opimian muscadine.'"

"Well," I asked, "and what is your prognosis in this case?"

"Just now the two personal-reminiscence liars are driving each other back through ancient history at the rate of about three centuries a week. The flood isn't likely to stop them. Before long they will be matching reminiscences of the antediluvian patriarchs, and then they'll bring up square on Adam. They can't go any farther than Adam. By that time they will be ready for the truth-cure process; and after a few weeks spent in an atmosphere of strict veracity in the other wing of the Infirmary, they'll go out into the world again perfectly cured, and much more useful citizens than before they came to us."

We went up-stairs and saw the scrupulously neat bed-rooms which the patients occupy; through the separate wards where the isolated cases are treated; across to the right wing of the building and into a lecture-room, where the convalescent liars were gathered to hear a most interesting dissertation on "The Inexpediency of False-hood from the Legal Point of View." I was not surprised to recognize in the lecturer my railroad acquaintance, the Boston lawyer, Merkle.

On our way back to the reception-room, or office, we met a pleasant-looking gentleman about forty years old. "He is a well-known society man," the Assistant Superintendent whispered, as the inmate approached, " and he was formerly the most politely insincere person in America. Nobody could tell when he was uttering the truth, or, indeed, whether he ever did utter the truth. His habit became so exaggerated that his relatives induced him to come to Lugville for treatment. I am glad to have you see him, for he is a good example of a radical cure. We shall be ready to discharge him by the first of next week."

The cured liar was about to pass us, but the Assistant Superintendent stopped him. " Mr. Van Ransevoort," he said, " let me make you acquainted with this gentleman, who has been inspecting our system."

"I am glad to meet you, Mr. Van Ransevoort," I said.

He raised his hat and made me an unexceptionable bow. "And I," he replied, with a smile of charming courtesy, " am neither glad nor sorry to meet you, sir. I simply don't care a d——n."

The somewhat startling candor of his words was so much at variance with the perfect politeness of his manner that I was taken aback. I stammered something about not desiring to intrude. But, as he still stood there as if expecting the conversation to be continued, I added,—

" I suppose you are looking forward to your release next week ?"

"Yes, sir," he replied, "I shall be rather glad to get out again ; but my wife will be sorry."

I looked at the Assistant Superintendent. He returned a glance full of professional pride. " Well, good-by, Mr. Van Ransevoort," I said. "Perhaps I shall have the pleasure of meeting you again."

"I hope not, sir; it's rather a bore," said he, shaking my hand most cordially, and giving the Assistant Superintendent a friendly nod as he passed on.

I could fill many more pages than I have time to write with descriptions of what I saw in the Infirmary. Intelligence and thoroughness were apparent in all of the arrangements. I encountered and conversed with liars of more varieties and degrees of mendacity than you would believe had distinct existence. The majority of the cases were commonplace enough. Liars of real genius seem to be as rare inside the establishment as they are outside. I became convinced from my observations during the profitable afternoon which I spent at Lugville that chronic mendacity is a disease, as the Assistant Superintendent said, and that it is amenable, in a great number of cases, to proper treatment. On the importance of the experiment that is being carried on at Lugville with so much energy and apparent success, it is not necessary to dilate.

CORN-SHUCKING IN SOUTH CAROLINA.

WILLIAM CULLEN BRYANT.

[We have given Bryant's "Mosquito" as perhaps his only instance of poetical humor. The following is a well-told prose description of a lively and amusing negro frolic, from his "Letters of a Traveller." As the selection is short, we add to it two other brief sketches, by authors of the same period.]

But you must hear of the corn-shucking. The one at which I was present was given on purpose that I might witness the humors of the Carolina negroes. A huge fire of *light-wood* was made near the corn-house. Light-wood is the wood of the long-leaved pine, and it is so called, not because it is light, for it is almost the heaviest wood in the world, but because it gives more light than any other fuel. In clearing land, the pines are girdled and suffered to stand : the outer portion of the wood decays and falls off; the inner part, which is saturated with turpentine, remains upright for years and constitutes the planter's provision of fuel. When a supply is wanted, one of these dead trunks is felled by the axe. The abundance of light-wood is one of the boasts of South Carolina. Wherever you are, if you happen to be chilly, you may have a fire extempore; a bit of light-wood and a coal give you a bright blaze and a strong heat in an instant. The negroes make fires of it in the fields where they work, and, when the mornings are wet and chilly, in the pens where they are milking the cows. At a plantation where I passed a frosty night, I saw fires in a small enclosure, and was told by the lady of the house that she had ordered them to be made to warm the cattle.

The light-wood fire was made, and the negroes dropped in from the neighboring plantations, singing as they came. The driver of the plantation, a colored man, brought out baskets of corn in the husk and piled it in a heap; and the negroes began to strip the husks from the ears, singing with great glee as they worked, keeping time to the music, and now and then throwing in a joke and an extravagant burst of laughter. The songs were generally of a comic character; but one of them was set to a singularly wild and plaintive air, which some of our musicians would do well to reduce to notation. These are the words:

> " Johnny come down de hollow.
>   Oh, hollow !
> Johnny come down de hollow.
>   Oh, hollow !

De nigger-trader got me.
  Oh, hollow!
De speculator bought me.
  Oh, hollow!
I'm sold for silver dollars.
  Oh, hollow!
Boys, go catch the pony.
  Oh, hollow!
Bring him round the corner.
  Oh, hollow!
I'm goin' away to Georgia.
  Oh, hollow!
Boys, good-by forever.
  Oh, hollow!"

The song of "Jenny gone away" was also given, and another, called the monkey song, probably of African origin, in which the principal singer personated a monkey, with all sorts of odd gesticulations, and the other negroes bore part in the chorus, "Dan, dan, who's the dandy?" One of the songs commonly sung on these occasions represents the various animals of the woods as belonging to some profession or trade. For example,—

"De cooter is de boatman."—

The cooter is the terrapin, and a very expert boatman he is.

"De cooter is de boatman.
  John John Crow.

"De red-bird de sojer.
  John John Crow.

"De mocking-bird de lawyer.
  John John Crow.

"De alligator sawyer.
  John John Crow."

The alligator's back is furnished with a toothed ridge, like the edge of a saw, which explains the last line.

When the work of the evening was over, the negroes adjourned to a spacious kitchen. One of them took his place as musician, whistling, and beating time with two sticks upon the floor. Several of the men came forward and executed various dances, capering, prancing, and drumming with heel and toe upon the floor, with astonishing agility and perseverance, though all of them had performed their daily tasks and had worked all the evening, and some had walked from four to seven miles to attend the corn-shucking. From the dances a transition was made to a mock military parade, a sort of burlesque of our militia trainings, in which the words of command and the evolutions were extremely ludicrous. It became necessary for the commander to make a speech, and, confessing his incapacity for public speaking, he called upon a huge black man named Toby to address the company in his stead. Toby, a man of powerful frame, six feet high, his face ornamented with a beard of fashionable cut, had hitherto stood leaning against the wall, looking upon the frolic with an air of superiority. He consented, came forward, demanded a piece of paper to hold in his hand, and harangued the soldiery. It was evident that Toby had listened to stump-speeches in his day. He spoke of " de majority of Sous Carolina," " de interests of de State," " de honor of ole Ba'nwell district," and these phrases he connected by various expletives, and sounds of which we could make nothing. At length he began to falter, when the captain with admirable presence of mind came to his relief, and interrupted and closed the harangue with a hurrah from the company. Toby was allowed by all the spectators, black and white, to have made an excellent speech.

[The author of the following sketch was a popular writer of humorous novels and sketches forty or fifty years ago. From his "Life in a Liner" we select a passage indicative of one of the infelicities of ocean life.]

AN INTERRUPTED BANQUET.

Among the luxuries which the captain had provided for himself and passengers was a fine green turtle, which was not likely to suffer from exposure to salt water, so it was reserved until all the pigs and sheep and poultry had been eaten. A few days before we arrived it was determined to kill the turtle and have a feast the next day. Our cabin gentlemen had been long enough deprived of fresh meats to make them cast lickerish glances towards their hard-skinned friend, and there was a great smacking of lips the day before he was killed. As I walked aft occasionally, I heard them congratulating themselves on their prospective turtle-soup and force-meat balls; and one of them, to heighten the luxury of the feast, ate nothing but a dry biscuit for twenty-four hours, that he might be able to devour his full share of the unctuous compound. It was to be a gala-day with them; and, though it was not champagne day, that falling on Saturday and this on Friday, they agreed to have champagne a day in advance, that nothing should be wanting to give a finish to their turtle. It happened to be a rougher day than usual when the turtle was cooked, but they had become too well used to the motion of the ship to mind that. It happened to be my turn at the wheel the hour before dinner, and I had the tantalizing misery of hearing them laughing and talking about their turtle, while I was hungry from want of dry bread and salt meat. I had resolutely kept my thoughts from the cabin during all the passage but once, and now I found my ideas clustering around a tureen of turtle in spite of all my philosophy. Confound them, if they had gone out of hearing with their exulting smacks, I would not have envied their soup; but their hungry glee so excited my imagination that I could see nothing through the glazing of the binnacle but a white plate with a slice of lemon on the rim, a loaf of delicate bread, a silver spoon, a napkin, two or three wineglasses of different hues and shapes, and a water-goblet, clustering around it, and a stream of black, thick, and fragrant turtle pouring into the plate. By and by it was four bells; they dined at three. And all the gentlemen, with the captain at their head, darted below into the cabin, where their mirth increased when they caught sight of the soup-plates. "Hurry with the soup, steward," roared the captain. "Coming, sir," replied the steward. The cook opened the door of his galley, and out came the delicious steam of the turtle, such as people often inhale, and step across the street of a hot afternoon to avoid, as they pass by Delmonico's in South William Street. Then came the steward with a large covered tureen in his hand, towards the cabin gangway. I forgot the ship for a moment in looking at this precious cargo, the wheel slipped from my hands, the ship broached to with a sudden jerk, the steward had got only one foot upon the stairs, when this unexpected motion threw him off his balance and down he went by the run, the tureen slipped from his hands, and part of its contents flew into the lee scuppers, and the balance followed him in his fall.

I laughed outright. I enjoyed the turtle a thousand times more than I should have done if I had eaten the whole of it. But I was forced to restrain my mirth, for the next moment the steward ran upon deck, followed by the captain in a furious rage, threatening if he caught him to throw him overboard. Not a spoonful of the soup had been left in the coppers, for the steward had taken it all away at once to keep it warm. In about an hour afterwards the passengers came upon deck, looking more sober than I had seen them since they left Liverpool. They had dined upon cold ham.

Charles F. Briggs.

[Henry Augustus Wise, a cousin of the well-known Governor Wise of Virginia, and a lieutenant in the United States navy, was the author of several works of considerable popularity and displaying a strong sense of humor. His principal works were "Los Gringos," and "Tales for the Marines," from the latter of which we make a brief extract. He was born at Brooklyn, New York, in 1819, and died in 1869.]

THE SAGACITY OF LOBSTERS.

"Very sagacious creeters," chimed in an old salt, who was carefully laying up nettles for his hammock-clews: "I knowed a dog once as would tell the time o' day by the skipper's nose, and would drink grog, too, like a Christian."

"Bless ye," again broke out the gaunt, bony fisherman, "dogs isn't a circumstance to lobsters for sagaciousness! Why, mateys, I was on the p'int of telling you that after my trip to Greenland and the coast of Labrador the old people thought I had 'bout sowed my wild oats."—"I thought you said grass," twanged in the young mountaineer; but the whaler, without deigning a glance at the cub, went on. "And I settled down stiddy at the lobster business. Nat Pochick and me was 'prentices in a smack for better nor five years, in war times too, until our time was out, when we bought the old smack at a bargain and drove a lively trade in the same business. We used to take the lobsters, where the best of 'em comes from, along the moniment shore, down about Plymouth, and we ran 'em through the Vineyard Sound to York, by way of

Montauk. Well, one day, when we had the well of the
schooner as full as ever it could stick with claws and
feelers, like darned fools we tried to shorten the distance
by runnin' outside of Nantucket; but jest as we got off
Skonset, what should we see but the old Ramillies seventy-
four, the admiral's ship, a-hidin' under Tom Nevers' Head;
and in less than a minute an eighteen-pounder shot come
spinnin' across our bows, and two big double-banked boats
was making the water white as they pulled towards us.
We knowed as well as could be that them Britishers didn't
want the old smack, nor care a snap for the lobsters; but
we did believe sartin that they wouldn't mind clappin' hold
on two sich likely chaps as my partner and me, to sarve
under the king's flag. So we up helm and ran the smack
and the cargo slap on to the Old Man's Shoal; but jest
afore she struck we jumped into the yawl, and paddled to
the beach, where we saved bein' captured. Well, the
smack was knocked into splinters by the breakers in less
than an hour. Now, my hearties," said the whaler, as he
paused and gazed round the group of listeners, "every
blessid one of them lobsters went back to the ground
where they was took, as much as a hundred miles from
the reef where the old craft was wrecked! and there's
great Black Dan, of Mansfield, will tell ye the same; for
ye must bear in mind that every fisherman has his par-
tiklar shaped peg, to chock the claws of the lobsters with,
and every one of our lobsters was kitched ag'in with our
'dentical pegs in 'em. This, boys, was the last trip as
ever we made in that trade, though Nat Pochick, out of
fondness for the things, established himself on the old
Boston bridge, where he is to this day, a-bilin', maybe,
five or six thousand lobsters of a mornin', which he sells
off like hot cakes in the arternoons."

                                          HENRY A. WISE.

POETIC MISCELLANY.

VARIOUS.

[The following Half-hour selection is made up of a series of more or less humorous poems, varied in style, date, and author, but all good in their way.]

LOVE IN A COTTAGE.

They may talk of love in a cottage,
   And bowers of trellised vine,—
Of nature bewitchingly simple,
   And milkmaids half divine;
They may talk of the pleasure of sleeping
   In the shade of a spreading tree,
And a walk in the fields at morning
   By the side of a footstep free.

But give me a sly flirtation
   By the light of a chandelier,
With music to play in the pauses,
   And nobody very near:
Or a seat on a silken sofa,
   With a glass of pure old wine,
And mamma too blind to discover
   The small white hand in mine.

Your love in a cottage is hungry,
   Your vine is a nest for flies,
Your milkmaid shocks the Graces,
   And simplicity talks of pies.
You lie down to your shady slumber
   And wake with a bug in your ear,
And your damsel that walks in the morning
   Is shod like a mountaineer.

True love is at home on a carpet,
  And mightily likes his ease,
And true love has an eye for a dinner,
  And starves beneath shady trees.
His wing is the fan of a lady,
  His foot's an invisible thing,
And his arrow is tipped with a jewel
  And shot from a silver string.

N. P. WILLIS.

THE RETORT.

Old Nick, who taught the village school,
  Wedded a maid of homespun habit;
He was stubborn as a mule,
  She was playful as a rabbit.

Poor Jane had scarce become a wife
  Before her husband sought to make her
The pink of country-polished life
  And prim and formal as a Quaker.

One day the tutor went abroad,
  And simple Jenny sadly missed him;
When he returned, behind her lord
  She slyly stole, and fondly kissed him.

The husband's anger rose,—and red
  And white his face alternate grew:
"Less freedom, ma'am!"—Jane sighed, and said,
  Oh, dear! I didn't know 'twas you!"

GEORGE P. MORRIS.

ODE TO FORTUNE.

Fair lady with the bandaged eye,
　I'll pardon all thy scurvy tricks,
So thou wilt *cut* me and deny
　Alike thy kisses and thy kicks:
I'm quite contented as I am,—
　Have cash to keep my duns at bay,
Can choose between beefsteaks and ham,
　And drink Madeira every day.

My station is the middle rank,
　My fortune just a competence,—
Ten thousand in the Franklin Bank,
　And twenty in the six-per-cents:
No amorous chains my heart enthrall,
　I neither borrow, lend, nor sell;
Fearless I roam the City Hall,
　And bite my thumb at Mr. Bell.*

The horse that twice a year I ride
　At Mother Dawson's eats his fill;
My books at Goodrich's abide,
　My country-seat is Weehawk Hill;
My morning lounge is Eastburn's shop,
　At Poppleton's I take my lunch;
Niblo prepares my mutton-chop,
　And Jennings makes my whiskey-punch.

When merry, I the hours amuse
　By squibbing bucktails, guards, and balls;
And when I'm troubled with the blues,
　Damn Clinton and abuse canals:

---

* The Sheriff.

Then, Fortune, since I ask no prize,
    At least preserve me from thy frown :
The man who don't attempt to rise
    'Twere cruelty to tumble down.

                    JOSEPH RODMAN DRAKE.

SONG—IMITATED FROM THE FRENCH.

If Jove, when he made this beautiful world,
    Had only consulted me,
An ocean of wine should flow in the place
    Of the brackish and bitter sea.
Red wine should pour from the fruitful clouds
    In place of the tasteless rain,
And the fountains should bubble in ruby rills
    To brim the sparkling main.

No fruit should grow but the round, full grape,
    No bowers but the shady vine,
And of all earth's flowers the queenly rose
    Should alone in her beauty shine ;
I'd have a few lakes for the choicest juice,
    Where it might grow mellow and old,
And my lips should serve as a sluice to drain
    Those seas of liquid gold.

                    EDWARD SANFORD.

THE RAILROAD-CROSSING.

I can't tell much about the thing, 'twas done so powerful
    quick,
But 'pears to me I got a most outlandish heavy lick ;
It broke my leg, and tore my skulp, and jerked my arm
    most out.
But take a seat : I'll try and tell jest how it kem about.

You see, I'd started down to town, with that 'ere team of
    mine,
A-haulin' down a load o' corn to Ebenezer Kline,
And drivin' slow; for, jest about a day or two before,
The off-horse run a splinter in his foot, and made it sore.

You know the railroad cuts across the road at Martin's
    Hole:
Well, thar I seed a great big sign, raised high upon a
    pole;
I thought I'd stop and read the thing, and find out what
    it said,
And so I stopped the hosses on the railroad-track, and
    read.

I ain't no scholar, rekollect, and so I had to spell:
I started kinder cautious like, with R-A-I- and L;
And that spelt "rail" as clear as mud; R-O-A-D was
    "road."
I lumped 'em: "railroad" was the word, and that 'ere much
    I knowed.

C-R-O and double S, with I-N-G to boot,
Made "crossing" jest as plain as Noah Webster dared to
    do't.
"Railroad crossing" — good enough! — L double-O-K,
    "look;"
And I was lookin' all the time, and spellin' like a book.

O-U-T spelt "out" jest right; and there it was, "look out:"
I's kinder cur'us, like, to know jest what 'twas all about;
F-O-R and T-H-E; 'twas then "look out for the—"
And then I tried the next word; it commenced with E-N-G.

I'd got that fur, when suddintly there came an awful
    whack;
A thousand fiery thunderbolts just scooped me off the
    track;
The hosses went to Davy Jones, the wagon went to
    smash,
And I was h'isted seven yards above the tallest ash.

I didn't come to life ag'in fur 'bout a day or two;
But, though I'm crippled up a heap, I sorter struggled
    through;
It ain't the pain, nor 'tain't the loss o' that 'ere team of
    mine;
But, stranger, how I'd like to know the rest of that 'ere
    sign!

HEZEKIAH STRONG.

TEACHING PUBLIC SCHOOL.

[Saxe's " Riding on a Rail" is here very neatly imitated.]

Forty little urchins
    Coming through the door,
Pushing, crowding, making
    A tremendous roar.
Why don't you keep quiet?
    Can't you keep the rule?—
Bless me, this is pleasant,
    Teaching public school!

Forty little pilgrims
    On the road to fame;
If they fail to reach it,
    Who will be to blame?

High and lowly stations,
  Birds of every feather,
On a common level
  Here are brought together.

Dirty little faces,
  Loving little hearts,
Eyes brimful of mischief,
  Skilled in all its arts.
That's a precious darling!
  What are you about?
"May I pass the water?"
  "Please, may I go out?"

Boots and shoes are shuffling,
  Slates and books are rattling,
And in the corner yonder
  Two pugilists are battling;
Others cutting didoes,—
  What a botheration!
No wonder we grow crusty
  From such association!

Anxious parent drops in,
  Merely to inquire
Why his olive-branches
  Do not shoot up higher;
Says he wants his children
  To mind their p's and q's,
And hopes their brilliant talents
  - Will not be abused.

Spelling, reading, writing,
  Putting up the young ones;
Fuming, scolding, fighting,
  Spurring on the dumb ones;

Gymnasts, vocal music,—
  How the heart rejoices
When the singer comes to
  Cultivate the voices!

Institute attending,
  Making out reports,
Giving object-lessons,
  Class-drills of all sorts,
Reading dissertations,
  Feeling like a fool,—
Oh, the untold blessing
  Of the Public School!

ANONYMOUS.

THE TALL GENTLEMAN'S APOLOGY.

Upbraid me not! I never swore
  Eternal love to thee;
For thou art only four feet high,
  And I am six feet three:
I wonder, dear, how you supposed
  That I could look so low;
There's many a one can tie a knot
  Who cannot tie a beau!

Besides, you must confess, my love,
  The bargain's scarcely fair;
For never could we make a match,
  Although we made a pair;
Marriage, I know, makes one of two,
  But there's the horrid bore,
My friends declare if you are *one*
  That I at least am *four!*

'Tis true, the moralists have said
    That Love has got no eyes;
But why should all my sighs be heaved
    For one who has no size?
And on our wedding-day I'm sure
    I'd leave you in the lurch,
For you never saw a steeple, dear,
    In the inside of a church!

'Tis usual for a wife to take
    Her husband by the arm,
But pray excuse me if I hint
    A sort of fond alarm
That when I offered *you* my arm,
    That happiness to beg,
Your highest efforts, dear, would be
    To take me by the leg!

I do admit I wear a glass,
    Because my sight's not good,
But were I always quizzing you
    It might be counted rude.
And, though I use a convex lens,
    I still cannot but hope
My wife will ne'er "look up to me"
    Through Herschel's telescope!

Then fare thee well, my gentle one;
    I ask no parting kiss;
I must not break my back, to gain
    So exquisite a bliss;
Nor will I weep, lest I should hurt
    So delicate a flower:
The tears that fall from such a height
    Would be a thunder-shower!

Farewell! and pray don't throw yourself
  In a basin or a tub;
For that would be a sore disgrace
  To all the Six-Feet Club.
But if you ever love again,
  Love on a smaller plan,
For why extend to six feet three
  The life that's but a span?

ANONYMOUS.

THE STORY OF DEACON BROWN.

Have you heard the story of Deacon Brown,—
How he came near losing his saintly crown
By uttering language so profane?
But it wasn't his fault, as I maintain.
Listen, Maria, and you will see
How it might have happened to you or me.

A worthy man was Deacon Brown
As ever lived in Clovertown;
Bland of manner and soft of speech,
With a smile for all and a word for each.
"There's odds in deacons," as I've heard tell;
But one who has known him for quite a spell
Has often told me that Brown stood well
Not only in church, but among his neighbors,
Esteemed and loved for his life and labors.
Not a man in the town at Brown would frown,
There wasn't a stain on his fair renown;
His soul was white, though his name was Brown.

One morning the deacon started down
To purchase some goods at the store in town,—

Sugar and salt, and a calico gown,
And a pair of shoes for the youngest Brown,
And other things which he noted down,—
A good provider was Deacon Brown.
His guileless heart was light as a feather,
As he rode along in the sweet May weather,
Till he came at length to the garden gate
Of the widow Simpson, and there did wait
For a moment's chat with the pious dame
Who, years agone, was the deacon's flame.

The widow Simpson was meek and mild,
With a heart as pure as an innocent child.
She dwelt in a cottage small and neat
A little way back from the village street;
And now, in sun-bonnet, with trowel in hand,
She was tickling the soil of her garden-land.

The widow looked up and said, " Du tell !
Is that you, deacon ?   I hope you're well."
And the deacon replied to the gentle dame,
" Quite well, I thank you; I hope you're the same."
Then they talked of the crops and the late spring storms,
Of the sparrowgrass and the currant-worms,
And she asked the deacon what she should do
For the varmints that riddled her bushes through.

The deacon, scratching his head, said, " Well,
If I were you I would give them hel—"
He bore too hard on the fence as he spoke,
When suddenly, swiftly, down it broke,
And prostrate there at the widow's feet
Lay the fence, and the deacon pale as a sheet !

The deacon's pride was sadly humbled ;
His teeth dropped out and he wildly mumbled,

As blindly there in the dirt he fumbled;
And the widow's faith as suddenly crumbled
When she found how her good friend Brown had stumbled
And her beautiful fence to the ground had tumbled,
While it seemed to her that an earthquake rumbled;
In fact, as you see, things were generally jumbled.
The widow turned pale, and well she might,
As she looked at the ruin with womanly fright;
But her pious soul was shocked still more
As she thought 'twas an oath the deacon swore.

The deacon, too, in his grief intense,
Was afraid he had given the widow offence.
He looked around in a vague surprise,
While he tried to dam the tears that would rise
(Of pain and shame) in his dust-filled eyes.
But when he recovered his teeth and sense
He borrowed a hammer and fixed the fence,
And endeavored with meekness to explain
His late remark, which was cut in twain
By the fall of the fence and his sad refrain;
No man could say he ever swore!
He was only speaking of *hellebore*,
A drug she could buy at what's-his-name's store,
To kill the bugs which her bushes bore.
I cannot tell all that the deacon said,
But he started for home with an aching head,
And a heavy heart that could not rest;
For a guilty feeling was in his breast
Which he couldn't get out, though he tried his best.
And the widow she was ill at ease,
In spite of the deacon's apologies.
She left the garden, went up the stair,
Threw herself into her rocking-chair,

And rocked and rocked till the soothing balm
Of the breeze and the sunshine made her calm,
Then she searched the Scriptures to find a text
That would somewhat ease her mind perplext;
For her righteous soul was sorely vext,
And she wondered, " What ever will happen next!"
And she thinks to this day, as I've heard her say,
Brown shouldn't have spoken in just that way.
But as for myself, I question whether,
If he'd just put his syllables nearer together,
There had been the least trouble or scandal; but then
Such mistakes will occur with the wisest of men.
In viewing such things with our moral eyes,
There's a tendency, always, to moralize;
And this is the moral I offer for all:
When you think you are standing take heed lest you fall!

ANONYMOUS.

JENKS'S WHISKERS.

SOLOMON F. SMITH.

[We have already given an extract from Sol. Smith's " Theatrical Apprenticeship," but an additional specimen will not be amiss.]

THERE lived in Macon a dandified individual, whom we will call Jenks. This individual had a tolerably favorable opinion of his personal appearance. His fingers were hooped with rings, and his shirt-bosom was decked with a magnificent breastpin; coat, hat, vest, and boots were made exactly to fit: he wore kid gloves of remarkable whiteness; his hair was oiled and dressed in the latest and best style; and, to complete his killing appearance, he sported an enormous pair of *real whiskers!* Of these whiskers Jenks was as proud as a young cat is of her tail when she first discovers she has one.

I was sitting one day in a broker's office, when Jenks came in to inquire the price of exchange on New York. He was invited to sit down, and a cigar was offered him. Conversation turning on the subject of buying and selling stocks, a remark was made by a gentleman present that he thought no person should sell out stock in such-and-such a bank at that time, as it *must* get better in a few days.

"I will sell anything I've got, if I can make anything on it," replied Jenks.

"Oh, no," replied one, "not anything: you wouldn't sell your whiskers!"

A loud laugh followed this chance remark. Jenks immediately answered, "I would; but who would want them? Any person making the purchase would lose money by the operation, I'm thinking."

"Well," I observed, "I would be willing to take the speculation, if the price could be made reasonable."

"Oh, I'll sell 'em cheap," answered Jenks, winking at the gentlemen present.

"What do you call cheap?" I inquired.

"I'll sell 'em for fifty dollars," Jenks answered, puffing forth a cloud of smoke across the counter and repeating the wink.

"Well, that *is* cheap. And you'll sell your whiskers for fifty dollars?"

"I will."

"Both of them?"

"Both of them."

"I'll take them. When can I have them?"

"Any time you choose to call for them."

"Very well: they're mine. I think I shall double my money on them, at least."

I took a bill of sale as follows:

"Received of Sol. Smith Fifty Dollars, in full for my crop of whiskers, to be worn and taken care of by me, and delivered to him when called for.

"J. Jenks."

The sum of fifty dollars was paid, and Jenks left the broker's office in high glee, flourishing five Central Bank X's, and telling all his acquaintances of the great bargain he had made in the sale of his whiskers.

The broker and his friends laughed at me for being taken in so nicely. "Never mind," said I: "let those laugh that win: I'll make a profit out of those whiskers, depend on it."

For a week after this, whenever I met Jenks, he asked me when I intended to call for my whiskers.

"I'll let you know when I want them," was always my answer. "Take good care of them: oil them occasionally; I shall call for them one of these days."

A splendid ball was to be given. I ascertained that Jenks was to be one of the managers, he being a great ladies'-man (on account of his whiskers, I suppose), and it occurred to me that before the ball took place I might as well call for my whiskers.

One morning I met Jenks in a barber's shop. He was adonizing before a large mirror, and combing up my whiskers at a devil of a rate.

"Ah! there you are, old fellow," said he, speaking to my reflection through the glass. "Come for your whiskers, I suppose?"

"Oh, no hurry," I replied, as I sat down for a shave.

"Always ready, you know," he answered, giving a final tie to his cravat.

"Come to think of it," I said, musingly, as the barber began to put the lather on my face, "perhaps now would be as good a time as another. You *may* sit down and let the barber try his hand at the whiskers."

"You couldn't wait until to-morrow, could you?" he asked, hesitatingly. "There's a *ball* to-night, you know——"

"To be sure there is, and I think you ought to go with a clean face: at all events, I don't see any reason why you should expect to wear *my* whiskers to that ball: so sit down."

He rather sulkily obeyed, and in a few moments his cheeks were in a perfect foam of lather. The barber flourished his razor, and was about to commence operations, when I suddenly changed my mind.

"Stop, Mr. Barber," I said: "you needn't shave off those whiskers just yet." So he quietly put up his razor, while Jenks started up from the chair in something very much resembling a passion.

"This is trifling!" he exclaimed. "You have claimed your whiskers: take them."

"I believe a man has a right to do as he pleases with his own property," I remarked, and left Jenks washing his face.

At dinner, that day, the conversation turned upon the whisker affair. It seems the whole town had got wind of it, and Jenks could not walk the streets without the remark being continually made by the boys, "There goes the man with old Sol's whiskers!" And they had grown to an immense size, for he dared not trim them. In short, I became convinced Jenks was waiting very impatiently for me to assert my rights in the property. It happened

that several of the party were sitting opposite me at
dinner who were present when the singular bargain was
made, and they all urged me to take the whiskers that
very day, and thus compel Jenks to go to the ball whisker-
less or stay at home. I agreed with them it was about
time to reap my crop, and promised that if they would all
meet me at the broker's shop, where the purchase had
been made, I would make a call on Jenks that evening
after he had dressed for the ball. All promised to be
present at the proposed shaving operation in the broker's
office, and I sent for Jenks and the barber. On the appearance of Jenks, it was evident he was much vexed at
the sudden call upon him, and his vexation was certainly
not lessened when he saw the broker's office was filled to
overflowing by spectators anxious to behold the barbarous
proceeding.

"Come, be in a hurry," he said, as he took a seat, and
leaned his head against the counter for support: "I can't
stay here long: several ladies are waiting for me to escort
them to the ball."

"True, very true: you are one of the managers, I recollect. Mr. Barber, don't detain the gentleman: go to
work at once."

The lathering was soon over, and with about three
strokes of the razor one side of his face was deprived of
its ornament.

"Come, come," said Jenks: "push ahead: there is no
time to be lost. Let the gentleman have his whiskers:
he is impatient."

"Not at all," I replied, coolly. "I'm in no sort of a hurry
myself; and, now I think of it, as *your* time must be
precious at this particular time, several ladies being in
waiting for you to escort them to the ball, I believe I'll
not take the other whisker to-night."

A loud laugh from the by-standers, and a glance in the mirror, caused Jenks to open his eyes to the ludicrous appearance he cut with a single whisker, and he began to insist upon my taking the whole of my property. But all wouldn't do. I had a right to take it when I chose; I was not obliged to take it all at once; and I chose to take but half at that particular period: indeed, I intimated to him very plainly that I was not going to be a very hard creditor, and that if he "behaved himself," perhaps I should *never* call for the balance of what he owed me.

When Jenks became convinced I was determined not to take the remaining whisker, he began, amidst the loudly-expressed mirth of the crowd, to propose terms of compromise,—first offering me ten dollars, then twenty, thirty, forty, fifty, to take off the remaining whisker. I said, firmly, "My dear sir, there is no use talking: I insist on your wearing that whisker for me for a month or two."

"What will you take for the whiskers?" he at length asked. "Won't you sell them back to me?"

"Ah," replied I, "now you begin to talk as a business-man should. Yes, I bought them on speculation: I'll sell them, if I can obtain a good price."

"What is your price?"

"One hundred dollars; *must* double my money."

"Nothing less?"

"Not a farthing less: and I'm not anxious to sell even at that price."

"Well, I'll take them," he groaned. "There's your money. And here, barber, shave off this d——d infernal whisker in less than no time. I shall be late at the ball."

ORATORY AND DIPLOMACY.

ANONYMOUS.

[We give in the present reading a series of sketches whose authors are unknown to us, but which contain enough of the element of fun to make them admissible.]

A QUENCHED ORATION.

Speaking of the ayes and noes reminds us of a story which may not prove unacceptable to legislative ears. Mike Walsh—he who made it lively in the lower House several decades ago—is the hero of it. One evening, the 21st of February, 184—, Mike occupied the chair in committee of the whole, while a bill was being considered having something to do with Indian affairs. The bill called out considerable debate, and prominent among those who proposed to make the discussion lengthy was a green and gushing law-maker who embraced each and every occasion to give vent to his impassioned eloquence. On this Indian bill he evidently intended to spread himself. A roll of manuscript lay on his desk, to which he frequently referred while his fellow-members were talking, and at length it got to be noised about that the Hon. Mr. —— was to make an elaborate speech before the committee. The ladies' gallery was filled with sweet inspirations, and the gentlemen's gallery did not lack the many boots that make rapturous applause. Those who had any objections to the Indian bill stated them as concisely as possible, and sat down so as to leave a smooth and unclaimed floor for the orator of the evening. At length he arose, spreading out his manuscript before him on his desk, and placing the glass of ice-water, brought him by a page, within easy reach. He began by remarking on the rush of memories brought to mind in considering what evening it was on which they were then assembled, and then proceeded as follows:

"Mr. Chairman and gentlemen, on this Washington's birthday eve, we who are assembled here for the good of our special State are forcibly reminded of the Father of his Country, who fought, bled, and labored incessantly and with thorough devotion for the good of all the States." At this point in his remarks the fluent speaker was interrupted by hearty applause; he took advantage of it to moisten his lips with a little ice-water, and then proceeded with a reference to the full-length portrait of George Washington, which hung then, as it hangs now, just behind the Speaker's chair. "Behold," said he, "that picture yonder, which stands a perpetual reminder of the virtues of patriotism and self-sacrifice. O lips of our first President, speak to us now with some golden motto of duty! Nose, whose nostrils have breathed defiance at the enemies of the country,—eyes, whose lightning glances were so magnetic, we call for thee and the rest of that noble form to be potent in our presence now, and during all our session to——"

The rest, residue, and remainder of the sentence were not spoken, for at this moment the chairman, Mike Walsh, brought down his gavel and announced, "The gentleman from —— is out of order in making the request he does. *The ayes and noes cannot be called for in committee of the whole.*" Those who were present when Mike made that ruling will never forget the scene it provoked. Ladies' and gentlemen's galleries, the floor and the lobbies, broke into a roar and yell of laughter which could not be restrained under ten minutes. The gushing law-maker did not resume after this interruption, although Mike very kindly said, "The gentleman from —— will proceed in order." He was seized with a sudden attack of not feeling very well, and withdrew. His views on that Indian bill were never known.

BASCOM'S BABY.

She brought it to our house, Mrs. Bascom did. It was their first,—a wee little, red-faced, pug-nosed, howling infant. It was one of the hottest days in July, but she had wrapped it up in three shawls and a bed-quilt, and was in agony every moment for fear it would sneeze.

"Do you see his darling, darling little face?" she said to me as she unwound him about forty times and looked to see which end his feet were on.

I looked. I have been the father of eleven just such howling little wopsies, and I don't see anything remarkable about Bascom's baby.

"See those eyes; that firmness of mouth; that temper in his look!" she went on.

I saw them.

The little wretch began to get red in the face and to beat the air, and his mother shouted,—

"He's being murdered by a pin!"

She turned him wrong end up, laid him on his face, then on his back, loosened his bands, rubbed the soles of his feet, and the tears stood in her eyes as she remarked,—

"I know he won't live: he's too smart."

The child recovered; and, as he lay on his back across her knees and surveyed the ceiling, she went on:

"Such a head! Why, every one who sees him says that he is going to be a Beecher. Do you notice that high forehead?"

I did. I thought he was all forehead, as his hair didn't commence to grow until the back of his neck was reached; but she assured me that I was mistaken.

" Wouldn't I just heft him once?"

I hefted him.

I told her that I never saw a child of his weight weigh so much, and she smiled like an angel. She said that she was afraid that I didn't appreciate children, but now she knew I did.

" Wouldn't I just look at his darling little feet,—his little red feet and cunning toes?"

She rolled him over on his face and unwound his feet and triumphantly held them up to my gaze. I contemplated the hundreds of little wrinkles running lengthwise and crosswise, the big toes and the little toes, and I agreed with her that, so far as I could judge from the feet and the toes and the wrinkles, a fortune of unexampled brilliancy lay before that pug-nosed infant.

He began to kick and howl, and she stood him on end, set him up, laid him down, and trotted him until she bounced his wind-colic into the middle of September.

" Whom did he look like?"

I bent over the scarlet-faced rascal, pushed his nose one side, chucked him under the chin, and didn't answer without due deliberation. I told her that there was a faint resemblance to George Washington around the mouth, but the eyes reminded me of Daniel Webster, while the general features had made me think of the poet Milton ever since she entered the house.

That was just her view exactly, only she hadn't said anything about it before.

" Did I think he was too smart to live?"

I felt of his ears, rubbed his head, put my finger down the back of his neck, and I told her that, in my humble opinion, he wasn't, though he had a narrow escape. If his nose had been set a little more to one side, or his ears had appeared in the place of his eyes, Bascom could have purchased a weed for his hat without delay. No; the child would live, there wasn't the least doubt of it; and any man or woman who said he wouldn't grow up to make the world thunder with his fame would steal the wool off a lost lamb in January.

She felt so happy that she rolled the imp up in his forty-nine bandages, shook him to straighten his legs and to take the kinks out of his neck, and then carried him home under her arm, while my wife made me go along with an umbrella, for fear the sun would peel his little nose.

BARRISTER AND WITNESS.

There is a point beyond which human forbearance cannot go, and the most even of tempers will become roused at times.

At an assize held recently, both judge and counsel had a deal of trouble to make the timid witnesses upon a trial speak sufficiently loud to be heard by the jury; and it is possible that the temper of the counsel may therefore have been turned from the even tenor of its way.

After this gentleman had gone through the various stages of bar pleading, and had coaxed, threatened, and even bullied witnesses, there was called into the box a young hostler, who appeared to be simplicity personified.

"Now, sir," said the counsel, in a tone that would at any other time have been denounced as vulgarly loud, "I hope we shall have no difficulty in making you speak out."

"I hope not, zur," was shouted, or rather bellowed out, by the witness, in tones which almost shook the building, and would certainly have alarmed any timid or nervous lady.

"How dare you speak in that way?" said the counsel.

"Please, zur, I can't speak any louder," said the astonished witness, attempting to speak louder than before, evidently thinking the fault to be in his speaking too softly.

"Pray, have you been drinking this morning?" shouted the counsel, who had now thoroughly lost the last remnant of his temper.

"Yes, zur," was the reply.

"And what have you been drinking?"

"Coffee, zur."

"And what did you have in your coffee, sir?" shouted the exasperated counsel.

"*A spune, zur*," innocently bawled the witness, in his highest key, amidst the roars of the whole court, excepting only the now thoroughly wild counsel, who flung down his brief and rushed out of court.

THE MAN WHO PUT UP AT GADSBY'S.

SAMUEL L. CLEMENS ("MARK TWAIN").

[Mark Twain is too notable a personage in American humor to be let off with the selection we have previously given from his writings. Yet out of the multitude of good things which have dropped from his pen it is by no means easy to select. Where there is a simultaneous attraction in a dozen different directions one is apt to stand still, and finally move almost at random. It is in this manner the following selection has been chosen, from "A Tramp Abroad." It may serve as an awful example to office- and claim-seekers at Washington.]

WHEN my old friend Riley and I were newspaper correspondents in Washington, in the winter of '67, we were coming down Pennsylvania Avenue one night, near midnight, in a driving storm of snow, when the flash of a street-lamp fell upon a man who was eagerly tearing along in the opposite direction. This man instantly stopped, and exclaimed,—

"This is lucky! You are Mr. Riley, ain't you?"

Riley was the most self-possessed and solemnly deliberative person in the republic. He stopped, looked his man over from head to foot, and finally said,—

"I am Mr. Riley. Did you happen to be looking for me?"

"That's just what I was doing," replied the man, joyously, "and it's the biggest luck in the world that I've found you. My name is Lykins. I'm one of the teachers of the high school, San Francisco. As soon as I heard the San Francisco postmastership was vacant, I made up my mind to get it; and here I am."

"Yes," said Riley, slowly, "as you have remarked, . . . Mr. Lykins, . . . here you are. And have you got it?"

"Well, not exactly *got* it, but the next thing to it. I've brought a petition, signed by the Superintendent of Public Instruction, and all the teachers, and by more than two hundred other people. Now I want you, if you'll be so good, to go around with me to the Pacific delegation, for I want to rush this thing through and get along home."

"If the matter is so pressing, you will prefer that we visit the delegation to-night," said Riley, in a voice that had nothing mocking in it,—to an unaccustomed ear.

"Oh, to-night, by all means! I haven't got any time to fool around. I want their promise before I go to bed: I ain't the talking kind, I'm the *doing* kind."

"Yes, . . . you've come to the right place for that. When did you arrive?"

"Just an hour ago."

"When are you intending to leave?"

"For New York to-morrow evening,—for San Francisco next morning."

"Just so. . . . What are you going to do to-morrow?"

"*Do!* Why, I've got to go to the President with the petition and the delegation, and get the appointment, haven't I?"

"Yes, . . . very true; . . . that is correct. And then what?"

"Executive session of the Senate at two P.M.,—got to get the appointment confirmed,—I reckon you'll grant that?"

"Yes, . . . yes," said Riley, meditatively, "you are right again. Then you take the train for New York in the evening, and the steamer for San Francisco next morning?"

"That's it,—that's the way I map it out."

Riley considered awhile, and then said,—

"You couldn't stay . . . a day . . . well, say two days longer?"

"Bless your soul, no! It's not my style. I ain't a man to go fooling around;—I'm a man that *does* things, I'll tell you."

The storm was raging, the thick snow blowing in gusts. Riley stood silent, apparently deep in a revery, during a minute or more, then he looked up and said,—

"Have you ever heard about that man who put up at Gadsby's, once? . . . But I see you haven't."

He backed Mr. Lykins against an iron fence, button-holed him, fastened him with his eye, like the Ancient Mariner, and proceeded to unfold his narrative as placidly and peacefully as if we were all stretched comfortably in a blossomy summer meadow instead of being persecuted by a wintry midnight tempest:

"I will tell you about that man. It was in Jackson's

II. 36*

time. Gadsby's was the principal hotel, then. Well, this man arrived from Tennessee about nine o'clock, one morning, with a black coachman and a splendid four-horse carriage and an elegant dog, which he was evidently fond and proud of; he drove up before Gadsby's, and the clerk and the landlord and everybody rushed out to take charge of him, but he said, 'Never mind,' and jumped out and told the coachman to wait,—said he hadn't time to take anything to eat, he only had a little claim against the government to collect, would run across the way, to the Treasury, and fetch the money, and then get right along back to Tennessee, for he was in considerable of a hurry.

"Well, about eleven o'clock that night he came back and ordered a bed and told them to put the horses up,—said he would collect the claim in the morning. This was in January, you understand,—January, 1834,—the 3d of January,—Wednesday.

"Well, on the 5th of February he sold the fine carriage, and bought a cheap second-hand one,—said it would answer just as well to take the money home in, and he didn't care for style.

"On the 11th of August he sold a pair of the fine horses, —said he'd often thought a pair was better than four, to go over the rough mountain-roads with, where a body had to be careful about his driving,—and there wasn't so much of his claim but he could lug the money home with a pair easy enough.

"On the 13th of December he sold another horse,—said two weren't necessary to drag that old light vehicle with, —in fact, one could snatch it along faster than was absolutely necessary, now that it was good solid winter weather, and the roads in splendid condition.

"On the 17th of February, 1835, he sold the old carriage and bought a cheap second-hand buggy,—said a buggy was just the trick to skim along mushy, slushy early-spring roads with, and he had always wanted to try a buggy on those mountain-roads, anyway.

"On the 1st of August he sold the buggy and bought the remains of an old sulky,—said he just wanted to see those green Tennesseans stare when they saw him come a-ripping along in a sulky; didn't believe they'd ever heard of a sulky in their lives.

"Well, on the 29th of August he sold his colored coachman,—said he didn't need a coachman for a sulky,— wouldn't be room enough for two in it, anyway,—and said it wasn't every day that Providence sent a man a fool who was willing to pay nine hundred dollars for such a third-rate negro as that,—been wanting to get rid of the creature for years, but didn't like to *throw* him away.

"Eighteen months later,—that is to say, on the 15th of February, 1837,—he sold the sulky and bought a saddle, —said horseback-riding was what the doctor had always recommended *him* to take, and dog'd if he wanted to risk *his* neck going over those mountain-roads on wheels in the dead of winter, not if he knew himself.

"On the 9th of April he sold the saddle,—said he wasn't going to risk *his* life with any perishable saddle-girth that ever was made, over a rainy, miry April road, while he could ride bareback and know and feel he was safe; always *had* despised to ride on a saddle, anyway.

"On the 24th of April he sold his horse,—said, 'I'm just fifty-seven to-day, hale and hearty,—it would be a *pretty* howdy-do for me to be wasting such a trip as that, and such weather as this, on a horse, when there ain't anything in the world so splendid as a tramp on foot through the fresh spring woods and over the cheery mountains, to a man that *is* a man; and I can make my dog carry my claim in a little bundle anyway, when it's

collected.   So to-morrow I'll be up bright and early, make
my little old collection, and mosey off to Tennessee, on
my own hind legs, with a rousing good-by to Gadsby's.'

"On the 22d of June he sold his dog, said, 'Dern a
dog, anyway, where you're just starting off on a rattling
bully pleasure-tramp through the summer woods and hills,
—perfect nuisance,—chases the squirrels, barks at everything, goes a-capering and splattering around in the fords,
—man can't get any chance to reflect and enjoy nature,—
and I'd a blamed sight rather carry the claim myself, it's
a mighty sight safer; a dog's mighty uncertain in a finan-
cial way,—always noticed it,—well, good-by, boys,—last
call,—I'm off for Tennessee with a good leg and a gay
heart, early in the morning.' "

There was a pause and a silence,—except the noise of
the wind and the pelting snow.   Mr. Lykins said, impatiently,—

"Well?"

Riley said,—

"Well, that was thirty years ago."

"Very well, very well: what of it?"

"I'm great friends with that old patriarch.   He comes
every evening to tell me good-by.   I saw him an hour
ago: he's off for Tennessee early to-morrow morning,—
as usual; said he calculated to get his claim through and
be off before night-owls like me have turned out of bed.
The tears were in his eyes, he was so glad he was going
to see his old Tennessee and his friends once more."

Another silent pause.   The stranger broke it:

"Is that all?"

"That is all."

"Well, for the *time* of night, and the *kind* of night, it
seems to me the story was full long enough.   But what's
it all for?"

"Oh, nothing in particular."

"Well, where's the point of it?"

"Oh, there isn't any particular point to it. Only, if you are not in *too* much of a hurry to rush off to San Francisco with that post-office appointment, Mr. Lykins, I'd advise you to '*put up at Gadsby*'s' for a spell, and take it easy. Good-by. *God* bless you!"

So saying, Riley blandly turned on his heel and left the astonished school-teacher standing there, a musing and motionless snow image shining in the broad glow of the street-lamp.

He never got that post-office.

RALPH STACKPOLE AND THE QUAKER.

ROBERT M. BIRD.

[Robert Montgomery Bird was born at New Castle, Delaware, in 1805. He studied medicine, but afterwards became joint editor and proprietor of the *North American and United States Gazette*. His literary productions comprise the successful tragedies "The Gladiator" and "Oraloosa," and several novels, one entitled "Calavar," which gives a vivid description of the conquest of Mexico by Cortez. He died in 1854. From his "Nick of the Woods," a story of life in the early days of Kentucky, we select the following description of the encounter of two notable characters. "Roaring Ralph" is the prototype of many later-drawn Western characters.]

ROARING RALPH was a stout, bandy-legged, broad-shouldered, and bull-headed tatterdemalion, ugly, mean, and villanous of look, yet with an impudent, swaggering, joyous self-esteem traced in every feature and expressed in every action of body, that rather disposed the beholder to laugh than to be displeased at his appearance. An old blanket-coat, or wrap-rascal, once white, but now of the same muddy brown hue that stained his visage, and once also of sufficient length to defend his legs, though the skirts had long since been transferred to the cuffs and elbows, where they appeared in huge patches, covered the upper part of his body; while the lower boasted a pair of buckskin breeches and leather wrappers, somewhat its junior in age, but its rival in mud and maculation. An old round fur hat, intended originally for a boy, and only made to fit his head by being slit in sundry places at the bottom, thus leaving a dozen yawning gaps, through which, as through the chinks of a lattice, stole out as many stiff bunches of black hair, gave to the capital excrescence an air as ridiculous as it was truly uncouth, which was not a little increased by the absence of one side of the brim, and by a loose fragment of it hanging down on the other. . . . As if there was not enough in his figure, visage, and attire to move the mirth of beholders, he added to his other attractions a variety of gestures and antics of the most extravagant kinds, dancing, leaping, and dodging about, clapping his hands and cracking his heels together, with the activity, restlessness, and, we may add, the grace of a jumping-jack. . . .

Had the gallant captain of horse-thieves boasted the blood, as he afterwards did the name, of an "alligator half-breed," he could scarce have conducted himself in a way more worthy of his parentage. He leaped into the centre of the throng, where, having found elbow-room for his purpose, he performed the gyration mentioned before, following it up by other feats expressive of his hostile humor. He flapped his wings and crowed, until every chanticleer in the settlement responded to the note of battle; he snorted and neighed like a horse; he bellowed like a bull; he barked like a dog; he yelled like an Indian; he whined like a panther; he howled like a wolf, until one would have thought he was a living menagerie, comprising within his single body the spirit of every animal noted for its love of conflict. Then, not content with such a display of readiness to fight the field, he darted from the centre of the area allowed him for his exercise, and invited the lookers-on individually to battle. "Whar's your buffalo-bull," he cried, "to cross horns with the roarer of Salt River? Whar's your full-blood colt that can shake a saddle off? h'yar's an old nag that can kick off the top of a buckeye! Whar's your cat of the Knobs? your wolf of the Rolling Prairies? h'yar's the old brown b'ar can claw the bark off a gum-tree! H'yar's a man for you, Tom Bruce! Same to you, Sim Roberts! to you, and to you, and to you! Ar'n't I a ring-tailed squealer? Can go down Salt on my back, and swim up the Ohio! Whar's the man to fight Roaring Ralph Stackpole?" . . .

"If you're ralely ripe for a fight, Roaring Ralph," cried Tom Bruce the younger, who had shown, like the others, a greater disposition to jest than to do battle with the champion, "here comes the very man for you. Look, boys, thar comes Bloody Nathan!" At which formidable name there was a loud shout set up, with an infinite deal of laughing and clapping of hands.

"Whar's the feller?" cried Captain Stackpole, springing six feet into the air, and uttering a whoop of anticipated triumph. "I've heered of the brute, and 'tarnal death to me, but I'm his super-superior! Show me the critter and let me fly! Cock-a-doodle-doo!"

[The new-comer was a man of very different appearance from Roaring Ralph. He was hollow-cheeked and weather-worn in aspect, with a good-natured and humble simplicity of countenance. He moved along with a shuffling and hesitating step, and a wistful look as if he feared insult from the men he was approaching. He bore a pack of deer-skins on his shoulders to relieve his miserable horse of their weight, thus showing a merciful disposition. Evidently he had received the name of Bloody Nathan in mockery.]

"Thar," exclaimed Tom Bruce, slapping Stackpole on the shoulder, with great glee, "thar's the man that calls himself Dannger! At him, for the honor of Salt River; but take care of his fore-legs, for, I tell you, he's the Pennsylvania war-horse."

"And ar'n't I the ramping tiger of the Rolling Fork?" cried Captain Ralph; "and can't I eat him, hoss, dog, dirty jacket, and all? Hold me by the tail, while I devour him!"

With that he executed two or three escapades, demivolts, curvets, and other antics of a truly equine character, and, galloping up to the amazed Nathan, saluted him with a neigh so shrill and hostile that even White Dobbin pricked up his ears and betrayed other symptoms of alarm.

"Surely, colonel, you will not allow that mad ruffian to assail the poor man?" [asked a visiting stranger.]

"Oh, Ralph won't hurt him; he's never ambitious, except among Indians and horses. He's only for skearing the old fellow."

"And who may the old fellow be? and why do you call him Bloody Nathan?"

"We call him Bloody Nathan," replied the commander, "because he's the only man in all Kentucky that won't fight! and thar's the way he beats us all hollow. Lord, captain, you'd hardly believe it, but he's nothing more than a poor Pennsylvania Quaker; and what brought him out to Kentucky, whar thar's nar another creatur' of his tribe, there's no knowing. . . . Some say his wits are unsettled, and I hold that's the truth of the creatur'."

[While this conversation was going on, Ralph continued to annoy Nathan, though more from a spirit of jest than actual hostility.]

"Bloody Nathan," said he, as soon as he had concluded his neighing and curveting, "if you ever said your prayers, now's the time. Down with your pack; for I can't stand deer's ha'r sticking in my swallow, nohow."

"Friend," said Bloody Nathan, meekly, "I beg thee will not disturb me. I am a man of peace and quiet."

And, so saying, he endeavored to pass onward, but was prevented by Ralph, who, seizing his heavy bundle with one hand, applied his right foot to it with a dexterity that not only removed it from the poor man's back, but sent the dried skins scattering over the road. This feat was rewarded by the spectators with loud shouts, all which, as well as the insult itself, Nathan bore with exemplary patience.

"Friend," he said, "what does thee seek of me, that thee treats me so?"

"A fight!" replied Captain Stackpole, uttering a war-whoop; "a fight, stranger, for the love of heaven!"

"Thee seeks it of a wrong person," said Nathan; "and I beg thee will get thee away."

"What!" cried Stackpole, "ar'n't thee the Pennsylvania war-horse, the screamer of the meeting-house, the bloody-mouthed ba'r of Yea-Nay-and-Verily?"

"I am a man of peace," said the submissive Slaughter.

"Yea verily, verily and yea!" cried Ralph, snuffing through the nostrils, but assuming an air of extreme indignation. "Stranger, I've heered of you! You're the man that holds it ag'in' duty and conscience to kill Injuns, the red-skin screamers,—that refuses to defend the women, the splendiferous critters! and the little children, the squal-a-baby d'ars! And wharfo'? Because as how you're a man of peace and no fight, you superiferous, long-legged, no-souled critter! But I'm the gentleman to make a man of you. So down with your gun, and, 'tarnal death to me, I'll whip the cowardly devil out of you."

"Friend," said Nathan, his humility yielding to a feeling of contempt, "thee is theeself a cowardly person, or thee wouldn't seek a quarrel with one, thee knows, can't fight thee. Thee would not be so ready with thee match."

With that, he stooped to gather up his skins, a proceeding that Stackpole, against whom the laugh was turned by this sally of Nathan's, resisted, by catching him by the nape of the neck, twirling him round, and making as if he really would have beaten him.

Even this the peaceful Nathan bore without anger or murmuring; but his patience fled when Stackpole, turning to the little dog, which, by bristling its back and growling, expressed a half inclination to take up its master's quarrel, applied his foot to its ribs with a violence that sent it rolling some five or six yards down the hill, where it lay for a time yelping and whining with pain.

"Friend," said Nathan, sternly, "thee is but a dog theeself to harm the creature! What will thee have with me?"

"A fight! a fight, I tell thee," replied Captain Ralph, "till I teach thy leatherified conscience the new doctrines of Kentucky."

"Fight thee I cannot, and dare not," said Nathan; and then added, "but if thee must have thee deserts, thee *shall* have them. Thee prides theeself upon thee courage and strength: will thee adventure with me a friendly fall?"

"Hurrah for Bloody Nathan!" cried the young men, vastly delighted at this unwonted spirit, while Captain

Ralph himself expressed his pleasure, by leaping into the air, crowing, and dashing off his hat, which he kicked down the hill with as much good will as he had previously bestowed upon the little dog.

"Off with your leather night-cap, and down with your rifle," he cried, giving his own weapon into the hands of a looker-on, "and scrape some of the grease off your jacket; for, 'tarnal death to me, I shall give you the Virginny lock, fling you head-fo'most, and you'll find yourself, in a twinkling, sticking fast right in the centre of the 'arth."

"Thee may find theeself mistaken," said Nathan, giving up his gun to one of the young men, but, instead of rejecting his hat, pulling it down tight over his brows. "There is locks taught among the mountains of Bedford that may be as good as them learned on the hills of Virginia.—I am ready for thee."

"Cock-a-doodle-doo!" cried Ralph Stackpole, springing towards his man, and clapping his hands, one on Nathan's left shoulder, the other on his right hip: "Are you ready?"

"I am," replied Nathan.

"Down then you go, war you a buffalo!" And with that the captain of horse-thieves put forth his strength, which was very great, in an effort that appeared quite irresistible; though, as it happened, it scarce moved Nathan from his position.

"Thee is mistaken, friend!" he cried, exerting his strength in return, and with an effect that no one had anticipated. By magic, as it seemed, the heels of the captain of horse-thieves were suddenly seen flying in the air, his head aiming at the earth, upon which it as suddenly descended with the violence of a bomb-shell; and there it would doubtless have burrowed, like the aforesaid im-

plement of destruction, had the soil been soft enough for
the purpose, or exploded into a thousand fragments, had
not the shell been double the thickness of an ordinary
skull.

"Huzza! Bloody Nathan forever!" shouted the delighted
villagers.

"He has killed the man," said Forrester; "but, bear
witness all, the fellow provoked his fate."

"Thanks to you, stranger! but not so dead as you
reckon," said Ralph, rising to his feet and scratching his
poll, with a stare of comical confusion. "I say, stranger,
here's my shoulders, but whar's my head?—Do you reckon
I had the worst of it?"

"Huzza for Bloody Nathan Slaughter! He has whipped
the ramping tiger of Salt River!" cried the young men of
the station.

"Well, I reckon he has," said the magnanimous Captain
Ralph, picking up his hat: then, walking up to Nathan,
who had taken his dog into his arms to examine into the
little animal's hurts, he cried, with much good-humored
energy, "Thar's my fo'-paw, in token I've had enough of
you, and want no mo'. But I say, Nathan Slaughter,"
he added, as he grasped the victor's hand, "it's nothing
you can boast of, to be the strongest man in Kentucky,
and the most sevagarous at a tussle, h'yar among murder-
ing Injuns and scalping runnegades, and keep your fists
off their top-knots. Thar's my idea; for I go for the
doctrine that every able-bodied man should sarve his
country and his neighbors, and fight their foes; and them
that does is men and gentlemen, and them that don't is
cowards and rascals,—that's my idea. And so fawwell."

POETICAL PROBLEMS.

VARIOUS.

[We present in the following selection a series of poems, mostly of old date in American literature, with the hope that they may be found agreeable reading.]

JUNGFRAU SPAIGER'S APOSTROPHE TO HER CAT.

A late London paper mentions that the celebrated Manheim Telescope, the masterpiece of the famous Spaiger, a Hungarian optician, was recently destroyed in a singular manner. A servant of the Observatory, having taken out the glasses to clean them, put them in again without observing that a cat had crept into the tube. At night, the animal, being alarmed at the strong powers of the lunar rays, endeavored to escape; but the effort threw down the instrument, which, falling to the ground from the top of a tower, was broken to pieces. The writer, presuming that the cat was killed by the fall, imagines the daughter of the astronomer as breaking forth in the following lament.

WHAT whiskered ghost, at this mild moonlight hour,
Invites my steps, and points to yonder tower?
'Tis Puss, my darling Puss; all bleeding! pale!
Gashed are her ears, and scotched her lengthy tail.
Oh, tell thy tale, and I will lend an ear,
Then sweep to my revenge, Grimalkin dear.
Oh, say, did boys, or other cruel hounds,
Conspire thy death and give those ghastly wounds?

Oh, tell me, puss, 'tis what I dread the most,
Did some Kilkenny cat make thee a ghost?
Canst thou not speak? Ah, then I'll seek the cause.
What see I here? the bloody prints of paws;
And, oh, chaste stars! what broken limbs appear!
Here lie thy legs; the telescope's lie here.

II.   37*

The telescope o'erturned,—too plain I see
The cause, the cause of thy cat-astrophe.

Was it for this my sire on topmost tower
Gazed at the stars till midnight's dewy hour,
Outwatched the Bear, and saw Orion rise,
While Hesper lent her light to other skies?
Was it for this he gave such strict command
To clean the glasses with a careful hand,
And then to search the tube with nicest care,
To see nor cat nor kit were nestling there,
Lest, like old Sidrophel, star-gazing wight,
Who wisely made a comet of a kite,
My cat, perhaps, 'twixt Mercury and Mars
Had helped to swell the cat-alogue of stars?

Oh, say, what led thee to that giddy height,
Thou queen of cats, that witching time of night?
Was it cat-optrics fired thy feline heart?
And didst thou dare to act the sage's part,
And, peeping at the moon, while stretched at ease,
Discover, with delight, 'twas all green cheese?
Or didst thou wish to take a near survey
Of that delicious stream, the Milky Way?
And, while the dog-star in the welkin raves,
To take a leap and lap its cream-clad waves?

Ah me! what terrors through thy frame were spread
When Luna's rays refracted on thy head
And filled thy gooseberry eyes with beams so thick!
No wonder thou becam'st a lunatic,
Lost all reflection, scarce retained a hope,
Immured in a reflecting telescope.

The concave mirror first thy fury bore,
The convex lens but vexéd thee the more:
Then all thy rage was to a focus brought;
To tilt the tube was now thy only thought.

Flounce—bounce, it tumbles from the turret wall,
Breaking itself, but breaking not thy fall!
Oh, direful fall! But why indulge this woe?
Can cat-aracts of tears avail thee now?
No; thou art bound to Hecate's wizard shore,
Where Whittington's famed cat has gone before;
And to appease thy ghost my task shall be
To consecrate a cat-acomb to thee.

Embalmed, dear shade, with true Egyptian care,
Across the Atlantic wave thy corpse I'll bear,
And where old Catskill props the western sky,
The fur-clad relics of my cat shall lie.
There shall thy favorite herbs and plants be found,
The cat-mint there shall shed its sweets around,
The savory mushroom from the sod shall start,
And to the breeze its catsup sweets impart,
While the tall cat-tail, on the reedy shore,
Shall hang his head, and thy sad fate deplore.

One warbler of the grove will ne'er forget
To pay to thee his grateful, tuneful debt:
The cat-bird, perched on the catalpa-tree,
Shall squall that note he learnt, poor puss, from thee.
While from the mount, the valley, and the plain
The weeping polecat shall repeat the strain.

ANTHONY BLEECKER.

EULOGY ON LAUGHING.

Like merry Momus while the gods were quaffing,
I come, to give an Eulogy on Laughing!
True, courtly Chesterfield, with critic zeal,
Asserts that laughing 's vastly ungenteel!
The boisterous shake, he says, distorts fine faces,
And robs each pretty feature of the graces!
But yet this paragon of perfect taste
On other topics was not over-chaste;
He like the Pharisees in this appears,
They ruined widows, but they made long prayers;
Tithe, anise, mint, they zealously affected,
But the law's weightier matters they neglected;
And while an insect strains their squeamish caul,
Down goes a monstrous camel, hunch and all!

    Yet others, quite as sage, with warmth dispute
Man's risibles distinguish him from brute;
While instinct, reason, both in common own,
To laugh is man's prerogative alone!

    Hail, rosy Laughter! thou deserv'st the bays!
Come, with thy dimples animate these lays,
Whilst universal peals attest thy praise.
Daughter of Joy! through thee we health attain
When Esculapian recipes are vain.

    Let sentimentalists ring in our ears
The tender joy of grief, the luxury of tears;
Heraclitus may whine, and oh! and ah!—
I like an honest, hearty ha, ha, ha!
It makes the wheels of nature gliblier play,
Dull care suppresses, smooths life's thorny way,
Propels the dancing current through each vein,
Braces the nerves, corroborates the brain,
Shakes every muscle, and throws off the spleen.

Old Homer makes yon tenants of the skies,
His gods, love laughing as they did their eyes!
It kept them in good humor, hushed their squabbles,
As froward children are appeased by baubles;
Ev'n Jove the thunderer dearly loved a laugh,
When of fine nectar he had ta'en a quaff!
It helps digestion when the feast runs high,
And dissipates the fumes of potent Burgundy.

But in the main, though laughing I approve,
It is not every kind of laugh I love;
For many laughs e'en candor must condemn!
Some are too full of acid, some of phlegm;
The loud horse-laugh (improperly so styled),
The idiot simper, like the slumbering child,
Th' affected laugh, to show a dimpled chin,
The sneer contemptuous, and broad vacant grin,
Are despicable all, as Strephon's smile,
To show his ivory legions, rank and file.

The honest laugh, unstudied, unacquired,
By nature prompted and true wit inspired,
Such as Quin felt, and Falstaff knew before,
When humor set the table on a roar,
Alone deserves th' applauding muse's grace!
The rest is all contortion and grimace.
But you exclaim, " Your Eulogy 's too dry;
Leave dissertation and exemplify;
Prove by experiment your maxims true,
And what you praise so highly make us do."

In truth I hoped this was already done,
And Mirth and Momus had the laurel won!
Like honest Hodge, unhappy should I fail,
Who to a crowded audience told his tale,
And laughed and sniggered all the while himself
To grace the story, as he thought, poor elf!

But not a single soul his suffrage gave,
While each long phiz was serious as the grave!
   "Laugh! laugh!" cries Hodge, "laugh loud! no halfing!
I thought you all, ere this, would die with laughing!"
This did the feat; for, tickled at the whim,
A burst of laughter like the electric beam,
Shook all the audience,—but it was at *him!*
Like Hodge, should every stratagem and wile
Through my long story not excite a smile,
I'll bear it with becoming modesty;
But should my feeble efforts move your glee,
Laugh, if you fairly can, but not at Me!

                       JONATHAN M. SEWALL.

TABITHA TOWZER.

Miss Tabitha Towzer is fair,
   No guinea-pig ever was neater;
Like a hackmatack slender and spare,
   And sweet as a musk-squash, or sweeter.

Miss Tabitha Towzer is sleek,
   When dressed in her pretty new tucker,
Like an otter that paddles the creek
   In quest of a mud-pout or sucker.

Her forehead is smooth as a tray,
   Ah! smoother than that, on my soul,
And turned, as a body may say,
   Like a delicate neat wooden bowl.

To what shall I liken her hair,
   As straight as a carpenter's line?
For similes sure must be rare
   When we speak of a nymph so divine.

Not the head of a Nazarite seer,
　　That never was shaven or shorn,
Naught equals the locks of my dear
　　But the silk of an ear of green corn.

My dear has a beautiful nose,
　　With a sled-runner crook in the middle,
Which one would be led to suppose
　　Was meant for the head of a fiddle.

Miss Tabby has two pretty eyes,
　　Glass buttons show never so bright:
Their love-lighted lustre outvies
　　The lightning-bug's twinkle by night.

And oft with a magical glance
　　She makes in my bosom a pother,
When, leering politely askance,
　　She shuts one and winks with the other.

The lips of my charmer are sweet
　　As a hogshead of maple molasses,
And the ruby-red tint of her cheek
　　The gill of a salmon surpasses.

No teeth like hers ever were seen,
　　Nor ever described in a novel,—
Of a beautiful kind of pea-green,
　　And shaped like a wooden-shod shovel.

Her fine little ears you would judge
　　Were wings of a bat in perfection;
A dollar I never should grudge
　　To put them in Peale's grand collection.

Description must fail in her chin,—
   At least till our language is richer;
Much fairer than ladle of tin,
   Or beautiful brown earthen pitcher.

So pretty a neck, I'll be bound,
   Never joined head and body together,
Like nice crook-necked squash on the ground,
   Long whitened by winter-like weather.

Should I set forth the rest of her charms,
   I might, by some phrase that's improper,
Give modesty's bosom alarms,
   Which I wouldn't do for a copper.

Should I mention her gait or her air,
   You might think I intended to banter:
She moves with more grace, you would swear,
   Than a foundered horse forced to a canter.

She sang with a beautiful voice,
   Which ravished you out of your senses;
A pig will make just such a noise
   When his hind leg stuck fast in the fence is.
             THOMAS G. FESSENDEN.

THE DECLARATION.

'Twas late, and the gay company was gone,
And light lay soft on the deserted room
From alabaster vases, and a scent
Of orange-leaves and sweet verbena came
Through the unshuttered window on the air,
And the rich pictures, with their dark old tints,

Hung like a twilight landscape, and all things
Seemed hushed into a slumber.   Isabel,
The dark-eyed, *spirituelle* Isabel,
Was leaning on her harp, and I had stayed
To whisper what I could not when the crowd
Hung on her look like worshippers.   I knelt,
And, with the fervor of a lip unused
To the cool breath of reason, told my love.
There was no answer, and I took the hand
That rested on the strings, and pressed a kiss
Upon it unforbidden, and again
Besought her that this silent evidence
That I was not indifferent to her heart
Might have the seal of one sweet syllable.
I kissed the small white fingers as I spoke
And she withdrew them gently, and upraised
Her forehead from its resting-place, and looked
Earnestly on me.   *She had been asleep!*

N. P. WILLIS.

MUSHROOMS.

In early days, ere Common Sense
  And Genius had in anger parted,
They made to friendship some pretence,
  Though each, heaven knows! diversely hearted.
To hunt for mushrooms once they went,
  Through nibbled sheepwalks straying onward,
Sense with his dull eyes earthward bent,
  While Genius shot his glances sunward.

Away they go!   On roll the hours,
  And toward the west the day-god edges;
See! Genius holds a wreath of flowers,
  Fresh culled from all the neighboring hedges.

Alas! ere eve their bright hues flit,
  While Common Sense (whom I so dote on!)
Thanked God "that he had little wit,"
  And drank his ketchup with his mutton.

Charles G. Halpine.

THAT GENTLEMAN.

EDWARD EVERETT.

[We have already given a short selection from Everett's humorous writings. The following story is an example of the older school of humor, of sufficient interest to reproduce. Everett's fame is that of an orator, scholar, and statesman. These examples show that he had a strong sense of the humorous as well.]

Among the passengers on board the steamer Chancellor Livingston, on one of her trips up the North River, last year, a middle-aged gentleman was observed by the captain, whose appearance attracted notice, but whose person and quality were unknown to him. The stranger was dressed in clothing of the latest style, but without being in the extreme of fashion or conspicuous for anything that he did or did not wear. He had not, however, availed himself of the apology of travelling, as many do, to neglect the most scrupulous care of his person, and seemed rather to be on a visit than a journey. His equipage had been noticed by the porters to correspond in appearance with its owner. The portmanteau was made to increase or diminish in capacity, the upper part rising on the under by screws, according to the contents; the whole of it was, besides, enveloped in a firm canvas. A cloak-bag of the best construction, a writing-apparatus, with a most inscrutable lock, an umbrella in a neat case, a hat in another, ready to take the place of the travelling seal-skin cap, which the stranger wore during the trip, were so many indications of a man who placed the happiness of life in the enjoyment of its comforts. The greatest of all comforts is yet to be told, and was in attendance upon him, in the shape of a first-rate servant, a yellow man by complexion, taciturn, active, gentle, just not too obsequious, and just not too familiar,—not above the name of servant, and well deserving that of friend.

This strange gentleman was quiet, moderate in his movements, somewhat reserved in his manners: all real gentlemen are so. A shade of melancholy settled over his face but rather lightening into satisfaction than dark and ominous of growing sorrow. It was a countenance which care had slightly furrowed, but in which the springing seeds of grief were not yet planted. There was a timid look of the one that had been deceived by appearances, and feared to trust himself to an exterior that might betray his heart into a misplaced confidence. There was an expression which one might almost call sly, of a man who had at length found a secret treasure, which he would not expose, lest it should be torn from him or he should be disturbed in its enjoyment. Of the beauties of the scene, though plainly a man of cultivated mind, he took little notice. He cast an eye of equal indifference on nature's Cyclopean masonry at the Palisades and on the elegant erections of art on the opposite side of the river. Even the noble entrance into the Highlands scarcely fixed his attention.

With all the appearance of a perfect gentleman, there was nevertheless conspicuous about this personage a punctuality in obeying the bell which summoned to the meals, and a satisfaction evinced while at them, which evidently proceeded from some particular association of ideas, to which the spectator wanted the key. It was not ravening appetite; it was not for want of being accustomed at home to what are commonly, and we think correctly, called "good things :" his whole appearance negatived such an idea. But he repaired to the table with a cheerful and active step, as if he were sure he could find things as they ought to be; and he partook of its provisions as if he had found them so. He did not praise the abundance and good quality of what he saw and enjoyed, but maintained the same rather mysterious silence here as elsewhere on board. But the expression of calm inward satisfaction which reigned in his face spoke volumes. In like manner, with respect to every part of the domestic economy of the boat,—the commodious berths, the conveniences of the washing-apparatus and of the barber's shop, the boot-brushing quarters,—in short, all the nameless accommodations and necessaries which will suggest themselves without being specified,—in regard to them all you might read in the stranger's looks and mien that he was perfectly satisfied; and, for some reason which did not suggest itself for want of knowledge of his history, he evidently enjoyed this satisfaction with a peculiar *relish*. In fact, the only words that had been heard to escape from "*that* gentleman" (for so the captain had called him, in pointing him out to the steward; and so the barber had called him, in speaking of him to the cook; and so the engineer had designated him, in describing his looks to the fireman),—the only words which "*that* gentleman" had been heard to utter to any one on board were his remarks to the captain after having finished a tour of observation round the boat: "Very convenient; very comfortable."

As they drew near to Albany, this air of satisfaction was evidently clouded. Nothing adverse had happened on board the boat, which was walking cheerily through the water at the rate of eleven miles and a half per hour. Mr. Surevalve, her engineer, was heard to say that he could double her steam without coming near her proof; "but then," he added to the fireman, "what good would that do, seeing the resistance of the water increases with the velocity of the boat?"—a remark to which the fireman returned what may be called a very *unknowing* look. The weather was fine, the company generally exhilarated at the thought of arriving at the journey's end, and all but the stranger rising in spirits, as they drew near to the landing-place. He, on the contrary, proceeded about the business of disembarking with the only discontented look he had worn during the trip.

But in the crowd and hurry of landing two hundred and fifty passengers, with as many trunks, carpet-bags, and bandboxes, and the tumult of conflicting porters, draymen, hackmen, and greeting friends, the stranger was lost sight of. Several of the passengers had secretly determined to keep an eye upon him, an idea having got abroad that he was a member of Parliament, or some said the Duke of Saxe-Weimar, which the engineer averred with an oath to be the case, adding that "it was hard if he could not tell a Frenchman." But it so happened that every man on board had an object of greater interest to look after in the crowd,—viz., himself; and what course the stranger took on landing, no one could say.

It was not long before the captain discovered that the stranger had not gone on shore, for he perceived him occupying a retired seat on the transom, aft in the cabin, and that he appeared to intend returning to New York the next trip. His countenance had recovered its prevailing expression, and he just opened his lips to say that he "believed he should take the boat back." Various speculations, no doubt, were made by the captain, the steward, the engineer, and the firemen, on a circumstance, upon the whole, so singular; but, recollecting his clouded aspect as he approached Albany, they came to the conclusion that he had forgotten something of importance in New York, that the recollection of it did not return to him till near the arrival of the boat, and consequently he was obliged to go down the river again. "You see *that* gentleman again?" says the engineer to the fireman. "I do," replied Mr. Manyscald. "I suppose he has forgotten something in New York," pursued the engineer, and thus closed a dialogue which a skilful novelist would have spread over three pages.

The stranger's demeanor on the return was the exact counterpart of that which he had worn on the ascent,— calm, satisfied, retired, perfectly at ease, a mind and senses formed to enjoy, reposing in the full possession of their objects. To describe his manner more minutely would be merely to repeat what we have already said in the former part of this account. But the hypothesis by which the engineer and fireman had accounted for his return, and his melancholy looks at Albany, was overthrown by the extraordinary fact that as they drew near to New York his countenance was overshadowed by the same clouds that had before darkened it. He was even more perplexed in spirit than he had before seemed; and he ordered his servant to look after the baggage, with a pettishness that contrasted strangely with his calm deportment. The engineer, who had noticed this, was determined to watch him closely; and the fireman swore he would follow him up to the head of Cortlandt Street. But just as the steamboat was rounding into the slip, a sloop was descending the river with wind and tide, and some danger of collision arose. It was necessary that the engineer should throw his wheels back, with all possible expedition. This event threw the fire-room into a little confusion, succeeded by some remarks of admiration at the precision with which the engine worked, and the boast of the fireman "how sweetly she went over her centres." This bustle below was followed by that of arriving; the usual throng of friends, porters, passengers, draymen, hackmen, and barrowmen breasting each other on the deck, on the plank which led from the boat, on the slip, and in the street, completed the momentary confusion; and when the engineer and fireman had readjusted their apartment, they burst out at once on each other with the question and reply, " Did you see which way *that* gentleman went?" " Hang it, no." The captain and the steward were much in the same predicament. " I meant to have had an eye after '*that* gentleman,' " said the captain, " but he has given me the slip."

It was, accordingly, with a good deal of surprise that, on descending to the cabin, he again saw the stranger, in the old place, again prepared to all appearance to go back to Albany, and again heard the short remark, " I believe I shall take the boat back." But the captain was well bred, and the stranger a good customer; so that no look escaped the former, expressive of the sentiments which this singular conduct excited in him. The same decorum, however, did not restrain the engineer and fireman. As soon as they perceived the stranger on his accustomed walk up and down deck, the engineer cried out, with a preliminary obtestation which we do not care to repeat, " Mr. Manyscald, do you see '*that* gentleman?' " " Ay, ay," was the answer. " Who can he be?" " Tell that if you can," rejoined the engineer; " it ain't every man that's willing to be known. For my own part, I believe it's Bolivar come to tap the dam over the Mohawk, and let the kanol waste out." The fireman modestly inquired his reason for thinking it was Bolivar, but the engineer, a little piqued at having his judgment questioned, merely muttered that "it was hard if a man who had been an engineer for ten years couldn't tell a Frenchman."

During the passage, nothing escaped the stranger that betrayed his history or errand ; nor yet was there any affectation of mystery or concealment. A close observer would have inferred (as is said to be the case with free-masonry) that no secret escaped him, because there was none to escape; that his conduct, though not to be accounted for by those unacquainted with him, was prob-ably consistent with the laws of human nature and the principles of a gentleman. It is precisely, however, a case like this which most stimulates the curiosity and awakens the suspicions of common men. They think the natural unaffected air but a deeper disguise; and it cannot be con-cealed that in the course of the third passage, very hard allusions were made by the engineer and fireman to the character of Major André as a spy. The sight of West Point probably awakened this reminiscence in the mind of the engineer, who, in the ardor of his patriotic feeling, forgot it was time of peace. The fireman was beginning to throw out a submissive hint that he did not know "that, in time of peace, even an Englishman could be hung for going to West Point;" but the engineer interrupted him, and expressed his belief with an oath, that "if General Jackson could catch '*that* gentleman'" (as he now called him with a little sneer on the word) "he would hang him, under the second article of the rules of war." "For all me," meekly responded the fireman, as he shouldered a stick of pitch-pine into the furnace.

It is remarked, by authors who have spoken on the sub-ject of juggling, that the very intensity with which a com-pany eyes the juggler facilitates his deceptions. He has but to give their eyes and their thoughts a slight misdirection, and then he may, for a moment, do almost anything unobserved, in full view. A vague impression, growing out of the loose conversation in the fire-room, had prevailed among the attendants and others in the boat that the gentleman was a foreigner, going to explore, if not to tap, the canal. With this view, they felt no doubt he would, on the return, land at Albany; a lookout was kept for him, and, though he was unnoticed in the throng at the place of debarkation, it was ascribed *to* the throng that the gentleman was unnoticed. "I tell you, you'll hear mischief from '*that* gentleman' yet," said the engineer, throwing off his steam.

What, then, was their astonishment, and even that of the captain and steward, to find the stranger was still in the cabin, and prepared to all appearance for a fourth trip! The captain felt he hardly knew how; we may call it *queer*. He stifled, however, his uneasy emotions, and endeavored to bow respectfully to the stranger's usual remark, "I think I shall take the boat back." Aware of the busy speculation which had begun to express itself in the fire-room, he requested the steward not to let it be known that "*that* gentleman" was going down again; and it remained a secret till the boat was under way. About half an hour after it had started, the gentleman left the cabin to take one of his walks on deck, and in passing along was seen at the same instant by the engineer and fireman. For a moment they looked at each other with an expression of displeasure and resolution strongly mingled. Not a word was said by either; but the fireman dropped a huge stick of pine, which he was lifting into the furnace, and the engineer as promptly cut off the steam from the engine and brought the wheels to a stand. The captain of course rushed forward, and inquired if the

boiler had *collapsed* (the modern polite word for *bursting*),
and met the desperate engineer coming up to speak for
himself. " Captain," said he, with a kind of high-pressure
movement of his arm, " I have kept up steam ever since
there was such a thing as steam on the river. Copper
boiler or iron, high pressure or low, give me the packing
of my own cylinder, and I'll knock under to no man. But
if we are to have '*that* gentleman' up and down, down and
up, and up and down again, like a sixty-horse piston, I
know one that won't raise another inch of steam if he
starves for it."

The unconscious subject of this tumult had already retreated to his post in the cabin, before the scene began,
and was, luckily, ignorant of the trouble he was causing.
The captain, who was a prudent man, spoke in a concili-
ating tone to the engineer, promised to ask the stranger
roundly who he was and what was his business, and, if he
found the least cause of dissatisfaction, to set him on shore
at Newburgh. The mollified engineer returned to his department, the fireman shouldered a huge stick of pine into
the furnace, the steam rushed hissing into the cylinder,
and the boat was soon moving her twelve knots an hour
on the river.

The captain, in the extremity of the moment, had
promised what it was hard to perform, and now experienced a sensible palpitation as he drew near to the
stranger to fulfil the obligation he had hastily assumed.
The gentleman, however, had begun to surmise the true
state of the case; he had noticed the distrustful looks of
the crew and the dubious expressions of the captain and
steward. As the former approached him, he determined
to relieve the embarrassment under which, it was plain,
he was going to address him, and said, " I perceive, sir,
you are at a loss to account for my remaining on board

the boat for so many successive trips, and, if I mistake
not, your people view me with suspicious eyes. The truth
is, captain, I believe I shall pass the summer with you."

The stranger paused to notice (somewhat wickedly) the
effect of this intelligence on the captain, whose eyes began
to grow round at the intimation; but in a moment pursued: "You must know, captain, I am one of those persons—favored I will not say—who, being above the necessity of laboring for a subsistence, are obliged to resort to
some extraordinary means to get through the year. I
am a Carolinian, and pass my summers in travelling. I
have been obliged to come by land, for the sake of seeing
friends and transacting business by the way. Did you
ever, captain, travel by land from Charleston to Philadelphia?"

The captain shook his head in the negative.

"You may thank heaven for that. Oh, captain, the
crazy stages, the vile roads, the rivers to be forded, the
sands to be ploughed through, the comfortless inns, the
crowd, the noise, the heat! But I must not dwell on it.
Suffice it to say, I have suffered everything, both moving
and stationary. I have been overturned, and had my
shoulder dislocated, in Virginia. I have been robbed between Baltimore and Havre de Grace. At Philadelphia I
have had my place in the mail-coach taken up by a way
passenger; I have been stowed by the side of a drunken
sailor in New Jersey; I have been beguiled into a fashionable boarding-house in the crowded season, in New York.
Once I have had to sit on a bag of turkeys which was
going to the stage-proprietor, who was also keeper of a
hotel; three rheumatic fevers have I caught by riding in
the night against a window that would not close; near
Elkton I was washed away in a gully, and three horses
drowned; at Saratoga I have been suffocated; at Montreal,

eaten of fleas; in short, captain, in the pursuit of pleasure I have suffered the pains of purgatory. For the first time in my life, I have met with comfort, ease, and enjoyment on board the Chancellor. I was following the multitude to the Springs. As I drew near to Albany, my heart sunk within me as I thought of the little prison in which I should be shut up at one of the fashionable hotels. In the very moment of landing, my courage failed me, and I returned to the comforts of another trip in your excellent boat. We went down to New York: I was about to step on shore, and saw a well-dressed gentleman run down by a swine in my sight. I shrunk back again into your cabin, where I have found such accommodations as I have never before met away from home; and, if you are not unwilling to have a season-passenger, I intend to pass the ensuing three months on board your boat."

The captain blushed and bowed, gratified and ashamed of his suspicions. He hurried up to put the engineer at ease, who was not less gratified at the high opinion the stranger had of the Chancellor, and, as long as the boat continued to ply for the rest of the season, remarked at least once a trip to the fireman, "' *That* gentleman' knows what's what."

A MUSICAL DUEL.

CHARLES GODFREY LELAND.

[We have given an extract from Leland's poetry. His prose also abounds in amusing situations, and we offer the following example from "Meister Karl's Sketch-Book."]

"I KNOW a story," suddenly exclaimed Count d'Egerlyn, one evening as we were taking supper at our parlor in the St. Nicholas, in New York. Now, if the count had suddenly sung, "I know a bank whereon the wild thyme blows," he would not have excited more astonishment. For, though the count was a gentleman of wit, a finished cosmopolite, and a thorough good fellow, and had moreover a beautiful wife, he was never known to tell tales of any description, either in school or out of it.

At the word upstarted Wolf Short and young C——, the latter declaring that he was, like Time, all ears, while the former, listening as if dreaming,—

> "heard him half in awe;
> While Cabaña's smoke came streaming
> Through his open jaw."

In a calm, bland voice, our good count proceeded to narrate a curious incident, which I long afterwards reduced to writing. As I remember it, the story would have been far better had it been given in the exact words in which it was originally told. But, alas! it was hardly concluded ere we had to scramble off to a party, and the next day we went all together to Boston; and it probably would never have been written out at all, had I not just been reminded of it by hearing "our nigger" Tom whistling through the hall the air on which it is founded:

MENDELSSOHN was a great musician.

Mendelssohn signifies "the son of an almond." Had he been a twin, they would have christened him *Philip-ina.*

But, as he was a Jew, they could not *christen* him. And, as he was not a twin, he consequently remained single.

Which did not, however, prevent him from being wedded to Divine Lady Music, as amateurs call her.

Mendelssohn composed "Songs without Words." Many modern poets give us words without songs.

" They shouldn't do so."

The story which I am about to relate is that of a duel which was fought as Mendelssohn's songs were sung, — without words. The insult, the rejoinder, the rebutter, the sur-rebutter, and the challenge were all *whistled.*

But as, according to Fadladeen in " Lalla Rookh," it is impossible even for an angel to carry *a sigh* in his hand, the reader will not find it strange that such an imperfect sinner as myself should find it difficult to whistle on paper or in print.

I will, therefore, take the liberty of representing by words the few notes which were whistled upon this melancholy occasion. The which notes are given at the beginning of this story.

And here the intelligent reader may remark that most authors put their notes at the *end* of their works. Mine, however, come before.

An Englishman was once seated in solitary silence in the Café de France, solemnly sipping sherry and smoking a cigar. His revery was unbroken, and his only desire on earth was that it should continue so.

Suddenly entered (as from the Grand Opera) a gay Frenchman, merrily whistling that odd little air from " Robert le Diable," so well known to all admirers of Meyerbeer and contemners of worldly wealth or sublunary riches,—

> " Oh, but gold is a chimera !
> Money all a fleeting dream !" *

Now, the interruption vexed our Englishman. At any
time he would have wished the Frenchman in Jerusalem.
At present the whistling so much disturbed him that he
wished him in a far less holy place. Mind! I do not mean
New York, though it be, like Milton's scaly sorceress, close
by the " Gate of Hell."

Therefore, in a firm and decided tone (which said, as
plainly as if he had spoken it, " I wish, sir, you would
hold your tongue"), he whistled,—

> " Oh, but gold is a chimera !
> Money all a fleeting dream !"

But the Frenchman was in high feather, and not to be
bluffed. He had had a dinner and a *gloria* of coffee and
brandy, and some *eau sucrée* and a glass of *bruleau* (which,
like *crambambuli*, consists of burnt brandy or rum, with
sugar). He had had a cigarette, or a four-cent government cigar (I forget which), had winked at a pretty girl in
the opera, and finally had heard the opera and Grisi. In
fact, he had experienced a perfect bender. Now, a bender
is a batter, and a batter is a spree, and a spree is a jollification. And the tendency of a jollification is to exalt the
mind and elevate the feelings. Therefore the feelings of
the Frenchman were exalted, and in the coolest, indiffer-
entest, impudentest, provokingest manner in the world,
he answered in whistling,—

> * " *Folle è quei che l'oro aduna*
> *E nol sa come goder,*
> *Non provó giammai fortuna,*
> *Che sta lunga dal piacer.*"

> " Oh, but gold is a chimera!
> Money all a fleeting dream !''

Which being interpreted, signified, "I care not a fig for
the world in general,—or you, sir, in particular! Stuff
that you are! Out upon you! *Parbleu!* BAH!

"Do you think that because you are silent all the world
must be mum? *Par-'r-'r-'r-'r-bleu!* Am I to sneeze because you snuff? *Par-'r-'r-'r-bleu!* Ought I to blush because you are well *read? Par-'r-'r-'r-'r-'r-'r-bleu! Tra-li-ra!*
Go to !''

All these words were distinctly intelligible in the chimes,
intonations, and accentuations of the Frenchman's whistle.
And, to make assurance doubly sure, he sat himself down
at the same *tête-à-tête* table whereon the Englishman
leaned, at the opposite seat, and, displacing, with an impudent little shove, his cigar-case, continued to whistle,
with all manner of irritating variations and aggravating
canary-bird trills, his little air,—

> " Oh, but gold is a chimera!
> Money all a fleeting dream !''

What I now wish you to believe is that John Bull was
in no wise either flattered or gratified by these little marks
of attention. Drawing back in his chair, he riveted a
stare of silent fury on the Frenchman, which might have
bluffed a buffalo, and then, in deliberate, cast-iron accents,
slowly whistled, as he rose from the table and beckoned
his foe to follow, the air which had so greatly incensed
him,—

> " Oh, but gold is a chimera!
> Money all a fleeting dream !''

Now, this last instrumento-vocal effort did not express

much, but the little it *did* express went, like the widow's
oil or a Paixhan shot, a great way. It simply signified
" Coffee and pistols for two,—without the coffee !"

To which the Frenchman, with a bow of the intensest
politeness, replied,—*toujours en sifflant*—always in whistling,—

> " Oh, but gold is a chimera !
> Money all a fleeting dream !"

Which was not much more, and certainly no less than
" Oh, if you come to that, two can play at that game.
Poor devil! what a loss you will be to the worthy and
estimable society of muffs and slow coaches! What will
that excellent individual Milady Popkins remark when
she hears that I have settled the account of her son without a surplus? After you, sir, if you please! I will
directly have the pleasure of following and killing you."

Out of the café, and along the boulevards, strode the
Englishman, followed by his new acquaintance, both
" whistling as they went,"—certainly not " from want
of thought." Whether it was " to keep their courage
up," is not written in history.

They soon reached a hall, where the Englishman offered
the only weapons in his possession, excepting " maulies,"
or fists ; and these were a pair of rapiers.

And here it would appear, gracious reader (if you are
gracious), that either I, or the Frenchman, or both of us,
made a great mistake when we understood the Englishman, by the sounds he uttered in his challenge, to signify
the whistle of pistol-bullets. It appears that it was the
whizz of swords to which he had reference. But the
Frenchman, who believed himself good at all things in
general and the *fleurette* in particular, made no scruples,
but—drawing his sword with a long whistle—struck a

II.   39*

salute, and held up a beautiful guard, accompanying every
movement with a note from the original air of

> "Oh, but gold is a chimera!
> Money all a fleeting dream!"

And now, reader, had I the pen of the blind old man
of Scio's rocky isle, I would describe thee a duel in the
real *comme il faut*, two-thirty style.   Every note of the air
was accompanied by a thrust or a parry.   When the Englishman made a thrust of *low carte seconde*, the Frenchman
guarded with a semicircle parade, or an octave (I forget
which).   When the Frenchman made an appel, a beat, or
a glissade, the Englishman, in no wise put out, either remained firm or put in a time thrust, both marking time
with the endless refrain,—

> "Oh, but gold is a chimera!
> Money all a fleeting dream!"

At last an untimely thrust from the Englishman's rapier
settled the business.   The Frenchman fell, dropped his
sword, and whistled in slower, slower measure and broken
accents, for the last time, his little melody.

Reader, I have no doubt that you have heard, ere now,
the opera of "Lucia di Lammermoor," and can well recall
the dying struggles and perishing notes of Edgardo :

> "Se di-vi-si fummo in ter-ra,
>   Ne cong-iun-ga, ne congiung-a il Nume in ciel!
>   Ne con-giun-ga, ah! oh!—Num' in ciel—
>   I-o—ti-i—se-guo!—oh!—oh!"

And so it was with our poor Frenchman, who panted
forth, game to the last,—

> "Oh,—but g-'g-'gold is a chi-mera!
>   M-'m-'mon-ey but a fleeee—"

And here—borne on the wings of a last expiring whistle —his soul took its flight.

Not a word had been spoken by either of the combatants!

A MARRIED MAN'S REVERY.

JOHN INMAN.

[The author of the following sketch, a brother of Henry Inman, the noted portrait-painter, was born at Utica, New York, in 1805, and was an associate editor of the *New York Mirror* and *The Commercial Advertiser*. He died in 1850.]

WHAT a blockhead my brother Tom is, not to marry! or rather, perhaps I should say, what a blockhead not to marry some twenty-five years ago!—for I suppose he'd hardly get any decent sort of a body to take him, as old as he is now. Poor fellow! what a forlorn, desolate kind of a life he leads! no wife to take care of him,—no children to love him,—no domestic enjoyment,—nothing snug and comfortable in his arrangements at home,—nice sociable dinners,—pleasant faces at breakfast. By the way, what the deuce is the reason *my* breakfast does not come up? I've been waiting for it this half-hour. Oh, I forgot; my wife sent the cook to market to get some trash or other for Dick's cold. She coddles that boy to death. But, after all, I ought not to find fault with Tom for not getting a wife, for he has lent me a good deal of money that came quite convenient, and I suppose my young ones will have all he's worth when he dies, poor fellow! They'll want it, I'm afraid; for, although my business does very well, this housekeeping eats up the profits, with such a large family as mine. Let us see: how many mouths have I to feed every day? There's my wife and her two sisters,—that's three; and the four boys,—seven; and Lucy, and Sarah, and Jane, and Louisa, four more,—eleven; then there's the cook and the housemaid and the boy,—fourteen; and the woman that comes every day to wash and do odd jobs about the house,—fifteen; then there's the nursery-maid, —sixteen; surely there must be another; I'm sure I made out seventeen when I was reckoning up last Sunday morning at church; there must be another somewhere. Let me see again; wife, wife's sisters, boys, girls—oh! it's myself. Faith, I have so many to think of and provide for that I forget myself half the time. Yes, that makes it,—seventeen. Seventeen people to feed every day is no joke; and, somehow or other, they all have most furious appetites; but then, bless their hearts, it's pleasant to see them eat. What a havoc they do make with the buck-wheat-cakes of a morning, to be sure! Now, poor Tom knows nothing of all this. There he lives all alone by himself in a boarding-house, with nobody near him that cares a brass farthing whether he lives or dies. No affectionate wife to nurse him and coddle him up when he's sick; no little prattlers about him to keep him in a good humor; no dawning intellects, whose development he can amuse himself with watching day after day; nobody to study his wishes and keep all his comforts ready. Confound it, hasn't that woman got back from the market yet? I feel remarkably hungry. I don't mind the boy's being coddled and messed if my wife likes it, but there's no joke in having the breakfast kept back for an hour. Oh, by the way, I must remember to buy all those things for the children to-day. Christmas is close at hand, and my wife has made out a list of the presents she means to put in their stockings. More ex-pense; and their school-bills coming in, too. I remember

before I was married I used to think what a delight it
would be to educate the young rogues myself; but a man
with a large family has no time for that sort of amusement. I wonder how old my young Tom is! let me see,—
when does his birthday come? next month, as I'm a
Christian; and then he will be fourteen. Boys of fourteen
consider themselves all but men, nowadays, and Tom is
quite of that mind, I see. Nothing will suit his exquisite
feet but Wellington boots, at thirty shillings a pair; and
his mother has been throwing out hints for some time as
to the propriety of getting a watch for him,—gold, of
course. Silver was quite good enough for me when I was
a half a score years older than he is; but times are awfully
changed since my younger days. Then, I believe in my
soul, the young villain has learned to play billiards; and
three or four times lately when he has come in late at
night his clothes seemed to be strongly perfumed with
cigar-smoke. Heigho! Fathers have many troubles, and
I can't help thinking sometimes that old bachelors are not
such wonderful fools, after all. They go to their pillows
at night with no cares on their mind to keep them awake;
and, when they have once got to sleep, nothing comes to
disturb their repose; nothing short of the house being on
fire can reach their peaceful condition. No getting up in
the cold to walk up and down the room for an hour or two
with a squalling young varlet, as my luck has been for the
last five or six weeks. It's an astonishing thing to perceive what a passion our little Louisa exhibits for crying;
so sure as the clock strikes three she begins, and there's
no getting her quiet again until she has fairly exhausted
the strength of her lungs with good, straightforward
screaming. I can't for the life of me understand why the
young villains don't get through all their squalling and
roaring in the daytime, when I am out of the way. Then,

II.—*ee*

again, what a delightful pleasure it is to be routed out of one's first nap and sent off post-haste for the doctor, as I was on Monday night, when my wife thought Sarah had got the croup, and frightened me half out of my wits with her lamentations and fidgets. By the way, there's the doctor's bill to be paid soon: his collector always pays me a visit just before Christmas. Brother Tom has no doctors to fee, and that certainly is a great comfort. Bless my soul, how the time slips away! Past nine o'clock and no breakfast ready yet,—wife messing with Dick and getting the three girls and their two brothers ready for school. Nobody thinks of me, starving here all this time. What the plague has become of my newspaper, I wonder? That young rascal Tom has carried it off, I dare say, to read in school when he ought to be poring over his books. He's a great torment, that boy. But no matter; there's a great deal of pleasure in married life, and, if some vexations and troubles do come with its delights, grumbling won't take them away. Nevertheless, brother Tom, I'm not very certain but that you have done quite as wisely as I, after all.

[To piece out the short selection above given we add two others, the first being an extract from John Neal's well-known and popular essay on "Children."]

CHILDREN.

You have but to go abroad for half an hour in pleasant weather, or to throw open your doors or windows on a Saturday afternoon, if you live anywhere in the neighborhood of a school-house, or a vacant lot with here and there a patch of green or a dry place in it, and steal behind the curtains, or draw the blinds and let the fresh wind blow through and through the chambers of your heart for a few

minutes, winnowing the dust and scattering the cobwebs
that have gathered there while you were asleep, and, lo!
you will find it ringing with the voices of children at
play, and all alive with the glimmering phantasmagoria
of leap-frog, prison-base, or knock-up-and-catch.

Let us try the experiment. There! I have opened the
windows, I have drawn the blinds, and, hark! already
there is the sound of little voices afar off, like "sweet bells
jangling." Nearer and nearer come they, and now we
catch a glimpse of bright faces peering round the corners,
and there, by that empty enclosure, a general mustering
and swarming, as of bees about a newly-discovered flower-
garden. But the voices we now hear proceed from two
little fellows who have withdrawn from the rest. One
carries a large basket, and his eyes are directed to my
window: he doesn't half like the blinds being drawn.
The other follows him with a tattered book under his arm,
rapping the posts, one after the other, as he goes along.
He is clearly on bad terms with himself. And now we
can see their faces. Both are grave, and one rather pale,
and trying to look ferocious. And, hark! now we are
able to distinguish their words. "Well, I ain't skeered o'
you," says the foremost and the larger boy. "Nor I ain't
skeered o' you," retorts the other; "but you needn't say
you meant to lick me." And so I thought. Another, less
acquainted with children, might not be able to see the
connection; but I could: it was worthy of Aristotle himself or John Locke. "I *didn't* say I meant to lick ye,"
rejoined the first; "I said I *could* lick ye, and so I can."
To which the other replies, glancing first at my window
and then all up and down street, "I should like to see you
try it." Whereupon the larger boy begins to move away,
half backwards, half sideways, muttering, just loud enough
to be heard, "Ah, you want to fight now, jest 'cause you're

close by your own house." And here the dialogue finished, and the babies moved on, shaking their little heads at each other, and muttering all the way up street. Men are but children of a larger growth; children but empires in miniature. . . .

"Ah, ah, hourra! hourra! here's a fellow's birthday!" cried a boy in my hearing once. A number had got together to play ball, but one of them having found a birthday, and not only the birthday, but the very boy to whom it belonged, they all gathered about him, as if they had never witnessed a conjunction of the sort before. The very fellows for a committee of inquiry!—into the affairs of a national bank, if you please.

Never shall I forget another incident which occurred in my presence between two other boys. One was trying to jump over a wheelbarrow. Another was going by; he stopped, and, after considering a moment, spoke. "I'll tell you what you can't do," said he. "Well, what is it?" "You can't jump down your own throat." "Well, *you* can't." "*Can't I, though!*" The simplicity of "Well, you can't," and the roguishness of "Can't I, though!" tickled me prodigiously. They reminded me of a sparring I had seen elsewhere,—I should not like to say where, having a great respect for the temples of justice and the halls of legislation. . . .

I saw three children throwing sticks at a cow. She grew tired of her share in the game at last, and, holding down her head and shaking it, demanded a new deal. They cut and run. After getting to a place of comparative security, they stopped, and, holding by the top of a board fence, began to reconnoitre. Meanwhile, another troop of children hove in sight, and, arming themselves with brick-bats, began to approach the same cow. Whereupon two of the others called out from the fence, "You Joe! you'd better

mind! that's our cow!" The plea was admitted without
a demurrer, and the cow was left to be tormented by the
legal owners. Hadn't these boys the law on their side?

JOHN NEAL.

["The Hive of the Bee-Hunter" is the source of the following
amusing sketch.]

A "HOOSIER" IN SEARCH OF JUSTICE.

About one hundred and twenty miles from New Orleans
reposes, in all rural happiness, one of the pleasantest little
towns in the South, that reflects itself in the mysterious
waters of the Mississippi.

To the extreme right of the town, looking at it from
the river, may be seen a comfortable-looking building,
surrounded by China-trees,—just such a place as senti-
mental misses dream of when they have indistinct notions
of "settling in the world."

This little "burban bandbox," however, is not occupied
by the airs of love nor the airs of the lute, but by a strong
limb of the law, a gnarled one too, who knuckles down to
business, and digs out of the "uncertainties of his profession" decisions, and reasons, and causes, and effects, nowhere to be met with except in the science called, *par
excellence*, the "perfection of human reason."

Around the interior walls of this romantic-looking place
may be found an extensive library, where all the "stat-
utes," from Moses's time down to the present day, are
ranged side by side: in these musty books the owner
revels day and night, digesting "digests," and growing the
while sallow with indigestion.

On the evening-time of a fine summer's day the sage
lawyer might have been seen walled in with books and
manuscripts, his eye full of thought, and his bald high

forehead sparkling with the rays of the setting sun, as if his genius was making itself visible to the senses: page after page he searched, musty parchments were scanned, an expression of care and anxiety indented itself on the stern features of his face, and with a sigh of despair he desisted from his labors, uttering aloud his feelings that he feared his case was a hopeless one.

Then he renewed again his mental labor with tenfold vigor, making the very silence with which he pursued his thoughts ominous, as if a spirit were in his presence.

The door of the lawyer's office opened. There pressed forward a tall, gaunt figure of a man, a perfect model of · physical power and endurance,—a Western flatboatman. The lawyer heeded not his presence, and started, as if from a dream, as the harsh tones of inquiry grated upon his ear, of,—

"Does a 'squire live here?"

"They call me so," was the reply, as soon as he had recovered from his astonishment.

"Well, 'squire," continued the intruder, "I have got a case for you, and I want jestess, if it costs the best load of produce that ever come from In-di-an."

The man of the law asked what was the difficulty.

"It's this, 'squire: I'm bound for Orleans, and put in here for coffee and other little fixin's. A chap with a face whiskered up like a prairie-dog says, says he,—

" 'Stranger, I see you've got cocks on board of your boat: bring one ashore, and I'll pit one against him that'll lick his legs off in less time than you could gaff him.' Well, 'squire, *I never take a dar'*. Says I, 'Stranger, I'm thar at wunce;' and in twenty minutes the cocks were on the levee, like parfect saints.

"We chucked them together, and my bird, 'squire,— uow mind, 'squire, my bird never struck a lick, not a single blow, but tuck to his heels and run, and, by thunder, threw up his feed,—actewelly vomited. The stakeholder gave up the money ag'in' me, and now I want jestess: as sure as fogs, my bird was physicked, or he'd stood up to his business like a wild-cat."

The lawyer heard the story with patience, but flatly refused to have anything to do with the matter.

"Prehaps," said the boatman, drawing out a corpulent pocket-book, "prehaps you think I can't pay. Here's the money; help yourself: give me jestess, and draw on my purse like an ox-team."

To the astonishment of the flatboatman, the lawyer still refused, but, unlike many of his profession, gave his would-be client, without charge, some general advice about going on board of his boat, shoving off for New Orleans, and abandoning the suit altogether.

The flatboatman stared with profound astonishment, and inquired of the lawyer "if he was a sure enough 'squire."

Receiving an affirmative reply, he pressed every argument he could use to have him undertake his case and get him "jestess;" but when he found that his efforts were unavailing, he quietly seated himself for the first time, put his hat aside, crossed his legs, then, looking up to the ceiling with an expression of great patience, he requested the 'squire to read to him the Louisiana laws on cock-fighting.

The lawyer said that he did not know of a single statute in the State upon the subject. The boatman started up as if he had been shot, exclaiming,—

"No laws in the State on cock-fighting? No, no, 'squire, you can't possum me; give us the law."

The refusal again followed; the astonishment of the boatman increased, and, throwing himself in a comicoheroic attitude, he waved his long fingers around the sides of the room, and asked,—

"What's all them thar books about?"

"All about the law."

"Well, then, 'squire, am I to understand that not one of them thar books contain a single law on cock-fighting?"

"You are."

"And, 'squire, am I to understand that thar ain't no laws in Louisiana on cock-fighting?"

"You are."

"And am I to understand that you call yourself a 'squire and that you don't know anything about cock-fighting?"

"You are."

The astonishment of the boatman at this reply for a moment was unbounded, and then suddenly ceased; the awe with which he looked upon "the 'squire" also ceased, and, resuming his natural awkward and familiar carriage, he took up his hat, and, walking to the door, with a broad grin of supreme contempt in his face, he observed,—

"That a 'squire that did not know the laws of cock-fighting, in his opinion, was distinctly an infernal old chuckle-headed fool!"

THOMAS B. THORPE.

NATIONAL ANTHEMS.

ROBERT H. NEWELL ("ORPHEUS C. KERR").

[The author of the following "poems," whose pen-name has a suspicious resemblance to "office-seeker," is a humorist who became well known through his satirical papers on the civil war, and who has also done good work in poetry, romance, and humorous fiction. He was born in New York in 1836, and was long connected with the New York press. Our selection purports to consist of poems received in response to an advertised call for a " National Anthem," answered, if we may believe their editor, by characteristic productions from our leading poets, but, as we are rather inclined to imagine, by poetic squibs for which said editor is alone responsible.]

NATIONAL ANTHEM.

BY H. W. L——, OF CAMBRIDGE.

BACK in the years when Phlagstaff, the Dane, was monarch
    Over the sea-ribbed land of the fleet-footed Norsemen,
Once there went forth young Ursa to gaze at the heavens,—
    Ursa, the noblest of all Vikings and horsemen.

Musing he sat in his stirrups and viewed the horizon,
    Where the Aurora lapt stars in a north-polar manner ;
Wildly he started,—for there in the heavens before him
    Fluttered and flew the original star-spangled banner.

Two objections are in the way of the acceptance of this anthem by the committee : in the first place, it is not an anthem at all ; secondly, it is a gross plagiarism from an old Sclavonic war-song of the primeval ages.

Next we quote from a

NATIONAL ANTHEM.

BY THE HON. EDWARD E——, OF BOSTON.

Ponderous projectiles, hurled by heavy hands,
    Fell on our Liberty's poor infant head,
Ere she a stadium had well advanced
    On the great path that to her greatness led ;
Her temple's propylon was shatter-ed ;
    Yet thanks to saving grace and Washington,
Her incubus was from her bosom hurled,
    And, rising like a cloud-dispelling sun,
She took the oil with which her hair was curled
    To grease the "hub" round which revolves the world.

II.   40*

This fine production is rather heavy for an "anthem," and contains too much of Boston to be considered strictly national. To set such an "anthem" to music would require a Wagner; and, even were it really accommodated to a tune, it could only be whistled by the populace.

We now come to a

NATIONAL ANTHEM.

BY JOHN GREENLEAF W——.

My native land, thy Puritanic stock
Still finds its roots firm bound in Plymouth Rock,
And all thy sons unite in one grand wish,—
To keep the virtues of Preserv-ed Fish.

Preserv-ed Fish, the deacon stern and true,
Told our New England what her sons should do;
And should they swerve from loyalty and right,
Then the whole land were lost indeed in night.

The sectional bias of this "anthem" renders it unsuitable for use in that small margin of the world situated outside of New England. Hence the above must be rejected.

Here we have a very curious

NATIONAL ANTHEM.

BY DR. OLIVER WENDELL H——.

A diagnosis of our history proves
Our native land a land its native loves,
Its birth a deed obstetric without peer,
Its growth a source of wonder far and near.

To love it more, behold how foreign shores
Sink into nothingness beside its stores,
Hyde Park at best—though counted ultra grand—
The "Boston Common" of Victoria's land.

The committee must not be blamed for rejecting the above after reading thus far, for such an " anthem" could only be sung by a college of surgeons or a Beacon Street tea-party.

Turn we now to a

NATIONAL ANTHEM.

BY RALPH WALDO E——.

Source immaterial of material naught,
 Focus of light infinitesimal,
Sum of all things by sleepless Nature wrought,
 Of which abnormal man is decimal.

Refract, in prism immortal, from thy stars
 To the stars blent incipient on our flag,
To beam translucent, neutrifying death,
 . And raise to immortality " the rag."

This " anthem" was greatly praised by a celebrated German scholar, but the committee will feel obliged to reject it on account of its too childish simplicity.

Here we have a

NATIONAL ANTHEM.

BY WILLIAM CULLEN B——.

The sun sinks softly to his evening post,
 The sun swells grandly to his morning crown,
Yet not a star our flag of heaven has lost,
 And not a sunset stripe with him goes down.

So thrones may fall; and from the dust of those
 New thrones may rise, to totter like the last;
But still our country's nobler planet glows,
 While the eternal stars of heaven are fast.

Upon finding that this does not go well to the air of " Yankee Doodle," the committee feel justified in declining it, being furthermore prejudiced against it by a suspicion that the poet has crowded an advertisement of a paper which he edits into the first line.

Next we quote from a

NATIONAL ANTHEM.

BY GENERAL GEORGE P. M——.

In the days that tried our fathers
    Many years ago,
Our fair land achieved her freedom,
    Blood-bought, you know.
Shall we not defend her ever,
    As we'd defend
That fair maiden, kind and clever,
    Calling us friend?

Yes! Let all the echoes answer
    From hill and dale;
Yes! Let other nations hearing
    Joy in the tale,
Our Columbia is a lady
    High-born and fair;
We have sworn allegiance to her,—
    Touch her who dare.

The tone of this "anthem" not being devotional enough to suit the committee, it should be printed on an edition of linen-cambric handkerchiefs for ladies especially.

Observe this

NATIONAL ANTHEM.

BY N. P. W——.

One hue of our flag is taken
    From the cheeks of my blushing pet,
And its stars beat time and sparkle
    Like the studs on her chemisette.

Its blue is the ocean shadow
      That hides in her dreamy eyes,
And it conquers all men, like her,
      And still for a Union flies.

Several members of the committee find that this "anthem" has too
much of the Anacreon spice to suit them.
   We next peruse a

NATIONAL ANTHEM.

BY THOMAS BAILY A——.

The little brown squirrel hops in the corn,
      The cricket quaintly sings;
The emerald pigeon nods his head,
      And the shad in the river springs;
The dainty sunflower hangs its head
      On the shore of the summer sea;
And better far if I were dead,
      If Maud did not love me.

I love the squirrel that hops in the corn,
      And the cricket that quaintly sings,
And the emerald pigeon that nods his head,
      And the shad that gayly springs.
I love the dainty sunflower, too,
      And Maud with her snowy breast;
I love them all; but I love—I love—
      I love my country best.

   This is certainly very beautiful, and sounds somewhat like Tenny-
son. Though it may be rejected by the committee, it can never lose
its value as a piece of excellent reading for children. It is calculated
to fill the youthful mind with patriotism and natural history, besides
touching the youthful heart with an emotion palpitating for all.
   We close the list with the following:

NATIONAL ANTHEM.

BY R. H. STOD——.

Behold the flag! Is it not a flag?
Deny it, man, if you dare!
And midway spread 'twixt earth and sky
It hangs like a written prayer.

Would impious hand of foe disturb
Its memories' holy spell,
And blight it with a dew of blood?
Ha, tr-r-raitor! . . . It is well.

THE FAMILY HORSE.

FREDERICK S. COZZENS.

[The "Sparrowgrass Papers" have already figured in our lists, but Mr. Sparrowgrass's experiences in horse-buying are sufficiently interesting to warrant a second extract.]

I HAVE bought me a horse. As I had obtained some skill in the *manège* during my younger days, it was a matter of consideration to have a saddle-horse. It surprised me to find good saddle-horses very abundant soon after my consultation with the stage-proprietor upon this topic. There were strange saddle-horses to sell almost every day. One man was very candid about his horse: he told me, if his horse had a blemish, he wouldn't wait to be asked about it; he would tell it right out; and, if a man didn't want him then, he needn't take him. He also proposed to put him on trial for sixty days, giving his

note for the amount paid for the horse, to be taken up in
case the animal were returned. I asked him what were
the principal defects of the horse. He said he'd been fired
once, because they thought he was spavined; but there
was no more spavin to him than there was to a fresh-laid
egg: he was as sound as a dollar. I asked him if he
would just state what were the defects of the horse. He
answered that he once had the pink-eye, and added,
"Now, that's honest." I thought so, but proceeded to
question him closely. I asked him if he had the bots.
He said, not a bot. I asked him if he would go. He said
he would go till he dropped down dead; just touch him
with a whip, and he'll jump out of his hide. I inquired
how old he was. He answered, just eight years, exactly:
some men, he said, wanted to make their horses younger
than they be; he was willing to speak right out, and own
up he was eight years. I asked him if there were any
other objections. He said no, except that he was inclined
to be a little gay; "but," he added, "he is so kind, a child
can drive him with a thread." I asked him if he was a
good family horse. He replied that no lady that ever
drew rein over him would be willing to part with him.
Then I asked him his price. He answered that no man
could have bought him for one hundred dollars a month
ago, but now he was willing to sell him for seventy-five, on
account of having a note to pay. This seemed such a very
low price, I was about saying I would take him, when
Mrs. Sparrowgrass whispered that I had better *see the
horse first.* I confess I was a little afraid of losing my
bargain by it, but, out of deference to Mrs. S., I did ask
to see the horse before I bought him. He said he would
fetch him down. "No man," he added, "ought to buy a
horse unless he's saw him." When the horse came down,
it struck me that, whatever his qualities might be, his

personal appearance was against him. One of his fore-legs was shaped like the handle of our punch-ladle, and the remaining three legs, about the fetlock, were slightly bunchy. Besides, he had no tail to brag of; and his back had a very hollow sweep, from his high haunches to his low shoulder-blades. I was much pleased, however, with the fondness and pride manifested by his owner, as he held up, by both sides of the bridle, the rather longish head of his horse, surmounting a neck shaped like a pea-pod, and said, in a sort of triumphant voice, "Three-quarters blood!" Mrs. Sparrowgrass flushed up a little when she asked me if I intended to purchase *that* horse, and added that, if I did, she would never want to ride. So I told the man he would not suit me. He answered by suddenly throwing himself upon his stomach across the backbone of his horse, and then, by turning round as on a pivot, got up a-straddle of him; then he gave his horse a kick in the ribs that caused him to jump out with all his legs, like a frog, and then off went the spoon-legged animal with a gait that was not a trot, nor yet precisely pacing. He rode around our grass-plot twice, and then pulled his horse's head up like the cock of a musket. "That," said he, "is *time.*" I replied that he did seem to go pretty fast. "Pretty fast!" said his owner. "Well, do you know Mr. —— ?" mentioning one of the richest men in our village. I replied that I was acquainted with him. "Well," said he, "you know his horse?" I replied that I had no personal acquaintance with him. "Well," said he, "he's the fastest horse in the country: jist so,—I'm willin' to admit it. But do you know I offered to put my horse ag'in' his to trot? I had no money to put up, or, rayther, to spare; but I offered to trot him, horse ag'in' horse, and the winner to take both horses; and I tell you—*he wouldn't do it!*"

Mrs. Sparrowgrass got a little nervous, and twitched me

by the skirt of the coat. "Dear," said she, "let him go."
I assured her that I would not buy the horse, and told the
man firmly I would not buy him. He said, very well; if
he didn't suit 'twas no use to keep a-talkin'; but, he added,
he'd be down agin' with another horse, next morning, that
belonged to his brother; and if he didn't suit me, then I
didn't want a horse. With this remark he rode off. . . .

"It rains very hard," said Mrs. Sparrowgrass, looking
out of the window next morning. Sure enough, the rain
was sweeping broadcast over the country, and the four
Sparrowgrassii were flattening a quartet of noses against
the window-panes, believing most faithfully the man would
bring the horse that belonged to his brother, in spite of
the elements. It was hoping against hope: no man having
a horse to sell will trot him out in a rain-storm, unless he
intend to sell him at a bargain; but childhood is so credulous! The succeeding morning was bright, however, and
down came the horse. He had been very cleverly groomed,
and looked pleasant under the saddle. The man led him
back and forth before the door. "There, 'squire, 's as good
a hoss as ever stood on iron." Mrs. Sparrowgrass asked me
what he meant by that. I replied, it was a figurative way
of expressing, in horse-talk, that he was as good a horse
as ever stood in shoe-leather. "He's a handsome hoss,
'squire," said the man. I replied that he did seem to be a
good-looking animal; "but," said I, "he does not quite come
up to the description of a horse I have read." "Whose hoss
was it?" said he. I replied it was the horse of Adonis.
He said he didn't know him; "but," he added, "there is so
many hosses stolen, that the descriptions are stuck up now
pretty common." To put him at his ease (for he seemed
to think I suspected him of having stolen the horse),
I told him the description I meant had been written some
hundreds of years ago by Shakespeare, and repeated it:

" Round-hooft, short-joynted, fetlocks shag and long,
    Broad breast, full eyes, small head, and nostrils wide,
High crest, short ears, straight legs, and passing strong,
    Thin mane, thick tail, broad buttock, tender hide."

"'Squire," said he, "that will do for a song, but it ain't no
p'ints of a good hoss. Trotters nowadays go in all shapes,
big heads and little heads, big eyes and little eyes, short
ears and long ears, thick tail and no tail; so as they have
sound legs, good l'in, good barrel, and good stifle, and
wind, 'squire, and speed well, they'll fetch a price. Now,
this animal is what I call a hoss, 'squire; he's got the
p'ints, he's stylish, he's close-ribbed, a free goer, kind in
harness,—single or double,—a good feeder." I asked him
if being a good feeder was a desirable quality. He replied
it was; "of course," said he, "if your hoss is off his feed,
he ain't good for nothin'. But what's the use," he added,
"of me tellin' you the p'ints of a good hoss. You're a
hoss man, 'squire; you know——" "It seems to me," said
I, "there is something the matter with that left eye."
"No, *sir*," said he, and with that he pulled down the horse's
head, and, rapidly crooking his forefinger at the suspected
organ, said, "See thar: don't wink a bit." "But he should
wink," I replied. "Not onless his eye are weak," he said.
To satisfy myself, I asked the man to let me take the
bridle. He did so, and, as soon as I took hold of it, the
horse started off in a remarkable retrograde movement,
dragging me with him into my best bed of hybrid roses.
Finding we were trampling down all the best plants, that
had cost at auction from three-and-sixpence to seven shillings apiece, and that the more I pulled the more he backed,
I finally let him have his own way, and jammed him stern-
foremost into our largest climbing rose, that had been all
summer prickling itself, in order to look as much like a
vegetable porcupine as possible. This unexpected bit of

satire in his rear changed his retrograde movement to a sidelong bound, by which he flirted off half the pots on the balusters, upsetting my gladioluses and tuberoses in the pod, and leaving great splashes of mould, geraniums, and red pottery in the gravel walk. By this time his owner had managed to give him two pretty severe cuts with the whip, which made him unmanageable, so I let him go. We had a pleasant time catching him again, when he got among the Lima-bean poles; but his owner led him back with a very self-satisfied expression. "Playful, ain't he, 'squire?" I replied that I thought he was, and asked him if it was usual for his horse to play such pranks. He said it was not. "You see, 'squire, he feels his oats, and hain't been out of the stable for a month. Use him, and he's as kind as a kitten." With that he put his foot in the stirrup, and mounted. The animal really looked very well as he moved around the grass-plot, and, as Mrs. Sparrowgrass seemed to fancy him, I took a written guarantee that he was sound, and bought him. What I gave for him is a secret: I have not even told Mrs. Sparrowgrass. . . .

We had passed Chicken Island, and the famous house with the stone gable and the one stone chimney, in which General Washington slept, as he made it a point to sleep in every old stone house in Westchester County, and had gone pretty far on the road, past the cemetery, when Mrs. Sparrowgrass said, suddenly, "Dear, what is the matter with your horse?" As I had been telling the children all the stories about the river on the way, I managed to get my head pretty well inside of the carriage, and, at the time she spoke, was keeping a lookout in front with my back. The remark of Mrs. Sparrowgrass induced me to turn about, and I found the new horse behaving in a most unaccountable manner. He was going down-hill with his nose almost to the ground, running the wagon first on this side and then on the other. I thought of the remark made by the man, and, turning again to Mrs. Sparrowgrass, said, " Playful, isn't he ?" The next moment I heard something breaking away in front, and then the rockaway gave a lurch and stood still. Upon examination I found the new horse had tumbled down, broken one shaft, gotten the other through the check-rein so as to bring his head up with a round turn, and besides had managed to put one of the traces in a single hitch around his off hind-leg. So soon as I had taken all the young ones and Mrs. Sparrow-grass out of the rockaway, I set to work to liberate the horse, who was choking very fast with the check-rein. It is unpleasant to get your fishing-line in a tangle when you are in a hurry for bites, but I never saw fishing-line in such a tangle as that harness. However, I set to work with a penknife, and cut him out in such a way as to make getting home by our conveyance impossible. When he got up, he was the sleepiest-looking horse I ever saw. " Mrs. Sparrowgrass," says I, " won't you stay here with the children until I go to the nearest farm-house ?" Mrs. Sparrowgrass replied that she would. Then I took the horse with me to get him out of the way of the children, and went in search of assistance. The first thing the new horse did when he got about a quarter of a mile from the scene of the accident was to tumble down a bank. Fortu-nately, the bank was not over four feet high, but, as I went with him, my trousers were rent in a grievous place. While I was getting the new horse on his feet again, I saw a colored person approaching, who came to my assistance. The first thing he did was to pull out a large jack-knife, and the next thing he did was to open the new horse's mouth and run the blade two or three times inside of the new horse's gums. Then the new horse commenced bleeding. "Dah, sah," said the man, shutting up his jack-knife; "ef 't hadn't been for dot yer hoss would 'a' bin a goner." "What was the matter with him?" said I. "Oh, he's only jis got de blind-staggers, das all. Say," said he, before I was half indignant enough at the man who had sold me such an animal, "say, ain't your name Sparrowgrass?" I replied that my name was Sparrowgrass. "Oh," said he, "I knows you. I brung some fowls once down to you place. I heerd about you and your hoss. Dat's de hoss dat's got de heaves so bad, heh! heh! You better sell dat hoss." I determined to take his advice, and employed him to lead my purchase to the nearest place where he would be cared for. Then I went back to the rockaway, but met Mrs. Sparrowgrass and the children on the road coming to meet me. She had left a man in charge of the rockaway. When we got to the rockaway we found the man missing, also the whip and one cushion. We got another person to take charge of the rockaway, and had a pleasant walk home by moonlight. I think a moonlight night delicious, upon the Hudson.

Does any person want a horse at a low price? A good stylish-looking animal, close-ribbed, good loin, and good stifle, sound legs, with only the heaves and blind-staggers, and a slight defect in one of his eyes? If at any time he slips his bridle and gets away, you can always approach him by getting on his left side. I will also engage to give a written guarantee that he is sound and kind, signed by the brother of his former owner.

NEGRO DOMESTICS.

CAROLINE GILMAN.

[Mrs. Caroline Gilman, born in Boston in 1794, was the author of a number of interesting works, among the most popular of which were "Recollections of a New England Housekeeper" "and Recollections of a Southern Matron." From the amusing descriptions of the ways of negro house-servants given in the latter we make a few extracts.]

That I might feel perfectly easy on one point, papa bought a professed cook, who was advertised in the papers, and, according to his frequent custom, brought home two gentlemen to dine the very day mamma went away. There had been so much regularity in our family heretofore that I should as soon have thought of interfering with the solar system as with the routine of the kitchen, and I felt perfectly at ease when summoned to the dining-room.

As I dipped the ladle into the tureen, and saw, instead of the usual richly-concocted turtle-soup, a few pieces of meat in a thin reddish fluid, sailing about like small craft in an open bay, my mind misgave me; but, knowing little of such matters, I helped round.

"What is this?" said papa, as he elevated a spoonful and let it drop back into his plate.

No one spoke.

"In the name of common sense, Mark," said he, in a louder tone, to one of the servants, "what have we got here?"

"Cuffee call 'em French bully, sir," said Mark, bowing, and trying to keep his countenance.

"French fire!" shouted papa, dislodging a mouthful into the grate: "my tongue is in a flame! Gentlemen, for heaven's sake put down your spoons, and don't be martyred through politeness. Mark, tell Cuffee, with my compliments, to eat it all, or he gets no Sunday money."

The soup was taken away, and the covers removed, when, lo! there stood before papa a pig on his four feet, with a lemon between his teeth, and a string of sausages round his neck. His grin was horrible.

Before me, though at the head of many delicacies provided by papa, was an immense field of *hopping John,** a good dish, to be sure, but no more presentable to strangers at the South than baked beans and pork in New England. I had not self-possession to joke about the unsightly dish, nor courage to offer it. I glanced at papa.

"What is that mountain before you, my daughter?" said papa, looking comically *over* his pig.

"*Ossa* on Pelion," said Lewis, laughing, and pointing at the almost bare bones that surmounted the rice. . . .

Have housekeepers never found that conversation has often taken a turn which seemed doubly to aggravate after misfortunes?

The subject of coffee was discussed at dinner in all its various bearings: our guests were Europeans, and evidently *au fait* in its mysteries. One contended for Mocha, the other for Java; one was for infusion, another for decoction. The greatest traveller had drank it in Turkey, and seen persons employed in watching it while it was parching on tin plates, who took out each separate bean as it became brown enough: he argued that it should be pounded not ground.

The other thought, and he thumped the table to add force to his assertion, that the French must have arrived at greater perfection than the Asiatics in this delicious beverage; and his eyes sparkled as if he were under its

---

* Bacon and rice.

influence, as he described its richness and flavor when taken from the hands of a pretty *limonadière* at the Café des Mille Colonnes at Paris.

Papa threw down his gauntlet for home-made coffee, and boasted (papa sometimes boasted a little) of his last purchase of Mocha, and the superior skill with which it was made by Kate, who usually superintended it.

The conversation was prolonged throughout the sitting, —indeed, until the beverage appeared in the drawing-room to assert its own claims, with its rich brown hue, its delightful perfume, and the vapor curling in beautiful wreaths from the gilt cups. As papa dipped his spoon in his cup, a glance told him that the chemical affinities were all rightly adjusted to the palate. It was tasted—augh! There was a moment's silence; Lewis looked ready for laughter; Anna and I were distressed; papa was angry; and our guests, with their eyes fixed on the carpet, were doubtless ruminating on Turkey and France. The taste was so utterly abominable that papa was alarmed and summoned Kate.

"Kate," said papa, "what have you put in the coffee?"

"Me ain't put nottin 'tall in 'em, sir. He mak like he always been mak."

"Did you grind or pound it?"

"He de poun', sir."

"In what?"

"In de mortar, sir."

"Go and ask the cook what was in the mortar."

Little was said during Kate's absence: we sat as solemn as members of the Inquisition. Kate entered.

"De cook say he spec' he lef *leetle* bit pepper and salt in de mortar."

Our visitors soon departed, probably minuting on their journals that Americans season their coffee with pepper and salt.

The cook was then summoned to his trial. Papa eyed him sternly, and said,—

"You call yourself a French cook, do you?"

"No, sir; maussa and de 'vertise call me French cook. I follows de mason trade, but didn't want to disoblige nobody."

In the sequel, Cuffee repaired our dilapidated chimneys, while a less pretending cook performed her duties better.

The distance of the kitchen from the house at the South often repulses housekeepers, both in cold and warm weather, from visiting it frequently; indeed, a young woman often feels herself an intruder, and as if she had but half a right to pry into the affairs of the negroes in the yard. In my rare visits, I was struck by one mode of fattening poultry. Two fine-looking turkeys were always kept tied to a part of the dresser, and fed by the cook, who talked to them by name, partly as pets and partly as victims, as they picked up the crumbs at her feet. On another occasion, I found her applying a live coal to the tail of a turtle. I exclaimed against her cruelty.

"He too stubborn, Miss Nelly."

As she spoke, he put out his head, which was her object, and a sharp knife, being near, terminated his troubles by decapitation.

Some of the mistakes that occurred in mamma's absence were as ludicrous as mortifying.

One day, as a field-boy was scrubbing the entry leading to the street door, I heard his voice in pretty strong remonstrance. Supposing him to be talking with a fellow-servant, I took no notice of it until I heard him roar out at the foot of the stairs, in a tremendous passion,—

"Miss Neely, one buckra woman want for track up all de clean floor."

I ran down as rapidly as I could, and found the elegant

Miss Lawton on the off side of his tub of water, held in abeyance by Titus's scrubbing-brush.

The social and agreeable habit of calling at tea-time is almost peculiar to Charleston. One evening, having several extra guests, Titus was summoned to carry the cake-tray. Long acquaintance and Lewis's jocose manner made him feel on particularly easy terms with him; and as Lewis was helping himself, Titus called to me,—

"Miss Neely, if Maus Lewis tak two piece of cake, he ain't lef enough for sarve all."

Passing from Lewis, he came to a gentleman who was occupied in looking at the paper to ascertain a point of intelligence; and, seeing him thus engaged, Titus took up a piece of toast carefully with his thumb and finger and laid it on a plate in the gentleman's lap. Having served us all, he deposited the tray on a table, and stood still.

After due time I said, "Hand the cake round, Titus."

Titus approached the table, took hold of the cake-basket with an air of importance, and deliberately turned it round, almost wrenching his arm in his attempt to do it thoroughly, and then, with a satisfied air, retreated. . . .

I was amusing myself, one morning, by seeing Patsey's efforts to get her big toe into her mouth, as she lay upon the floor, for her figure was too rotund to admit of walking. Puckering up her red lips with as intense an interest as if the world depended on the effort, she at length succeeded, and smacked them with a flavorous relish. As I began to frolic with her, she showed her teeth, white as rice-grains, and her round, fresh laugh rang out in musical peals. At length I jumped over her. Binah, her nurse, caught me by the arm in anger, exclaiming,—

"What for you ben walk over *my child*, Miss Neely? Just go back same fashion, or my child ain't gauin for grow no more agen."

I was really obliged to skip back to pacify her, but I soon offended anew by snatching her from her nurse's arms through the open window, as I stood on the piazza.

"My lor, Miss Neely," cried her nurse, "how you ben do sich a ting! Put Miss Patsey straight back; if you carry him troo one door 'fore you ben put 'em back, he just keep *leetle* so!"

It would be interesting to know the origin of these and other superstitions. Perhaps they have some more rational beginning than is dreamed of in our philosophy. No nurse at the South will allow a child to be carried to a looking-glass before it is a month old, and its infant sneeze must never be unanswered by "God bless you!"

ANECDOTES OF WESTERN TRAVEL.

ANONYMOUS.

[The excessive primitiveness of life in the "Wild West" of a former period has been described by many writers. We give here an example of Wisconsin ways some fifty years ago.]

AFTER a long and fatiguing day's ride over the prairies of Wisconsin, in the summer of 184–, Judge D——, upon his semi-annual circuit through the territory, arrived at a farm-house upon the borders of a large prairie, where he proposed passing the night. The proprietor of the establishment was absent, and his worthy spouse was left to do the honors of the house to such travellers as were occasionally forced to put up with the scanty accommodation she could offer.

Settlers were far apart in those days, and she was certain to get a call from all whom night happened to overtake in her vicinity. Mammy R—— was a native of the "Sucker State," and inherited many of the peculiarities of the primitive settlers. She scorned the luxuries and superfluities of the pampered matrons of the older States. Her domestic arrangements were such as to require the least amount of labor or care from her. There were no sofas, carpets, or other useless trumpery about her premises. Her wants were few and easily satisfied. She cared not what was the latest style of hat or dress; and as for shoes and stockings, they were regarded by her with the most "lofty despise." She had never cramped her understanding with any such effeminate finery. She stood five feet eleven without shoes and stockings; her hair, which was the color of a red fox (in the spring), was allowed to fall loosely about her brown shoulders, very much to the annoyance of her guests, who often fancied they saw the ends of her locks making fantastic gyrations in the dish intended for their repast.

The old woman was purely democratic in her domestic economy. She permitted her pigs, chickens, and all other live-stock to have free ingress to her house, and it was sometimes difficult, in a general *mêlée* of pigs, calves, and half-naked children, to distinguish one from the other. All appeared to possess an equal share in her good graces. She was assisted in her *ménage* by a lank, half-starved Sucker, who officiated, in the absence of her lord, as major-domo, barkeeper, and hostler.

As the judge drove up to the door, the old woman came out and said,—

"Strang-ger, will ye tell me whar yer mought be gowin to put up, or prehaps you moughtn't?"

"Yes, my dear madam: I fear we shall be under the necessity of throwing ourselves upon your hospitality for the night. I trust you will not put yourself to any inconvenience on our account, as any little spare corner you may be so kind as to allow us will suffice to make us perfectly snug and comfortable. I hope, madam, your health has been very good since I had the pleasure of seeing you last; and how are all the little ones? Ah, I see they are looking superbly! Come here, my little man, and give me a kiss."

The mammy twisted her face into what she intended for a smile, at this gracious salutation; but she looked more as if she was attempting Davy Crockett's feat of grinning the bark off a white oak, while she replied, "Wal, old hoss, trot along into the cabin, and I'll yell for Sucker to tote your hanimals to the crib."

At this she set up a scream that would not have disgraced the lungs of a Sioux warrior.

Sucker soon made his appearance, and assisted the judge's servant to attend to the horses. Upon entering the cabin, and inquiring if they could have supper, he was told that such a luxury as meat had not been seen in their larder for several weeks; that corn-dodgers and milk were the best fixings the house afforded, and these were very scarce. Fortunately for the judge, he had provided himself with a ham, to meet such contingencies, before he left home. This was soon drawn from his pannier, and placed in the hands of mammy, to be cooked for supper.

A very savory odor, issuing from the frying-pan, soon diffused itself throughout the cabin, and found its way through the chinks of the logs to the olfactories of the Sucker at the stables, and made known to him the fact that a different kind of food was preparing from what he had seen for a long time. He soon found himself seated near the fire, and cast very significant and approving glances at the meat, as it hissed and burned over the hot coals of the mammy's fire.

Supper was, in due course of time, upon the table, and the old woman announced the welcome intelligence by saying, "Men, haul up!"

Before the judge clearly comprehended this singular summons, the Sucker was seated near the plate of ham, had commenced operations on the largest slice, and as the judge drew his chair to the table he said,—

"Stranger, if that thar bacon ain't some, may I be choked to death with a raw corn-dodger. Don't be bashful, hoss; make a dash and go ahead; don't be backward 'bout goin for'ard!"

The judge was so much astonished at the impudence of the fellow that he could say nothing, but looked on in amazement. The Sucker laid in lustily: slice after slice disappeared through his voracious jaws, until only one piece remained upon the platter. As bacon was rather scarce at this time of year, he concluded he would, upon this particular occasion, infringe a little upon the rules of etiquette, and made a thrust with his fork at the remaining slice. The judge, who had been watching his operations in mute astonishment, had hardly commenced. As every slice disappeared from the platter, the chances of going to bed supperless continued to increase; this, together with the fact that his servant had not supped, threw him completely off his balance when the last piece was about to be taken. He thereupon seized a fork in both hands, raised it perpendicularly over the meat, and thrust it with tremendous force, just as the Sucker was in the act of raising it from the platter, and, leaning over the table towards him at the same time, he said,—

"Are you aware, sir, that this meat is mine, and that I do not intend you shall have any more?"

"I war not aware of that, hoss; but a ham, like a tur-

key, are a monstrous convenient bird,—a little too much
for one, and not quite enough for two. I'm done. I'll
absquatulate."

He then retired from the table, and left the judge to
finish his supper. This over, they collected around the
fire, and passed off the evening in listening to several
amusing anecdotes from the judge. One of them I venture to relate, although it will appear in print but weak
and feeble when compared to the rich, racy, quaint, and
humorous style in which it came from his lips :

When I came to the Western country, I took the route
by New Orleans, and then embarked on a steamboat for
St. Louis. Boats were much longer in making the trip
then than they are at present, and passengers were compelled to resort to every expedient to while away the dull
monotony of the voyage. We had on board a heteroge-
neous mass of humanity, from all parts of the United
States. There was the backwoodsman and the Yankee,
whose manners presented a very striking contrast, although originally coming from the same primitive stock.
Yet the force of habit, association, and necessity have
made them antipodes. The latter of my countrymen has
the reputation of being very inquisitive, yet, as far as my
experience goes, I must confess the Western man mani-
fests as great a desire to obtain personal information as
his countrymen farther East. For example, I met with
one man who approached me, and, without any prelimi-
naries, said,—

" Wal, steamboat, whar ar you from ?"

Knowing from his enunciation that he was a Western
man, and might be prejudiced against a Yankee, I replied,
" I'm from Virginia."

" What part of Virginia ?"

" Let me see : I'm from Norfolk."

"Ah! I know a heap of folks in Norfolk. You know Mike Trotter?"

"No."

"Know Jake Johnson?"

"No, I believe not."

"Don't know Jake? I thought everybody knew Jake. I suppose you know Billy Bennet?"

"I believe I——that is, I presume I do."

"Presume! of course you do, if you war raised in Norfolk. How did Billy get out of that scrape with Sam Smith?"

"Well, I declare I've almost forgotten; but it strikes me that he settled it by arbitration, or something of that sort."

"Settled the devil! Look here, steamboat, I b'lieve you're a d—d sight more of a Yankee than a Virginian!"

It was not long before another son of the West walked up to me, and said,—

"Wal, hoss, I reckon thar's no harm in asking whar you war raised?"

Having a compunctious streak pass over me about this time, I concluded that I would set at defiance local prejudices, and tell the truth. I replied, "Me? I'm from Connecticut, sir."

"Connecticut! Connecticut! Connecticut!" Closing up his left eye, and turning up the right towards the hearers, —"I never hearn of that place afore: if I did, d—n me."

Among the passengers who came aboard at New Orleans was a "split me" young buck from New York, on a tour of pleasure through the Western States. He had never before been far from Broadway, and he regarded the time spent away from that fashionable resort as so much time thrown away: it was a blank in his existence that could never be filled up. He had been but a few weeks absent, and was already becoming disgusted with the country, and longed to return to the gayeties of the city. His peculiarities were new to the backwoodsmen, and he was looked upon by them as an original, as belonging to a genus of the race biped of which they had before no conception. He had brought with him from the city all the paraphernalia of the wardrobe and toilet, and, among other things, a very beautiful rosewood dressing-case, one of Tiffany's latest importations. It stood in a conspicuous place in the gents' cabin, and soon attracted the observation of the backwoodsmen.

Their curiosity was raised, and there were numerous speculations as to its use. One thought it a money-box, one a gun-case, and others, and the most knowing ones, thought that it was a faro-box. The latter opinion, after a good deal of discussion, prevailed, and they arrived at the unanimous conclusion that the Broadway gent was a travelling "leg" in disguise.

Thereupon they resolved to give him an invitation to "open," and, collecting together in the forward cabin, they appointed one of their number to intimate to the gentleman that his presence there with the necessary "tools" would be agreeable to them.

The messenger was a double-fisted Mississippian, who soon found the exquisite, and, approaching him, with the right side of his face screwed up until the eye on that side closed (intending it for a sly wink), and beckoning with his finger towards him at the same time, said, in a low tone of voice,—

"It's all right, my boy : get out your old 'sody-box' and come along and give us a 'turn.'"

The dandy looked in perfect amazement as he said, "Ah—ah—ah !—what do you mean, fellow ?"

"I say it's all O. K. down there,"—pointing with his finger over his left shoulder: "thar's three or four of us down-river boys ready to start the fires with a small pile o' 'chips.' You understand, now: so come along; come along."

"Dem you, sah, what do you mean? I declare I don't comprehend you, fellar."

"Oh, come along: we'll put 'er through straight from the mark, and pile on the chips until we bust you, or get bust ourselves: so don't try to play 'possum on this child. I say it ain't no use."

At this, the dandy walked off in a furious passion, considering himself most grossly insulted, saying, "Ah, captain, I believe—'pon my honor I do—that the savage fellar means to blow up the boat!"

The sporting gents could not understand this, and they watched his motions all day, following him from one place to another. Go where he would, they were sure to keep him in sight. Having occasion to go to his dressing-case before night, they all collected around him, and looked over his shoulder while he was unlocking it. On raising the lid, the first article that presented itself was a pair of boot-hooks. When they saw this, one of them turned away with an air of disgust, saying to the others, "Why, he's one of them d—d dentistry chaps, after all."

Finding that they were not likely to get up a game, they were forced to resort to other expedients to while away the dull monotony of the voyage; and, as the New-Yorker was very credulous, some of them amused themselves at his expense by relating to him the most improbable tales of backwoods adventures, hair-breadth escapes from savage wild beasts, the dangers of navigating Western rivers, blowing up of steamboats, running foul of snags, etc., etc. He swallowed them all, and they had such an effect upon his imagination that he was afraid to venture out of sight of the boat when it stopped to take in wood, for fear, as he said, of "encountewing a bear, or some other howible cweture." He was constantly on the *qui vive* at night, expecting some accident to the boat, and would pace the deck for hours together, trembling at every pull of the engine, as if he expected the next to send him to the bottom. Seeing the captain come on deck one night, he approached him, when the following dialogue ensued:

"Ah—ah—ah, capting, do you really have any sewious accidents on this howible river?"

"Accidents, my dear fellow! as a matter of course we do."

"Ah! and pray, capting, what is the nature of them?"

"Oh, sometimes we run foul of a snag or sawyer; then again we occasionally collapse a boiler, and blow up sky-high."

"The devwal you do! you don't say so! Does anybody ever get killed, capting?"

"Nothing is more common, my good fellow; but we soon get used to such little things, and don't mind them. If we get up to St. Louis without an accident, we may consider ourselves extremely fortunate."

The dandy looked perfectly aghast, and turned blue at this announcement.

"How perfwectly howible, capting! I wish I was back in Bwoadway again,—by quist I do."

By the time the judge had finished this story it was bedtime, and the mammy made up a field-couch upon the floor in front of the fire, to which she consigned all her guests: the judge took the soft side of a pine puncheon, and, ensconcing himself as comfortably as possible, was soon courting the embraces of Morpheus. The family dis-

appeared one by one, until finally none remained. Everything had become perfectly still and quiet, except the
measured and sonorous breathing of the Sucker, upon
whom the ham appeared to operate as a powerful opiate.
The judge had fallen into a restless doze, and was dreaming of hungry Suckers and cannibals. He fancied himself
upon a boundless prairie, pursued by a pack of Suckers
on all fours, following him with the speed of race-horses
and giving tongue at every jump like so many blood-
hounds: but, instead of unmeaning howls, their enunciation was distinct and audible, every note of which fell
upon his ears like a death-knell: it seemed to say, "h-a-m!
h-a-m! h-a-a-m!" He exerted himself to the utmost to
escape his savage pursuers, but, notwithstanding all his
efforts, they appeared to gain on him.

> "And on, on, on! no stop, no stay!
> Up hill, down dale, and far away!"

He occasionally cast his eyes back, to see if they did
not begin to tire; but no; the farther they went the
faster they came. They bounded over hill and valley,
with the constant cry of h-a-m, h-a-m, h-a-m! until finally
the judge, becoming weak and exhausted, sank down upon
the prairie, and awaited the coming of the foremost Sucker,
who, foaming at the mouth and snapping his teeth like a
hungry wolf, seized him by the thigh with his teeth and
threw him over his head. Turning around, he seized him
again, and repeated the operation, until the judge fancied
the features of his face became changed into those of a
hog. He ventured to put out his hand to ascertain if it
was tangible, when a sensation of cold ran through his
frame, and a tremendous punch in the ribs, accompanied
with an ugh—ugh—ugh—awoke him.

He found, to his great astonishment, that his hand was

holding a hog by the snout, that had taken possession of the side of his bed nearest the door and was manifesting his displeasure at the familiarity of the judge by the savage grunts that had awakened him. Being an old voyager, he did not let this little mishap disturb him in the least, but very quietly and deliberately raised a puncheon which he found loose under his bed, and, thrusting down mister hog, he closed the hole, and slept quietly until morning.

The next morning he arose early and resumed his journey, leaving the Sucker and the mammy in great distress at the supposed loss of their pig.

INDEX TO VOLS. I. AND II.

503